The 1998 Stagecoach Bus Handbook

C000115258

Body codes used in the Bus Handbook series:

Type:
A	Articulated vehicle
B	Single-deck bus
C	Coach - High-back seating
D	Low floor double-deck bus (4-metre)
DP	Express - high-back seating in a bus body
H	Full-height double-deck
L	Low-height double-deck
M	Minibus
N	Low-floor bus
O	Open-top bus (CO = convertable)
P	Partial or convertible open-top

Seating capacity is then shown. For double-decks the upper deck first,

Door position:-
C	Centre entrance/exit
D	Dual doorway
F	Front entrance/exit
R	Rear entrance/exit (no distinction between doored and open)
T	Three or more access points

Equipment:-
L	Lift for wheelchair
T	Toilet

e.g. - H32/28F is a high-bridge bus with thirty-two seats upstairs, twenty-eight down and a front entrance/exit.
B43D is a bus with two doorways.

Re-registrations:-
Where a vehicle has gained new index marks the details are listed at the end of each fleet showing the current mark, followed in sequence by those previously carried starting with the original mark.

Other books in the series:
The Scottish Bus Handbook
The Ireland & Islands Bus Handbook
The North East Bus Handbook
The Yorkshire Bus Handbook
The Lancashire, Cumbria and Manchester Bus Handbook
The Merseyside and Cheshire Bus Handbook
The North and West Midlands Bus Handbook
The East Midlands Bus Handbook
The South Midlands Bus Handbook
The North and West Wales Bus Handbook
The South Wales Bus Handbook
The Chilterns and West Anglia Bus Handbook
The East Anglia Bus Handbook
The South West Bus Handbook
The South Central Bus Handbook (New in 1998)
The South East Bus Handbook (New in 1998)

Annual books are produced for the major groups:
The 1998 Stagecoach Bus Handbook (Editions for 1995, 1996 and 1997 are available direct from the publishers)
The 1998 FirstBus Bus Handbook
The 1998 Cowie Bus Handbook (Arriva Group)

Associated series:
The Hong Kong Bus Handbook
The Leyland Lynx Handbook
The Model Bus Handbook
The Toy & Model Bus Handbook - Volume 1 - Early Diecasts
The Fire Brigade Handbook (fleet list of each local authority fire brigade)
The Fire Brigade Handbook - Special Appliances Volume 1
The Fire Brigade Handbook - Special Appliances Volume 2

1998 Stagecoach Bus Handbook

The 1998 Stagecoach Bus Handbook is the fifth edition of this Bus Handbook dedicated to the various bus fleets of Stagecoach Holdings, both within the United Kingdom and overseas.

Although this book has been produced with the encouragement of, and in co-operation with, Stagecoach management, it is not an official Stagecoach fleet list and the vehicles included are subject to variation, particularly as substantial new vehicle deliveries lead to older vehicles being 'cascaded' to other subsidiaries. Some vehicles listed are no longer in regular use on service but are retained for special purposes or preserved by the company. The services operated and the allocation of vehicles to subsidiary companies are subject to variation at any time, although accurate at the time of going to print. The contents are correct to January 1998, and include the vehicles of Glasgow, Rhondda (which is now part of Red & White), and the new Australia acquisition.

The publishers would be glad to hear from readers should any information be available which corrects or enhances that given in this publication, or to receive any suitable photographs for use in future editions, particularly those covering the overseas operations.

Principal Editors: Bill Potter, David Donati and Stuart Martin

Acknowledgements:
We are grateful to Keith Grimes, Mark Jameson, Colin Lloyd, Steve Sanderson, Malcolm Tranter, Tony Wilson, the PSV Circle and the Management and officials of Stagecoach Holdings and their operating companies for their kind assistance and co-operation in the compilation of this book.
To keep up to date with the fleets we recommend *Buses*, published monthly by Ian Allan Ltd and for more in-depth information the news sheets of the PSV Circle.

The front cover photo is by Les Peters, the frontispieces for the UK section by Paul Wigan and the overseas by Swebus, Norway. The rear cover photographs are by Bob Docherty and Tony Wilson.

ISBN 1 897990 25 1
Published by *British Bus Publishing* Ltd
The Vyne, 16 St Margarets Drive, Wellington,
Telford, Shropshire, TF1 3PH
© British Bus Publishing Ltd, January 1998

Contents

Stagecoach

The Stagecoach Group is one of the larger private sector operators of buses in the United Kingdom, with a growing involvement in surface transport throughout the world. This Bus Handbook details the latest fleets of constituent companies, both in Britain and overseas in Africa, Portugal, Scandinavia and New Zealand.

Stagecoach can trace its roots back to a small self-drive caravan and caravanette rental business which was formed in Perth in 1976. Trading as Gloagtrotter (later GT Coaches), the business expanded a couple of years later to include minibus private hire under the original partnership of Ann Gloag, now an Executive Director of Stagecoach Holdings, and her husband, Robin. Her brother, Brian Souter, now Executive Chairman (an accountant by profession), joined the fledgling organisation in 1980 just prior to its starting regular long distance services at which time the Stagecoach name was adopted, at the suggestion of Ann's other brother, David. This move into regular services was made possible by coach deregulation, introduced in the 1980 Transport Act.

Stagecoach was born out of deregulation and developed through privatisation. The freedom of deregulation and the opportunities of privatisation have facilitated the rapid growth of Stagecoach.

The first service began in October 1980, an overnight run from Dundee to London. Subsequently further legs were added that brought in Aberdeen and Glasgow. Soon a network of express services was developed that operated throughout Scotland and ran south of the border to London via Manchester and Birmingham. The quality of vehicle provided on these services quickly improved, exotic foreign double deck coaches in a bright unconventional livery becoming the norm from 1982 onwards in marked contrast to the traditional single deck coaches with a rather dowdy image used by their main competitor - the Scottish Bus Group.

In December 1982 Mrs Gloag's husband left the business and set up his own company trading as Highwayman Coaches at Errol near Perth. In tandem with the coach service expansion, a number of school contracts had been secured. These were operated primarily with second hand Bristol Lodekkas and, by the mid 1980s, Stagecoach was the largest operator of that type, with a fleet of over 20. In December 1980 Stagecoach took its first step into regular bus service operation when the Perth to Errol route of A & C McLennan of Spittalfield was taken over. It was this route which five years later was to see the birth of the

'Provincial Routemaster Revival' started by Stagecoach when it introduced Routemasters between Perth and Errol in the spring of 1985. In the early 1980s a number of other Scottish coach operations were absorbed into Stagecoach including Adamson & Low of Edinburgh and parts of Bennetts of Kilwinning in Ayrshire, although both were subsequently disposed of. After a period of consolidation, a further expansion into local bus services was achieved when, in November 1985, the remaining business of McLennan's of Spittalfield was purchased. This gave the Stagecoach company a significant presence in the Tayside region, and most importantly McLennan's extensive workshops and engineering facilities at Spittalfield which were needed to maintain the ever-growing express coach fleet.

The 1985 Transport Act resulted in the deregulation of bus services outside of London. As implementation of the Act drew near, the Stagecoach company prepared its plans for a major expansion in the bus market. A new company was formed called Magicbus, and on 26th October 1986 it commenced operating a number of services in Glasgow and East Kilbride. The vehicles utilised were primarily Routemasters formerly with London Buses or Northern General and these vehicles brought back conductor operation to the city along with the Routemasters of Kelvin and Clydeside. At the same time there was some expansion of services in Tayside, Stagecoach taking over commercially a number of rural routes left for the tendering process by Strathtay Scottish, including the routes north of Perth to Aberfeldy and Pitlochry.

With established operations in Tayside and Glasgow, and an extensive network of express services, the Stagecoach team considered for the first time acquiring operators outside their native Scotland, and took an interest in the pending privatisation of National Bus Company's subsidiaries. An unsuccessful bid for City of Oxford did not deter the directors who turned their attention to Hampshire Bus. A new holding company, Skipburn Limited, was formed by directors Brian Souter and Ann Gloag together with their uncle Fraser McColl and the General Manager of Hampshire Bus. Hampshire Bus together with Pilgrim Coaches was successfully purchased on 2nd April 1987. The new owners did not waste time in rationalising their new acquisition, with Pilgrim Coaches, which had been loss-making from the outset, closing down on 26th April 1987. By 3rd October, the Grosvenor Square depot was sold for re-development and the Southampton area operations had been sold to Southern Vectis who formed a new company, trading as Solent Blue Line, to operate the routes. The residual Hampshire Bus operation continues as part of the Stagecoach South company with depots at Andover, Basingstoke and Winchester.

In 1987 Derek Scott joined the board as Finance Director, and has subsequently played a key role in shaping the growth of the group, before taking a more of a back seat as Company Secretary in 1996. While still digesting Hampshire Bus, the Stagecoach board turned its attention to the acquisition of a second NBC subsidiary. This time Cumberland was the target and, following a successful offer, Stagecoach took control of Cumberland Motor Services on 23rd July 1987. The Cumberland operations were based at Whitehaven with depots in Carlisle, Penrith, Keswick, Workington and Millom. The new owners quickly recast the Carlisle city network and introduced crew-operated Routemasters to that city. The Cumberland company acquired a number of its competitors during 1988 including Yeowart's of Whitehaven and Kirkpatrick of Brigham, near Cockermouth.

In July 1987 the McColl interests in Skipburn were acquired. However, further expansion of the group was still being sought. Under the NBC privatisation rules only three subsidiaries could be acquired by any purchaser. However, Hampshire Bus and Pilgrim Coaches had been classed as one unit, Cumberland a second and, therefore, Stagecoach was able to acquire United Counties as its third NBC company. The area of operation encompassed Bedford, Corby, Huntingdon, Kettering and Northampton and was the group's first presence in the Midlands. As with Cumberland, it was not long before the potential of Routemasters was realised and the Corby and Bedford networks received a fleet of these vehicles soon after the Stagecoach acquisition.

During 1988 Ewan Brown joined the board of directors in a non-executive capacity. Being a Merchant Banker by profession, based in Edinburgh and a former director of the Scottish Transport Group as well as being a native of Perth, he brought valuable skills and knowledge to the management team.

Up to this point the Stagecoach Group had acquired three NBC companies. All were operating a typical mix of National Bus Company standard vehicles which primarily consisted of Leyland Nationals and Leopards, and Bristol VRTs. Additionally, the fleet in Scotland was mainly secondhand Routemasters and Bristol Lodekkas together with Volvo B58 and Neoplan double-deck coaches for the express network. Vehicles in Scotland were in the now standard Stagecoach livery of white with blue, red and mustard (later to become orange) stripes and it was decided that in order to provide flexibility and enable vehicles to be transferred between fleets, all vehicles in the group would be painted in this corporate style. Very quickly the new livery began to appear on all three English fleets but local trading names were retained

New vehicle purchases had to be made in order that the bus companies could maintain and develop their business into the 1990s and early purchases of Alexander-bodied Mercedes 709 minibuses and Leyland Olympians were to be a portent of large numbers of vehicles of these types in years to come. The importance of investing in new vehicles, and its consequent increase in patronage and reduction of maintenance costs, has continued to the present.

The most significant event of 1988 was the private placing of a quantity of Stagecoach shares with institutional investors. This raised £5 million and set the financial scene for Stagecoach to develop into a major force within the bus industry. It was also a sign of things to come, that is the Stock Market flotation five years later.

1989 saw the first Stagecoach acquisition overseas when, in March of that year, it purchased a 51% share in United Transport Malawi Limited from United Transport International, a British Electric Traction (BET) subsidiary.

The vehicles operated in Africa were somewhat strange to British eyes with large numbers of ERF Trailblazer and Leyland Victory single deckers, all built to meet the rough African conditions where much mileage is run on dirt roads. Stagecoach did, however, introduce double decker operation to the Malawi fleet with Daimler CVG6 double deckers previously operated in Hong Kong by the Kowloon Motor Bus Company. All of these, together with a Bristol FLF, are now withdrawn as the company took delivery of Dennis Dragons, former Durban single-decks and new single-decks. City services and long distance express routes are operated from depots based in Blantyre (Makata Road and Chichiri), Lilongwe and Mzuzu.

Having ventured into Africa, Stagecoach soon returned to the acquisition trail in England. East Midland Motor Services had been sold to its management by NBC, but in April 1989 the management decided to sell its entire share holding to Stagecoach. The operation was conducted under East Midland, Mansfield & District, and Rainworth Travel names in the East Midland area, and in addition there were two Frontrunner operations, one based in Essex and the other in north west Derbyshire and eastern Greater Manchester. The Frontrunner South East operation was quickly sold on to Ensign Bus of Purfleet while the Derbyshire/Manchester operation was absorbed by Ribble and subsequently sold to Drawlane. This left the East Midland management to concentrate in its own territory and soon its coaching operations were consolidated into Rainworth Travel which was renamed Midland Travel. The bus operations are based on Worksop, Chesterfield and Mansfield and, as with other acquisitions, former London Routemasters were again tried, this time in Mansfield where Routemaster operation lasted until 1991. In May 1993 the Midland Travel coaching operation was sold to Skills of Nottingham.

Only a matter of days after the East Midland acquisition, a further company was acquired from its management. Ribble Motor Services Limited, based in the north west of England, had been bought by its management team and had subsequently purchased, from United Transport, the Bee Line Buzz Company - a large minibus operation based in Manchester, together with the Zippy minibus operation based in Preston.

Having added two major bus companies in North West England to one it already owned, Stagecoach embarked upon a reorganisation and rationalisation of its interests in the area. The Barrow-in-Furness municipal undertaking had been in financial difficulties for some time, following heavy competition with Ribble, and its services and depot were acquired from the administrator in May 1989. For operational control reasons, and to align with the county boundaries, Ribble's South Cumbrian and Lake District operations were transferred to Cumberland Motor Services which also took control in Barrow. This concentrated Cumberland into the county of Cumbria and Ribble into Lancashire and Greater Manchester. In September of 1989 Ribble sold its Bee Line Buzz subsidiary and some of its own Ribble Manchester operations to the Drawlane Group (now part of the Arriva Group) though it retained the Preston-based Zippy minibuses, a name now used for all Ribble minibus operations. Having lost depots at Barrow, Ulverston and Kendal to Cumberland and the Manchester operation passing to Drawlane, Ribble was left to concentrate on the central area which consists of the Lancashire towns of Blackburn, Bolton, Chorley, Clitheroe, Fleetwood, Lancaster, Morecambe and Preston. Future acquisitions by Ribble included parts of Lancaster City Transport, Burnley & Pendle Transport and Hyndburn Transport.

Despite the activity in England there were still changes taking place in Scotland during 1989. On 19th June new bus services in and around the cities of Perth and Dundee were introduced, primarily in competition with Strathtay Scottish, whose managing director, Neil Renilson was recruited by Stagecoach at the same time. This new network was branded Perth Panther and, after a prolonged period of competition, in which both operators used Routemasters on Perth City services, Strathtay (which became part of Yorkshire Traction at privatisation) closed their Crieff depot and operations in 1991 and their Perth depot and operations in the summer of 1993.

Perhaps the most surprising development of 1989 was the decision by Stagecoach to sell the express coach operations that had been the genesis of the company. On 4th August 1989 the company announced the sale of its express network to National Express who re-branded the operation as Caledonian Express. With this sale Stagecoach clearly indicated that it was to concentrate on local bus operations in future. The Scottish operations saw further expansion when Inverness Traction was purchased from receivership in November. Inverness Traction had been competing with Highland Scottish on town services in Inverness since 1987. Stagecoach placed this Inverness operation under the Magicbus and Perth Panther management, and renamed the Magicbus company Stagecoach Scotland Ltd as the holding company for its Glasgow, Tayside and Inverness operations. All of these operations were carving out their market through head to head competition with established state-owned and municipal operators, whereas in England established operators had been purchased, and competitive pressures were the other way round.

The south coast of England was not neglected either. In August 1989 the management of Southdown decided to sell out to Stagecoach. This brought a sixth former NBC subsidiary into the fold and Stagecoach then acquired, in October, the operations of Portsmouth City Bus from Southampton City Bus who held 75% and a workers co-operative which owned the remaining 25%. In December 1989 Hastings and District was added when the management sold the company which it had bought from NBC.

In 1990 there was expansion overseas with the purchase of Gray Coach Lines of Toronto, Canada. This brought to the Stagecoach Group an extensive network of express coach services throughout eastern Canada together with Niagara Falls sightseeing tours and the Toronto City/Airport express coach service. The venture proved to be unsuccessful in financial terms and the Group's interest in Gray Coach Lines was sold in two stages to Ontario Northern in June 1992 and Greyhound Lines of Canada in December 1992, but not before a number of Stagecoach Scotland Bristol FLFs had been transferred for sightseeing tour work.

One result of the large expansion on the south coast of England was an inquiry by the Monopolies and Mergers Commission and the DTI subsequently instructed Stagecoach to divest themselves of Portsmouth City Bus, and this operation was subsequently sold to Transit Holdings in January 1991. The South of England subsidiaries that remained were then restructured and consolidated in April 1992 when a new company, Stagecoach South Limited, was given overall control of Hastings Buses, Southdown and Hampshire Bus as well as United Counties. As part of the reorganisation Southdown was split into two operating companies, Sussex Coastline Buses and South Coast Buses, the latter also taking in Hastings Buses. The Southdown name was discontinued, and South Coast Buses operates at Eastbourne and Hastings with Coastline Buses trading from Chichester, Havant and Worthing.

Following on from the privatisation of NBC the Government decided to extend privatisation to the Scottish Bus Group. It was decreed that only two companies could be acquired by any one purchaser and Stagecoach completed its quota with the purchase of Bluebird Northern and Fife Scottish during the first half of 1991. Bluebird is based in Aberdeen and also has depots at Ballater, Elgin, Fyvie, Macduff, Peterhead and Stonehaven, together with several outstations. Bluebird was acquired in March and its archaic legal company name of Northern Scottish Omnibuses Ltd was quickly changed to Bluebird Buses Ltd. Bluebird was placed under common management with Stagecoach Scotland Ltd and its fleet renumbered into a single series.

By July of 1991 the Fife company was also under the Stagecoach umbrella. In line with the company name operations are concentrated in the Kingdom of Fife with depots at Aberhill (Methil), Cowdenbeath, Dunfermline, Glenrothes, Kirkcaldy and St Andrews. In the autumn of 1991 Stagecoach Scotland further expanded when it took over the remaining Inverness and Easter Ross area operations from Highland, adding some 30 extra buses to the Inverness Traction Fleet, plus the former Highland depot at Tain.

With two former SBG companies now under its wing, plus the Perth and Inverness operations, Stagecoach had established a strong presence on the eastern side of Scotland. In line with Stagecoach policy the corporate colours started to appear on the newly-acquired fleets and fleet renewal commenced, primarily involving Alexander-bodied Mercedes minibuses and Leyland Olympians. There were also transfers north of the border of vehicles from the English companies which resulted in some unfamiliar types of vehicle being introduced into Scotland, especially ECW-bodied Bristol VRTs. The VRT had been despised by SBG with all its initial examples being exchanged for NBC-owned Bristol FLFs.

November 1991 saw further expansion in Africa following BETs decision to divest itself of local bus operations throughout the world and Stagecoach saw potential in acquiring its Kenya operations to add to those of Malawi. As a result of the deal Stagecoach acquired a 75% share of Kenya Bus Services (Nairobi), and a 51% share in Kenya Bus Services (Mombasa). The remaining share holdings were held by the local city councils and both operations are maintained under franchising arrangements. As in Malawi the ERF Trailblazer and Leyland Victory tend to dominate the fleets though there are a number of unusual vehicles including some manufactured by Isuzu in Japan. Mombasa was sold to local operators in 1996.

There is one company in the Stagecoach Group which plays a not insignificant part in the UK transport system as a whole, but operates no buses. National Transport Tokens was formed in the 1970s to manufacture and distribute concessionary travel tokens to various bodies, mostly local authorities and national operators, and a minority shareholding came to Stagecoach with the purchase of Ribble in April 1989. The aluminium tokens produced by National Transport Tokens are accepted by a variety of operators in lieu of cash fares, including bus companies, taxi firms and rail services and currently NTTs annual turnover is £14m. Stagecoach bought a controlling interest in the company in March 1992 and its headquarters were moved from Manchester to Preston.

In October 1992 Brian Cox, Managing Director of Stagecoach South, and Barry Hinkley, Managing Director of North West joined the main board as executive appointments while Muir Russell and Barry Sealey (who had also previously been a director of the Scottish Transport Group) joined as non-executive directors in December. Muir Russell (who had expected to complete a three-year term) resigned in January 1995 following his promotion within The Scottish Office.

It came as a significant surprise in April 1992 when Stagecoach decided to sell another of its initial operations. Having disposed of the express network the deal was now to sell the Glasgow-based Magicbus operation to Kelvin Central Buses. The vehicles transferred included some newly-delivered Dennis Darts and a substantial number of Bristol VRTs and Routemasters, and the Glasgow depot was also acquired by Kelvin. The Magicbus name and Stagecoach livery continued in use with Kelvin Central until 1993 as part of the deal.

1992 also saw further expansion of the southern fleet when Stagecoach acquired Alder Valley's operations based at depots in Aldershot, Alton and Hindhead. Alder Valley had been through a particularly disturbed time having had a number of owners since privatisation from NBC and suffering from subsequent fragmentation. The operation acquired by Stagecoach was placed under the Stagecoach South umbrella and is operated under the brand name Hants & Surrey.

Having seen the deregulation and privatisation process in the United Kingdom the New Zealand Government decided to embark on a similar course of action. In October 1992 the Wellington City Transport undertaking was privatised and Stagecoach was the successful bidder. There are three companies involved: Wellington City Transport, with a depot at Karori and an outstation at Kilbirnie; Cityline Auckland based at Papakura and Cityline Hutt Valley with depots at Lower Hutt and Stokes Valley. With its new undertaking, Stagecoach now has experience of operating MAN and Hino vehicles but more interestingly, is now operating electric traction. The Wellington City Transport fleet contains over seventy Volvo trolleybuses while Wellington City

Transport's shareholding in Harbour City Cable Car Limited has resulted in Stagecoach having an operating interest in this funicular railway.

Overseas developments in 1992 were not confined to Africa and New Zealand. For some time Stagecoach had held a stake in Speedybus Enterprises Limited of Hong Kong, whose primary functions were to sell advertising space on double deckers it supplied to Chinese municipal bus companies, and to import vehicles to China through Hong Kong. Speedybus also supplied Hong Kong double deckers to Stagecoach Malawi. In 1992 Stagecoach Hong Kong Ltd was formed to tender for bus services in Hong Kong, and to gain an operating base in the colony. (Speedybus was primarily a bus dealer and bus advertising contractor rather than an operator, and Stagecoach's 50% interest was disposed of in 1993). In 1994 the company commenced operating services on two commuter routes with five Volvo B10Ms. These vehicles were almost the same as the Stagecoach standard Alexander PS-bodied Volvo B10Ms except that they were fitted with air conditioning to cope with the humid Hong Kong climate. In 1995 six tri-axle Volvo Olympians joined the operation and a second residents' route was introduced. The Hong Kong operations were sold in the summer of 1996 after attempts to enlarge the business through the tendering/franchising process had been unsuccessful.

In the spring of 1993 Lancaster City Council expressed an intention to sell its municipal bus undertaking, much of the network operated comprising joint services with Ribble. As Ribble already had a substantial presence in Lancaster and the surrounding area, Stagecoach was not expected to be a bidder for the operation. However, in order to protect its interests in the area, Ribble registered many of Lancaster City's routes and subsequently the City Council decided to liquidate their undertaking, selling the depot and some twelve buses to Ribble during 1993. As a result of this acquisition Ribble was able to close its own, smaller, depot in Morecambe and move into the former council depot in Heysham.

Expansion in the south of England continued in 1993 when the management of East Kent sold their company. This is yet another former NBC subsidiary that had been purchased originally by a management team. Again the new acquisition has been placed under the control of Stagecoach South and it now trades under the Stagecoach East Kent name. The East Kent purchase brought with it depots at Ashford, Canterbury, Thanet (Westwood), Dover, Folkestone and Herne Bay and contained a typical mix of former NBC vehicles with Leyland Nationals, Bristol VRs and Olympians together with a substantial number of minibuses. In addition, it contained several MCW and Scania products. In 1994 East Kent purchased four Dennis low-floor vehicles with Berkhof bodies for the Canterbury Park and Ride service, these being the first such vehicles in the Stagecoach Group with more of the type delivered during 1996 for a Greater Manchester PTE contract.

While the Government had not legislated for the privatisation of municipal bus companies, a number of councils took the opportunity to sell before the end of 1993 to allow all of the income from the sale to be used on other projects. (The proportion for retention by councils has since been reduced to 75% when sold before 31st March 1997).

Grimsby Cleethorpes Transport was jointly owned by the Boroughs of Grimsby and Cleethorpes and the two councils decided to sell the undertaking through a competitive tendering process and Stagecoach was the successful bidder. The deal was completed in November 1993 and brought the Stagecoach livery to South Humberside. The vehicles acquired were of a typical municipal nature and included substantial numbers of Dennis Dominators and Lances. The last of the five Lances delivered in 1993 was painted into Stagecoach livery before delivery. Grimsby Cleethorpes is operated as a division of the East Midland company.

The 1000th new bus to join Stagecoach was handed over to Ann Gloag and Brian Souter on the opening day of Coach & Bus 93; this was a Volvo B6 destined for United Counties. Stagecoach has been the largest UK purchaser of new buses in recent years, and has invested heavily in renewing its fleet and offering passengers modern, comfortable vehicles. The order for new vehicles for delivery in 1995 was the largest annual order for buses in the UK since privatisation began in the 1980s. Purchasing policy for the year continued to be based on Volvo double deck and single deck chassis together with Mercedes-Benz minibuses, though Dennis have supplied the Dart and Javelin in significant numbers. Alexander with assembly plants in Scotland and Northern Ireland are the preferred bus body builder with Plaxton as the coach body supplier, although some vehicles have been bodied by Northern Counties, particularly for the Group's urban operations.

December 1993 saw a further major acquisition by Stagecoach Holdings. Western Travel Ltd was formed on the privatisation of the Cheltenham and Gloucester company from NBC. Cheltenham and Gloucester operates in both the cities mentioned in its title together with services in Swindon and the Cotswolds based on Stroud. Western Travel itself went on the acquisition trail as part of the NBC privatisation process and acquired the Midland Red South company which brought with it operations in Leamington Spa, Nuneaton, Rugby, Stratford-upon-Avon and Warwick. Western Travel had also acquired G & G Coaches and the eastern part of the National Welsh operation part of which was trading as Red & White, adding operations around the Red & White historical base of Monmouthshire and the eastern valleys of South Wales. A further 650 vehicles were added to the Stagecoach Group with this purchase, the first being painted into corporate colours in December 1993.

1993 also saw the company become listed on the London Stock Exchange. The successful share flotation attracted much publicity and the proceeds gave the group access to considerable additional funds with which to expand. Some 18,000 (over 90%) of Stagecoach's UK employees are now shareholders, following the Buy One Get One Free (BOGOF) offer in 1991 and the award of free shares twice each year from 1994 based on up to 3% of pre-tax profits.

1994 saw the bus industry's consolidation accelerate and Stagecoach's development move into the larger metropolitan markets in which it had previously had limited operations. The year opened with the launch of Stagecoach Manchester at the end of January. Although a division of Ribble, it traded separately under its own brand name on the long established 192 route from central Manchester to Hazel Grove south of Stockport. Originally set up as a unit with sixteen B6s, rapid passenger growth called for more and larger vehicles, and the year finished with 23 B10Ms allocated to the route. In the autumn of 1995 this operation, with the vehicles, was sold to EYMS Group Ltd who also operated south Manchester services through their Finglands subsidiary.

The first full scale acquisition of 1994 was of Western Scottish, a former SBG company, which was owned by its management and employees. Western is based at Ayr with other depots at Cumnock, Dumfries, Kilmarnock and Stranraer, and a number of sub-depots both on the mainland and on the Isle of Arran and Bute. The operating area runs from the southern outskirts of Glasgow right down to Annan where the services meet those of Stagecoach North West's Cumberland division while the fleet comprised 340 vehicles, including a large number of different chassis and bodies. Shortly after aquisition the legal company name was changed to Western Buses Limited.

In July 1994 Busways Travel Services Ltd became a subsidiary company of Stagecoach. Busways Travel Services Ltd was a private limited company established by the Transport Act 1985 to acquire the bus undertaking of Tyne and Wear Passenger Transport Executive.

Busways commenced trading in October 1986 under the ownership of the PTA, though its origins can be found in the municipal transport undertakings in Newcastle upon Tyne, South Shields and Sunderland, and also the private companies acquired in 1973 (Armstrong and Galley) and 1975 (Economic). In May 1989 a management/employee buyout was successfully completed. Fifty-one per cent of the shares were purchased

Bus Points loyalty scheme was introduced by Stagecoach during 1997. Pictured heading for Newton Mearns is the only double-deck bus with Stagecoach Glasgow, 955, OHV762Y, which carries an advertisement for Bus Points. *Andrew Jarosz*

by the management of ten while 49% were purchased for employees through an ESOP. The Tyne and Wear Omnibus Company Ltd was acquired in November 1989 and in August 1993 Busways acquired a majority shareholding in Welcome Passenger Transport Ltd.

With a fleet of 590 buses and coaches Busways provides mainly urban local bus services in the Newcastle upon Tyne, South Shields and Sunderland areas whose combined population is approximately one million. The acquisition represented an important development for the group. Stagecoach had not previously had a significant presence in a metropolitan area as Stagecoach was effectively excluded from all the earlier privatisations of municipals in South Yorkshire, Aberdeen, Tyneside, Teeside, West Midlands and West Yorkshire because of council's unwillingness to open up to competitive tendering. The controversial Manchester privatisation also seemed biased against outsiders such as British Bus and Stagecoach.

Because of the strength of the brand names in the local market the group agreed that Busways should retain its distinctive liveries once Busways joined the group but the presentation of trading names was revised to include reference to group membership. However, during 1995 corporate livery was introduced following a local employee decision after market research showed the group livery to have a more modern image.

The 1998 Stagecoach Bus Handbook

Also in the summer of 1994, Stagecoach announced its intention to buy a 20% share in Mainline, the former South Yorkshire PTE bus operation based on Sheffield, Doncaster and Rotherham. In October, however, the Office of Fair Trading decided to investigate this purchase the result being a requirement for Stagecoach to divest its interest. While a sale to FirstBus was agreed, an appeal against the principle of forced divestment was taken to (but ultimately lost in) the London courts.

The breakthrough into London bus operation was achieved in September 1994 with the purchase of London Buses' subsidiaries East London and Selkent being announced as part of the privatisation of the capital's red bus fleets. In the case of East London this returned Stagecoach operations to that area of the city following the disposal of East Midland's Frontrunner South East in 1989 to Ensign Bus of Purfleet. Both companies run local suburban services in their respective areas of London as well as trunk routes into the central area. East London's fleet comprises 600 buses operating out of depots at Leyton, Barking, East Ham and Stratford, while Selkent's has 450 buses operating from depots at Bromley, Catford, Plumstead and Orpington, since closed as a result of the Roundabout route tender losses.

A few weeks later saw further expansion in the urban areas of the north east of England, with the acquisition of Cleveland Transit in October, and along with it 51% of the share capital of formerly troubled Kingston upon Hull City Transport. The remaining 49% of Kingston upon Hull City transport owned by the ESOP was also acquired. Days later, Darlington City Transport, which had been experiencing financial problems for some time, ceased trading after Busways established a competing network of services in the town, and with it the birth of Stagecoach Darlington. In the middle of the following month Hartlepool Transport joined Stagecoach in an agreed sale. Hartlepool, also based in the county of Cleveland, employed some 145 staff and operated 68 vehicles. In 1995 the management of the Darlington operation was transferred from Busways to Cleveland.

November 1994 was planned to see the return of Stagecoach into Glasgow with the introduction of Stagecoach Glasgow, a 69 vehicle quality operation, in similar fashion to the Manchester unit. However, two days before Stagecoach Glasgow was due to commence operations, Strathclyde Buses announced they would sell 20% of their shares to Stagecoach in a similar style deal to the Mainline share exchange, and the Stagecoach Glasgow operation, staff and 18 Volvo B10Ms passed to SBL. Like the Mainline operation, this holding attracted the attention of the DTI who, after a Monopolies and Mergers Commission investigation, instructed divestment. A legal appeal was lost in July

1996, although the DTI agreed in an out of court settlement not to seek any undertakings against Stagecoach in Strathclyde or South Yorkshire.

Further expansion in 1995 commenced in January with the acquisition of A1 Service. This was a complex sale in that Ayrshire Bus Owners was the last Scottish co-operative bus company and was owned by nine separate member families. Stagecoach took 75 vehicles with the purchase, not all constituent members sold all their vehicles, and Stagecoach declined to purchase some of the most elderly vehicles. As a result of this and an urgent need to replace many of those acquired, Leyland Titans and Bristol VRs were transferred from other companies to ensure operational needs were met. During the year no less than 21 new Volvo Olympians and many modern mid-life vehicles were placed with this operation to replace the very elderly A1 fleet which had been the subject of a Traffic Commissioner's maintenance hearing and warning shortly prior to the sale to Stagecoach.

Despite the small scale of this operation the Secretary of State for Trade and Industry directed the Monopolies and Mergers Commission to inquire into the purchase. Much criticism of the MMC has been voiced over this inquiry as each investigation costs the taxpayer a considerable amount of money and consumes valuable management time and energy. It was widely commented on at the time that often larger acquisitions by other groups were being cleared without referral. In November the report was published allowing the retention of the operation providing certain conditions on fares and service levels were adhered to.

May 1995 saw the announcement of a joint venture with Montagu Private Equity to buy part of Rodoviária de Lisboa, the main operator in and around the Portuguese capital. The main towns served are Cascais, Estoril and Sintra, with the 900mm gauge Sintra tram operation included. Some 151 buses and 330 staff from two depots and associated services transferred on 1st January 1996. This purchase brought many AECs and early Volvo products including articulated-buses into the group, though many of the older examples have been replaced with the arrival of sixty Scania single-deck buses.

In New Zealand Stagecoach acquired the operations of Cesta Travel in Wellington and Stokes Valley Coaches of Upper Hutt. The Runcimans Motors business was also acquired with bus services taken into the Cityline Hutt Valley operation initially while the remaining contract and hire business was acquired subsequently, retaining a local identity.

In July 1995 Stagecoach confirmed the acquisition of ailing Chesterfield Transport following an Extraordinary General Meeting at which over 99% of Chesterfield's employees voted in favour of the take over. The Chesterfield operation was placed under East Midlands management who moved its local depot to Stonegravels depot off Sheffield Road. This acquisition too became the subject of a Monopolies and Mergers Commission enquiry with vehicle repainting delayed pending the outcome of the MMC enquiry. Ten much travelled B10Ms were transferred in from Ribble. This purchase was cleared during 1996 allowing the fleet to be renumbered and brought together.

October brought Coach and Bus 95 at which four Stagecoach buses were exhibited by various suppliers. Mercedes-Benz displayed the 800th 709D for the group, destined for Cumberland. On the Northern Counties stand was the last of 52 Volvo Olympians destined for Selkent from the 1995 order. Also in red livery was an Alexander-bodied Dennis Dart for East London but the main Stagecoach attraction was the Volvo B10L demonstrator for the group. It operated in the Fife fleet for a year along side new B10Ms and featured the Säffle-designed body built by Alexander as its Ultra model, and was returned to Volvo after its one year trial.

The investment in new vehicles continued during the year with some 627 new vehicles delivered in the year ending 30th April. This represented a total expenditure in excess of £40 million. At Coach and Bus 95 substantial corporate orders were announced totalling over 1000 buses for delivery during 1996. In a statement Brian Souter said "The level of investment in new vehicles demonstrates our continued commitment to maintain our operating costs at the lowest possible levels, while at the same time offering our customers the highest standard of safety and comfort."

1996 was another year of outstanding growth with pre-tax profits up 34% despite adverse weather and fuel duty increases. In Scotland, Bluebird was granted the Royal Warrent for services to the Royal Family with vehicles at Ballater now displaying the Royal Coat of Arms. Western Buses saw the greatest change with many services revised and new routes introduced, including several Stagecoach Express inter-urban services providing links from the centres of operation to Glasgow and Edinburgh. Fife intoduced the first articulated coaches on its X27 service from Glasgow, these to be joined by some Plaxton-bodied examples from the ten to be used nationwide. The north west of England saw the acquisition of GM Buses South (now Stagecoach Manchester) in February after several months of speculation. Earlier, the initial Manchester unit was sold to Finglands to ensure there was no conflicting competition issues. Also in the north west, Ribble secured the Hyndburn operations during September, the services to be provided from several Ribble depots as the purchase did not include the Hyndburn premices in Accrington.

Busways and Transit now form the north east England operations. Highlights of 1996 here were the introduction of a Green Route in Stockton and the restructuring of Busways engineering and administration functions. The addition of 59 new buses was the largest delivery in the area for some twenty years. The Midlands fleets were joined by Cambus from December 1995 and the administration of Cambus and Chesterfield Transport have now been integrated into East Midlands at Chesterfield. Following the merger with Cambus undertakings were agreed with the DTI that the divestment of the United Counties Huntingdon depot and Milton Keynes operations of Cambus would be made.

In the west of England two operation units now function, Stagecoach West and Stagecoach Devon with the acquisition of Devon General and Bayline from Transit Holdings in February 1996. All three divisions of Stagecoach West (Cheltenham & Gloucester, Midland Red South and Red & White) received new single deck buses and minibuses during the year with the Volvo B10Ms being devoted to the important corridors of Nuneaton-Coventry, Cheltenham-Gloucester and Newport-Tredegar. The Devon operation was formed by the amalgamation into one company with two operational divisions for Exeter and Torbay, the latter acquiring open-top Bristol VRs to re-instate regular big-bus services in the Torquay area. 185 vehicles were delivered to Stagecoach South during the year, some 25% of the fleet strength. Stagecoach South also received Titans from Selkent as part of a group policy to cascade urban vehicles to lighter duties at mid-life and help minimise whole-life costs.

1996 in Africa saw a further batch of 30 ERF Trailblazer chassis for Speedlink express services between Lilongwe and Blantyre and other cities. Some 36 second-hand single-decks from Durban City Transport were also being introduced to Blantyre to replace life-expired vehicles including the last of the former KMB double-decks from Hong Kong. During March 1996 the small Hong Kong operation was sold, the B10Ms moving to New Zealand while the Olympians remain there, passing to Citybus.

The group was awarded a seven-year franchise for South West Trains in December 1995 and took over operations in February 1996. SWT operates urban and main line passenger rail services from London Waterloo to over 200 stations principally in south west London, Surrey, Hampshire and Dorset using 1022 vehicles, mainly electric multiple units and Class 159 diesel rail cars. One of the early developments has been the introduction of bus/rail feeder services between Romsey-Winchester and Bordon-Liphook using buses provided by East London though operated by Stagecoach South. The Isle of Wight rail line franchise was also awarded to Stagecoach during 1996.

August 1996 saw the aquisition of Porterbrook Leasing Company MEBO Limited, one of three railway rolling stock leasing operators (ROSCOs). This operation owns over 30% of the rail stock which is then leased to the various operators for them to operate. Porterbrook Group has its headquarters in Derby. It owns 3774 vehicles of rolling stock and supplies units to 16 of the 25 train operating companies. Approximately 70 per cent of Porterbrook's rolling stock is leased for eight to ten years of which the Government have guaranteed up to 80 per cent of the rentals payable to Porterbrook during these intitial periods. To allow Stagecoach to manage both Porterbrook and South West Trains, in November the Department of Trade and Industry indicated that it would accept certain undertakings in respect of this acquisition in lieu of reference to the MMC.

Swebus was finally acquired on 2nd October, though the announcement that Stagecoach was the preferred bidder was made several weeks earlier. Swebus has a fleet of approximately 3,450 buses. 90% of these are commuter buses of which 87% operate in Sweden. The remainder of the fleet consists of express buses and hire coaches. The principal operations are in Sweden and the largest component of this operation are tendered services for various authorities. As a result small batches of vehicles are often supplied to match the tender with some 200 buses, of various lengths and specifications, being delivered in 1997.

In November 1996 Bluebird won the prestigious Bus Company of the year award, at a ceremony in London where the Managing Director, Neil Renilson, received the award from John Watts, Minister of Transport.

Some 625 vehicles were ordered for 1997 delivery for Stagecoach's British fleets announced in November of 1996. The double-deck requirement was met by 140 Volvo Olympians of which forty were bodied

The Stagecoach name is carried proudly on the vehicles used for express service network in Scotland as illustrated here on R120OPS, one operated by Glasgow. During 1998 the express services are to gain 25 Jonckheere Modulo/Mistral articulated vehicles which should also see several operating in England.
Andrew Jarosz

by Northern Counties to London specification. One hundred minibuses were delivered during the year, and these are the new Mercedes-Benz Vario model. Fifty low-floor Dennis Darts, with Alexander ALX200 bodies augment the ninty Volvo B6BLEs from the 1996 delivery order. Requirements for full single-deck and coach needs were met by the Volvo B10M. The Darts SLFs signalled a switch to low floor units for general replacement. In addition, five Northern Counties-bodied Volvo B10BLEs wre trialled with Manchester and and used on the 192 service early in 1997 followed by 23 low-floor Volvo B10BLEs with Alexander ALX300 bodywork for Busways.

In the Chairman's Statement for the year ended 30th April 1997 he reported the increase in turnover by 130% to £1,153 million. On the rail side, an order for 30 new trains was placed which would replace slam-door trains and an extension of the franchise would enable the type to be eliminated. On 21st July 1997 the group concluded the acquisition of Thames Transit Ltd and Docklands Transit Ltd. Thames Transit operates 180 buses in Oxford and Docklands Transit operates 48 buses in London. The following day the group consolidated the acquisition of part of the business of Transit Australia comprising a 120 contracted bus operation in Queensland, Australia.

The year ended with the announcement that on 23rd December Stagecoach had acquired Rhondda Buses and its associate Parfitt's Motor Services Ltd in south east Wales.

In October of 1997 the 1998 order for new vehicles for the UK was announced, continuing the policy of investing heavily in new vehicles. The order sees the the introduction of MAN single-deck chassis to Stagecoach's UK fleet, with the first vehicles expected in late spring. The details of the order are:- 150 MAN 18.220LE - Alexander ALX300; 100 Dennis Trident SLF - Alexander ALX400; 100 Dennis Dart SLF - Alexander ALX200; 100 Volvo Olympian - Alexander RL; 40 Mercedes-Benz O810 Vario - Alexander ALX100 and 25 Volvo B10M coaches with Jonckheere Modulo/Mistral articulated vehicles.

As 1998 commences the corporate livery of white with orange, red and blue stripes is now a familiar sight throughout the United Kingdom and is also highly visible in a number of countries overseas. The company strives to develop its policy of expansion within the whole sphere of transport and the stated ambition of the group is to develop into a truly global surface transport provider, with a turnover of £2 billion by the year 2000.

Of one thing we can be certain. When writing the 1999 edition there will be a lot of further developments to report. Growth and development have been one of the hallmarks of Stagecoach for the past seventeen years, and surely will be so for 1998 as well!

BLUEBIRD

Bluebird Buses Ltd, Guild Street, Aberdeen, Grampian, AB9 2DR

002-007

Leyland Olympian ONLXB/1R   Alexander RL   H45/32F   1981

002	SSA2X	004	SSA4X	005	SSA5X	006	SSA6X	007	SSA7X
003	SSA3X						

008	K508ESS	Leyland Olympian ON2R50G13Z4	Alexander RL	DPH43/27F	1992	
009	K509ESS	Leyland Olympian ON2R50G13Z4	Alexander RL	DPH43/27F	1992	
010	K510ESS	Leyland Olympian ON2R50G13Z4	Alexander RL	DPH43/27F	1992	
011	K511ESS	Leyland Olympian ON2R50G13Z4	Alexander RL	DPH43/27F	1992	
012	TSO12X	Leyland Olympian ONLXB/1R	Eastern Coach Works	H45/32F	1982	Ex Stagecoach, 1994
013	TSO13X	Leyland Olympian ONLXB/1R	Eastern Coach Works	H45/32F	1982	Ex Stagecoach, 1994
014	TSO14X	Leyland Olympian ONLXB/1R	Eastern Coach Works	H45/32F	1982	Ex Stagecoach, 1994
015	K515ESS	Leyland Olympian ON2R50G13Z4	Alexander RL	DPH43/27F	1992	
017	TSO17X	Leyland Olympian ONLXB/1R	Eastern Coach Works	H45/32F	1982	Ex Stagecoach, 1994
018	K518ESS	Leyland Olympian ON2R50G13Z4	Alexander RL	DPH43/27F	1992	
019	OMS910W	Leyland Olympian B45-6LXB	Eastern Coach Works	H45/32F	1981	Ex Stagecoach, 1994

020-025

Leyland Olympian ONLXB/1R   Eastern Coach Works   H45/32F   1982   Ex Stagecoach, 1994

020	TSO20X	022	9492SC	023	TSO23X	024	TSO24X	025	TSO15X
021	TSO21X						

026	L26JSA	Volvo Olympian YN2RV18Z4	Northern Counties Palatine I	DPH43/25F	1993	
027	L27JSA	Volvo Olympian YN2RV18Z4	Northern Counties Palatine I	DPH43/25F	1993	
028	L28JSA	Volvo Olympian YN2RV18Z4	Northern Counties Palatine I	DPH43/25F	1993	
029	TSO29X	Leyland Olympian ONLXB/1R	Eastern Coach Works	H45/32F	1982	Ex Stagecoach, 1994
030	TSO30X	Leyland Olympian ONLXB/1R	Eastern Coach Works	H45/32F	1982	Ex Stagecoach, 1994
031	TSO31X	Leyland Olympian ONLXB/1R	Eastern Coach Works	H45/32F	1982	Ex Stagecoach, 1994
032	TSO32X	Leyland Olympian ONLXB/1R	Eastern Coach Works	H45/32F	1982	Ex Stagecoach, 1994

033-060

Leyland Olympian ONLXB/1R*   Alexander RL   H45/32F*   1983-85   *044 is DPH41/29F
*049 has a 5LXCT engine

033	YSO33Y	039	YSO39Y	045	A45FRS	051	B351LSO	056	B356LSO
034	YSO34Y	040	YSO40Y	046	A46FRS	052	B352LSO	057	B357LSO
035	YSO35Y	041	YSO41Y	047	A47FRS	053	B353LSO	058	B358LSO
036	YSO36Y	042	YSO42Y	048	B348LSO	054	B354LSO	059	B359LSO
037	YSO37Y	043	YSO43Y	049	B349LSO	055	B355LSO	060	B360LSO
038	YSO38Y	044	A44FRS	050	B350LSO				

The attractive Bluebird motif and name continues to be used on vehicles based around Aberdeen where the operation is a successor to the Alexander Northern fleet. The company have a share of the rights to the motif which is seen in Guild Street, Aberdeen on Olympian 051, B351LSO.
Tony Wilson

061-066

Leyland Olympian ONLXB/1RV   Alexander RL   DPH43/27F   1986

061	C461SSO	063	C463SSO	064	MHS4P	065	MHS5P	066	C466SSO
062	C462SSO								

067-071

Leyland Olympian ONLXB/1RV   Alexander RL   H47/30F   1986

067	C467SSO	068	C468SSO	069	C469SSO	070	C470SSO	071	GSO1V

072w	UWV605S	Bristol VRT/SL3/6LXB	Eastern Coach Works	CO43/31F	1977	Ex East Midland, 1992
074	UWV611S	Bristol VRT/SL3/6LXB	Eastern Coach Works	CO43/31F	1978	Ex Stagecoach South, 1996
075	UWV613S	Bristol VRT/SL3/6LXB	Eastern Coach Works	CO43/31F	1978	Ex Stagecoach South, 1996
077w	VTV171S	Bristol VRT/SL3/6LXB	Eastern Coach Works	H43/31F	1978	Ex Stagecoach South, 1996
078w	EAP996V	Bristol VRT/SL3/6LXB	Eastern Coach Works	H43/31F	1980	Ex Stagecoach South, 1996

080-084

Leyland Titan TNLXB2RR   Leyland   O44/26F   1984   Ex Stagecoach Selkent, 1997

080	B93WUV	081	B100WUV	082	B106WUV	083	B110WUV	084	B114WUV

085-089

Leyland Olympian ONLXB/1RV   Alexander RL   DPH43/27F   1987

085	D385XRS	086	D386XRS	087	D387XRS	088	D388XRS	089	D389XRS

090-099

Leyland Olympian ON2R56G13Z4 Alexander RL   DPH47/27F   1991-92

090	J120XHH	092	J122XHH	097	J197YSS	098	J198YSS	099	J199YSS
091	J121XHH	096	J196YSS						

100	L100JLB	Volvo Olympian YN2RV18Z4	Northern Counties Palatine I	DPH43/25F	1993	
101	L101JSA	Volvo Olympian YN2RV18Z4	Northern Counties Palatine I	DPH43/25F	1993	
102	L102JSA	Volvo Olympian YN2RV18Z4	Northern Counties Palatine I	DPH43/25F	1993	
103	FDV810V	Bristol VRT/SL3/6LXB	Eastern Coach Works	H43/31F	1980	Ex Stagecoach, 1994
104	JAK209W	Bristol VRT/SL3/6LXB	Eastern Coach Works	H43/31F	1980	Ex Western Scottish, 1995
105	FDV816V	Bristol VRT/SL3/6LXB	Eastern Coach Works	H43/31F	1980	Ex Stagecoach, 1994
106w	UWV608S	Bristol VRT/SL3/6LXB	Eastern Coach Works	CO43/31F	1977	Ex Stagecoach, 1991
107	FDV819V	Bristol VRT/SL3/6LXB	Eastern Coach Works	H43/31F	1980	Ex Stagecoach, 1994
108w	UWV609S	Bristol VRT/SL3/6LXB	Eastern Coach Works	CO43/31F	1977	Ex Stagecoach, 1991
109	FDV840V	Bristol VRT/SL3/6LXB	Eastern Coach Works	H43/31F	1980	Ex Stagecoach, 1994
110w	JAK210W	Bristol VRT/SL3/6LXB	Eastern Coach Works	H43/31F	1980	Ex Stagecoach, 1994
111	KWA213W	Bristol VRT/SL3/6LXB	Eastern Coach Works	H43/31F	1981	Ex Western Scottish, 1995
112	JAK212W	Bristol VRT/SL3/6LXB	Eastern Coach Works	H43/31F	1980	Ex Stagecoach, 1994
113w	HWG207W	Bristol VRT/SL3/6LXB	Eastern Coach Works	H43/31F	1980	Ex Western Scottish, 1995
114w	KWA219W	Bristol VRT/SL3/6LXC	Eastern Coach Works	H43/31F	1981	Ex Western Scottish, 1995
115w	FAO429V	Bristol VRT/SL3/6LXB	Eastern Coach Works	H43/31F	1980	Ex Western Scottish, 1995
116w	EWE205V	Bristol VRT/SL3/6LXB	Eastern Coach Works	H43/31F	1980	Ex Western Scottish, 1995
117w	KKY222W	Bristol VRT/SL3/6LXB	Eastern Coach Works	H43/31F	1981	Ex Western Scottish, 1995
120w	SAO410R	Bristol VRT/SL3/501	Eastern Coach Works	H43/31F	1977	Ex Cumberland, 1991
122w	SAO412R	Bristol VRT/SL3/501	Eastern Coach Works	H43/31F	1977	Ex Cumberland, 1991
123	EWE202V	Bristol VRT/SL3/6LXB	Eastern Coach Works	H43/31F	1980	Ex Western Scottish, 1995
126	KRM430W	Bristol VRT/SL3/6LXB	Eastern Coach Works	H43/31F	1980	Ex Western Scottish, 1995
128w	RJT155R	Bristol VRT/SL3/6LXB	Eastern Coach Works	H43/31F	1977	Ex Stagecoach, 1992
132w	RRS47R	Leyland Leopard PSU3E/4R	Duple Dominant I	C49F	1977	
134	PRA109R	Leyland Leopard PSU3C/4R	Alexander AT	C49F	1976	Ex East Midland, 1995
135w	RRS50R	Leyland Leopard PSU3E/4R	Duple Dominant I	C49F	1977	
136	PRA110R	Leyland Leopard PSU3C/4R	Alexander AT	C49F	1976	Ex East Midland, 1995
137	PRA112R	Leyland Leopard PSU3C/4R	Alexander AT	C49F	1976	Ex East Midland, 1995
138w	RRS53R	Leyland Leopard PSU3E/4R	Duple Dominant I	C49F	1977	

139-144

Leyland Leopard PSU3E/4R   Alexander AT   DP49F   1979

139	CRS60T	141	CRS62T	142	CRS63T	143	CRS68T	144	CRS69T
140	CRS61T								

145w	CRS70T	Leyland Leopard PSU3E/4R	Duple Dominant I	C49F	1979	
146w	CRS71T	Leyland Leopard PSU3E/4R	Duple Dominant I	C49F	1979	
147w	CRS73T	Leyland Leopard PSU3E/4R	Duple Dominant I	C49F	1979	
148w	CRS74T	Leyland Leopard PSU3E/4R	Duple Dominant I	C49F	1979	
149w	OSJ635R	Leyland Leopard PSU3C/3R	Alexander AY	B53F	1977	Ex East Midland, 1995
150w	OSJ643R	Leyland Leopard PSU3C/3R	Alexander AY	B53F	1977	Ex East Midland, 1995
151w	OSJ644R	Leyland Leopard PSU3C/3R	Alexander AY	B53F	1977	Ex East Midland, 1995

152-158

Leyland Leopard PSU3E/4R   Alexander AYS   DP49F*   1980   Ex Stagecoach, 1994
*155/7 are B53F

152	GSO89V	154	GSO91V	156	GSO93V	157	GSO94V	158	GSO95V
153	GSO90V	155	GSO92V						

No.	Reg	Chassis	Body	Seating	Year	Notes
160u	KRS531V	Leyland Leopard PSU3E/4R	Duple Dominant II Express	C49F	1980	
161u	KRS532V	Leyland Leopard PSU3E/4R	Duple Dominant II Express	C49F	1980	
162u	OSJ634R	Leyland Leopard PSU3C/3R	Alexander AY	B53F	1977	Ex East Midland, 1995
163	JSA101V	Leyland Leopard PSU3F/4R	Alexander AT	DP49F	1980	
164	JSA102V	Leyland Leopard PSU3F/4R	Alexander AT	DP49F	1980	
165	JSA103V	Leyland Leopard PSU3F/4R	Alexander AT	DP49F	1980	
166	JSA104V	Leyland Leopard PSU3F/4R	Alexander AT	DP49F	1980	
167	HSR136W	Leyland Leopard PSU3G/4R	Duple Dominant II Express	C49F	1981	Ex Stagecoach, 1994
169	NUF276	Leyland Leopard PSU3G/4R	Duple Dominant II Express	C49F	1981	Ex Stagecoach, 1994
170	VLT272	Leyland Leopard PSU3G/4R	Duple Dominant II Express	C49F	1981	Ex Stagecoach, 1994
171	866NHT	Leyland Leopard PSU3G/4R	Duple Dominant II Express	C49F	1981	Ex Stagecoach, 1994
172	KRS682V	Leyland Leopard PSU3E/4R	Duple Dominant II Express	C53F	1980	Ex Western Scottish, 1995
188w	DWF188V	Bristol VRT/SL3/6LXB	Eastern Coach Works	H43/31F	1979	Ex Stagecoach, 1994
190w	DWF190V	Bristol VRT/SL3/6LXB	Eastern Coach Works	H43/31F	1979	Ex Stagecoach, 1994
191w	DWF191V	Bristol VRT/SL3/6LXB	Eastern Coach Works	H43/31F	1979	Ex Stagecoach, 1994
193w	DWF193V	Bristol VRT/SL3/6LXB	Eastern Coach Works	H43/31F	1979	Ex Stagecoach, 1994
213	HNE252V	Leyland Leopard PSU5C/4R	Duple Dominant II Express	C53F	1980	Ex Stagecoach, 1994
214	HNE254V	Leyland Leopard PSU5C/4R	Duple Dominant II Express	C53F	1980	Ex Stagecoach, 1994
215	JND260V	Leyland Leopard PSU5C/4R	Duple Dominant II Express	C53F	1980	Ex Stagecoach, 1994
216	XRM772Y	Leyland Leopard PSU5C/4R	Duple Dominant III	C57F	1983	Ex Hardie's Coaches, Aberchirder, 1994
217w	D523KSE	Bedford YNV Venturer	Duple 320	C57F	1986	Ex Hardie's Coaches, Aberchirder, 1994
221	WFS135W	Leyland Leopard PSU3F/4R	Alexander AYS	B53F	1980	Ex Stagecoach, 1994
223	WFS137W	Leyland Leopard PSU3F/4R	Alexander AYS	B53F	1980	Ex Stagecoach, 1994
224	F164XCS	Mercedes-Benz 609D	Scott	C24F	1989	Ex Clyde Coast, Ardrossan, 1990
225	F862FWB	Mercedes-Benz 609D	Whittaker Europa	C24F	1989	Ex Metcalfe, Ferryhill, 1990
231	D436RYS	Mercedes-Benz 609D	Scott	C24F	1987	Ex Airpark, Linwood, 1990
232	D322MNC	Mercedes-Benz 609D	Made-to-Measure	DP25F	1986	Ex Western Buses, 1997
233	E364YGB	Mercedes-Benz 609D	Scott	C24F	1988	Ex Airpark, Linwood, 1990
234	E842KAS	Mercedes-Benz 609D	Reeve Burgess	C23F	1988	Ex Glenlivet & District, 1990
235	E947BHS	Mercedes-Benz 609D	Scott	C24F	1988	Ex Whitelaw, Stonehouse, 1990
236	F77HAU	Mercedes-Benz 609D	Scott	C24F	1988	Ex Skills, Sheffield, 1990

239-255

Mercedes-Benz 811D   Carlyle   B29F   1991   Ex Docklands Transit, 1997

239	H989FTT	243	H103HDV	248	H108HDV	251	H985FTT	254	H784GTA
241	H101HDV	244	H181GTA	250	H110HDV	252	H786GTA	255	H785GTA
242	H102HDV	245	H105HDV						

256-292

Mercedes-Benz 709D   Alexander Sprint   B25F*   1990   Ex Stagecoach, 1991-94
*279-292 are B23F

256	G256TSL	262	G262TSL	275	G275TSL	283	G283TSL	288	G288TSL
257	G257TSL	270	G270TSL	276	G276TSL	284	G284TSL	289	G289TSL
258	G258TSL	271	G271TSL	277	G277TSL	285	G285TSL	290	G290TSL
259	G259TSL	272	G272TSL	278	G278TSL	286	G286TSL	291	G291TSL
260	G260TSL	273	G273TSL	279	G279TSL	287	G287TSL	292	G292TSL
261	G261TSL	274	G274TSL	282	G282TSL				

No.	Reg	Chassis	Body	Seating	Year	Notes
293	E713LYU	Mercedes-Benz 811D	Optare StarRider	B28F	1988	Ex Western Scottish, 1995
294	E714LYU	Mercedes-Benz 811D	Optare StarRider	B28F	1988	Ex Western Scottish, 1995
295	F169FWY	Mercedes-Benz 811D	Optare StarRider	B26F	1989	Ex Western Scottish, 1995
296	F177FWY	Mercedes-Benz 811D	Optare StarRider	B26F	1989	Ex Western Scottish, 1995
297	F180FWY	Mercedes-Benz 811D	Optare StarRider	B26F	1989	Ex Western Scottish, 1995
298	G86KUB	Mercedes-Benz 811D	Optare StarRider	B26F	1989	Ex Western Scottish, 1995
299	L550JFS	Mercedes-Benz 814D	Dormobile Routemaker	B33F	1993	Ex John G Gordon, Dornoch, 1996
301	L301JSA	Mercedes-Benz 709D	Alexander Sprint	DP25F	1993	
302	L302JSA	Mercedes-Benz 709D	Alexander Sprint	DP25F	1993	
303	L303JSA	Mercedes-Benz 709D	Alexander Sprint	DP25F	1993	

Many of the services provided by Bluebird Buses cover longer distances than the metropolitan centres in England. To provide extra comfort many vehicles fitted with high-back seats are used on these routes, a trend which is also being followed in other rural operations. Seen arriving in Aberdeen from Port Lethen is 458, **WAO643Y.** *Tony Wilson*

304-314

Mercedes-Benz 709D — Alexander Sprint — DP25F — 1990 Ex Stagecoach, 1991-94

304	G193PAO	**307**	G196PAO	**309**	G198PAO	**311**	G200PAO	**313**	G202PAO
305	G194PAO	**308**	G197PAO	**310**	G199PAO	**312**	G201PAO	**314**	G203PAO
306	G195PAO								

315-321

Mercedes-Benz 709D — Alexander Sprint — DP25F — 1993-94

315	L315JSA	**317**	M317RSO	**319**	M319RSO	**320**	M320RSO	**321**	M321RSO
316	L316JSA	**318**	M318RSO						

336-352

Mercedes-Benz 709D — Alexander Sprint — B25F — 1996

336	N636VSS	**340**	N640VSS	**344**	P344ASO	**347**	P347ASO	**350**	P350ASO
337	N637VSS	**341**	P341ASO	**345**	P345ASO	**348**	P348ASO	**351**	P351ASO
338	N638VSS	**342**	P342ASO	**346**	P346ASO	**349**	P349ASO	**352**	P352ASO
339	N639VSS	**343**	P343ASO						

421	A116ESA	Leyland Tiger TRBTL11/2R	Alexander P	B52F	1983	
422	A117ESA	Leyland Tiger TRBTL11/2R	Alexander P	B52F	1983	
423	A118ESA	Leyland Tiger TRBTL11/2R	Alexander P	B52F	1983	

424-430

Leyland Tiger TRBLXB/2RH — Alexander P — B52F — 1984

424	A121GSA	**426**	A123GSA	**428**	A125GSA	**429**	A126GSA	**430**	A127GSA
425	A122GSA	**427**	A124GSA						

431	PES190Y	Leyland Tiger TRCTL11/3R	Duple Laser	C55F	1983	Ex Fife Scottish, 1994
432	NIB5455	Leyland Tiger TRCTL11/3RH	Duple Laser	C51F	1984	Ex Stagecoach, 1994
433	A940XGG	Leyland Tiger TRCTL11/3R	Duple Laser	C51F	1984	Ex Fife Scottish, 1994
434	A941XGG	Leyland Tiger TRCTL11/3R	Duple Laser	C51F	1984	Ex Fife Scottish, 1994
435	A942XGG	Leyland Tiger TRCTL11/3R	Duple Laser	C51F	1984	Ex Fife Scottish, 1994
436	B158WRN	Leyland Tiger TRCTL11/3RH	Duple Laser 2	C53F	1985	Ex Ribble, 1997
437	927GTA	Leyland Tiger TRCTL11/3RH	Duple Laser 2	C53F	1985	Ex Ribble, 1997

Mystery has always excercised the human mind, and one of the attractions of Bluebird's operating area is a chance to see the Loch Ness monster. For two seasons 455, HSK760 has been liveried for The Grand Loch Ness Tour and this vehicle is to be joined in 1998 by 557, a Volvo B10M with Plaxton Paramount bodywork. *Murdoch Currie*

438	TSU638	Leyland Tiger TRCTL11/3R		Plaxton Paramount 3200 E	C53F		1983	Ex Western Buses, 1997	
439	NIB5232	Leyland Tiger TRCTL11/3RH		Plaxton Paramount 3200 II	C51F		1985	Ex Western Buses, 1997	
440	NIB5233	Leyland Tiger TRCTL11/3RH		Plaxton Paramount 3200 II	C51F		1985	Ex Western Buses, 1997	
441	A663WSU	Leyland Tiger TRBTL11/2RP		Alexander TE	DP53F		1983	Ex Kelvin Central, 1993	

442-446		Leyland Tiger TRCTL11/2RP			Alexander TC		C51F*	1985	*443 is C49F; 446 is C47F
442	TSV718	443	TSV719	444	TSV720	445	TSV721	446	TSV722

447	126ASV	Leyland Tiger TRBTL11/2R		Alexander TE	C51F		1983	Ex Kelvin Scottish, 1986	
448	127ASV	Leyland Tiger TRBTL11/2R		Alexander TE	C51F		1983	Ex Kelvin Scottish, 1986	
449	128ASV	Leyland Tiger TRBTL11/2R		Alexander TE	C51F		1983	Ex Kelvin Scottish, 1986	

450-454		Leyland Tiger TRCTL11/3RH			Alexander TC		C57F	1987	
450	D744BRS	451	D437XRS	452	D438XRS	453	147YFM	454	BSK756

455	HSK760	Leyland Tiger TRCLXC/2RH	Duple 320	C53F		1986	Ex Central Scottish, 1989	
456	C111JCS	Leyland Tiger TRCLXC/2RH	Duple 320	C53F		1986	Ex Central Scottish, 1989	
458	WAO643Y	Leyland Tiger TRCTL11/2R	Alexander TE	C47F		1983	Ex Ribble, 1994	
459	RIB4309	Leyland Tiger TRCTL11/2R	Alexander TE	C49F		1983	Ex East Midland, 1991	

460-465		Leyland Tiger TRCTL11/3R			Duple Laser		C53F	1984	Ex National Welsh, 1992
460	AAX600A	461	AAX631A	463	AAX589A	464	AAX601A	465	AKG162A

466	NIB4138	Leyland Tiger TRCTL11/3RH	Duple Laser	C51F		1984	Ex Stagecoach, 1994

491-499		Volvo B6-9.9M			Alexander ALX200		B40F	1996	
491	P491BRS	493	P493BRS	495	P495BRS	497	P497BRS	499	P499BRS
492	P492BRS	494	P494BRS	496	P496BRS	498	P498BRS		

501-512

Dennis Dart 9.8SDL3017 — Alexander Dash — B41F — 1992

501	J501FPS	504	J504FPS	507	J507FPS	509	J509FPS	511	J511FPS
502	J502FPS	505	J505FPS	508	J508FPS	510	J510FPS	512	J512FPS
503	J503FPS	506	J506FPS						

513-522

Dennis Dart 9.8SDL3017 — Alexander Dash — B40F — 1993

513	K101XHG	515	K103XHG	517	K105XHG	519	K107XHG	521	K109XHG
514	K102XHG	516	K104XHG	518	K106XHG	520	K108XHG	522	K110XHG

527-544

Volvo B10M-62 — Plaxton Premiére Interurban DP51F — 1994

527	M527RSO	531	M531RSO	535	M535RSO	539	M539RSO	542	M542RSO
528	M528RSO	532	M532RSO	536	M536RSO	540	M540RSO	543	M543RSO
529	M529RSO	533	M533RSO	537	M537RSO	541	M541RSO	544	M544RSO
530	M530RSO	534	M534RSO	538	M538RSO				

545	1412NE	Volvo B10M-61	Van Hool Alizée	C53F	1986	Ex Hardie's Coaches, Aberchirder, 1994
546	TSV778	Volvo B10M-61	Van Hool Alizée	C53F	1986	Ex Hardie's Coaches, Aberchirder, 1994
547	TSV779	Volvo B10M-61	Van Hool Alizée	C53F	1987	Ex Rainworth Travel, 1992
548	TSV780	Volvo B10M-61	Van Hool Alizée	C53F	1987	Ex Shearings, 1991
549	TSV781	Volvo B10M-61	Van Hool Alizée	C53F	1987	Ex Shearings, 1991
550	CSU920	Volvo B10M-61	Van Hool Alizée	C53F	1987	Ex Rainworth Travel, 1992
551	CSU921	Volvo B10M-61	Van Hool Alizée	C53F	1987	Ex Shearings, 1991
552	CSU922	Volvo B10M-61	Van Hool Alizée	C53F	1987	Ex Shearings, 1991
553	CSU923	Volvo B10M-61	Van Hool Alizée	C53F	1987	Ex Shearings, 1991
554	F277WAF	Volvo B10M-61	Duple 320	C56F	1989	Ex Scotravel, Elgin, 1995
555	DDZ8844	Volvo B10M-61	Duple 320	C57F	1989	Ex Scotravel, Elgin, 1995
556	MIB7416	Volvo B10M-61	Plaxton Paramount 3500 III	C53F	1988	Ex Western Buses, 1996
557	F424GGB	Volvo B10M-61	Plaxton Paramount 3200 III	C57F	1988	Ex Gray, Fochabers, 1996
558	UOT648	Volvo B10M-61	Van Hool Alizée	C53F	1988	Ex Eastons, Inverurie, 1996
559	OSK784	Volvo B10M-61	Duple 320	C53F	1988	Ex Eastons, Inverurie, 1996
560	XRC487	Volvo B10M-61	Van Hool Alizée	DP49F	1985	Ex Eastons, Inverurie, 1996

561-570

Volvo B10M-60 — Plaxton Premiére Interurban DP51F — 1993 — 561/70 ex Stagecoach, 1994

561	K561GSA	563	K563GSA	565	K565GSA	567	K567GSA	569	K569GSA
562	K562GSA	564	K564GSA	566	K566GSA	568	K568GSA	570	K570GSA

571-578

Volvo B10M-55 — Alexander PS — B49F — 1993 — Ex Stagecoach, 1994

571	K571LTS	573	K573LTS	575	K575LTS	577	K577LTS	578	K578LTS
572	K572LTS	574	K574LTS	576	K576LTS				

579	L579JSA	Volvo B10M-60	Plaxton Premiére Interurban	DP51F	1993
580	L580JSA	Volvo B10M-60	Plaxton Premiére Interurban	DP51F	1993
581	L581JSA	Volvo B10M-60	Plaxton Premiére Interurban	DP51F	1993
582	N582XSA	Volvo B10M-62	Plaxton Premiére Interurban	DP51F	1996
583	N583XSA	Volvo B10M-62	Plaxton Premiére Interurban	DP51F	1996
584	N584XSA	Volvo B10M-62	Plaxton Premiére Interurban	DP51F	1996
585	L585JSA	Volvo B10M-60	Plaxton Premiére Interurban	DP51F	1993
586	L586JSA	Volvo B10M-60	Plaxton Premiére Interurban	DP51F	1993
587	L587JSA	Volvo B10M-60	Plaxton Premiére Interurban	DP51F	1993
588	L588JSA	Volvo B10M-60	Plaxton Premiére Interurban	DP51F	1993

589-598

Volvo B10M-55 — Alexander PS — DP48F — 1994

589	M589OSO	591	M591OSO	593	M593OSO	595	M595OSO	597	M597OSO
590	M590OSO	592	M592OSO	594	M594OSO	596	M596OSO	598	M598OSO

618	N618USS	Volvo B10M-62	Plaxton Expressliner 2	C44FT	1995
619	N619USS	Volvo B10M-62	Plaxton Expressliner 2	C44FT	1995
620	N620USS	Volvo B10M-62	Plaxton Expressliner 2	C44FT	1995

Opposite top:- 1996 was a particularly successful year for Bluebird Buses, gaining the Royal Warrant for its services and also winning the Bus Company of the Year award. Vehicles based at Ballater and many of the coaches carry the Royal Warrant as illustrated in this picture of 582, N582XSA. *Opposite, bottom:-* Buses based at Tain and Inverness carry *IT* fleet names signifying Inverness Traction. Pictured in Inverness is 594, M594OSO, a Volvo B10M with Alexander PS bodywork. Following the delivery of the latest fourteen PSs to Inverness and Aberdeen the 1994 batch are being transferred to Stagecoach operations in Perth, where they are displacing Leyland Leopards. *British Bus Publishing / Malc McDonald*

622	P622ESO	Volvo B10M-62	Plaxton Expressliner 2	C44FT	1997	
625	P625NSE	Volvo B10M-62	Plaxton Expressliner 2	C44FT	1997	
626	P626NSE	Volvo B10M-62	Plaxton Expressliner 2	C44FT	1997	
627	P627ESO	Volvo B10M-62	Plaxton Expressliner 2	C44FT	1997	

628-640

Volvo B10M-62 — Plaxton Premiére Interurban DP51F — 1996-97

628	N148XSA	631	N151XSA	634	N154XSA	637	R637RSE	639	R639RSE
629	N149XSA	632	N152XSA	636	R636RSE	638	R638RSE	640	R640RSE
630	N150XSA	633	N153XSA					

641-654

Volvo B10M-55 — Alexander PS — DP48F — 1997-98

641	R641LSO	644	R644LSO	647	R647LSO	650	R650LSO	653	R653VSE
642	R642LSO	645	R645LSO	648	R648LSO	651	R651VSE	654	R654VSE
643	R643LSO	646	R646LSO	649	R649LSO	652	R652VSE		

Special event vehicles - traditional liveries

1101	EDS50A	AEC Routemaster R2RH	Park Royal	H36/28R	1960	Ex Stagecoach, 1994
1102	NSG636A	AEC Routemaster R2RH	Park Royal	H36/28R	1962	Ex Stagecoach, 1994
1105	ALD968B	AEC Routemaster 2R2RH	Park Royal	H36/28R	1964	Ex Stagecoach, 1994
1106	LDS201A	AEC Routemaster 2R2RH	Park Royal	H36/24R	1963	Ex Stagecoach, 1994
1107	490CLT	AEC Routemaster R2RH	Park Royal	H32/25R	1962	Ex Stagecoach Selkent, 1994
1109u	FES831W	Volvo B58-61	Duple Dominant IV	DP59F	1981	Ex Stagecoach, 1994
1110u	NMY643E	AEC Routemaster R2RH2	Park Royal	H32/24F	1967	Ex Kelvin Scottish, 1993
1111	GRS343E	Albion Viking VK43AL	Alexander Y	DP40F	1967	Ex Stagecoach, 1994
1112	HDV639E	Bristol MW6G	Eastern Coach Works	C39F	1967	Ex preservation, 1996
1113u	HGM335E	Bristol FLF6G	Eastern Coach Works	H44/34F	1967	Ex Stagecoach, 1994
1114u	HFM561D	Bristol MW6G	Eastern Coach Works	C39F	1966	Ex preservation, 1996
1115	DGS625	Leyland Tiger PS1/2	McLennan	C39F	1951	Ex Stagecoach, 1994
1116	LDS210A	AEC Routemaster R2RH	Park Royal	H36/28R	1962	Ex Stagecoach, 1994
1117	SJW515	Guy Warrior WUF	Burlingham Seagull	C41F	1956	Ex Dodds, Troon, 1997
1118u	RRS46R	Leyland Leopard PSU3E/4R	Duple Dominant I	C49F	1977	

Previous Registrations:

126ASV	BMS511Y	KRS682V	GTO798V, 145CLT
127ASV	BMS513Y	L100JLB	L110JSA
128ASV	BMS515Y	LDS201A	607DYE
1412NE	C325DND	LDS210A	245CLT
147YFM	D439XRS	LSK548	D438XRS
490CLT	From new	MHS4P	C464SSO
866NHT	ORS110W, TSV722, PSO32W	MHS5P	C465SSO
927GTA	B157WRN	MIB7416	E408MSX, 174NJO, E898CGA, DJU704,
9492SC	TSO19X		E605CHS.
A663WSU	A120GLS, WLT976	NIB4138	A45YAK
A940XGG	A507PST, GSU344	NIB5232	D47DWE
A941XGG	A505PST, GSU342	NIB5233	D48DWE
A942XGG	A506PST, GSU343	NIB5455	A46YAK
AAX589A	A216VWO	NSG636A	164CLT
AAX600A	A219VWO	NUF276	ORS108W, TSV720, PSO27W, OVL473
AAX601A	A218VWO	OSK784	E748JAY, A3KRT
AAX631A	A222VWO	PES190Y	VTY130Y, GSU341
AKG162A	A223VWO	RBZ5497	D46UAO
B291YSL	B209FFS, GSU343	RIB4309	A40XHE
BSK756	E640BRS	SJW515	From new
CSU920	D550MVR	TSU638	BKK838Y
CSU921	D551MVR	TSV718	B328LSA
CSU922	D552MVR	TSV719	B329LSA
CSU923	D553MVR	TSV720	B330LSA
D437XRS	D437XRS, LSK547	TSV721	B331LSA
D744BRS	D436XRS, BSK744	TSV722	B332LSA
DGS625	From new	TSV778	C330DND
DDZ8844	F27LTO	TSV779	D547MVR
EDS50A	WLT560	TSV780	D548MVR
GSO1V	C471SSO	TSV781	D549MVR
HSR136W	ORS106W, TSV718, PSO27W, 4585SC	UOT648	E644UNE, LSK874
HSK760	C110JCS	VLT272	ORS109W, TSV721, PSO31W, LSK528
KRS531V	HSA97V, CSU921	XRC487	From new
KRS532V	HSA98V, CSU922		

Allocations:-

Aberdeen (Hillview Road, East Tullos) - Bluebird Buses

Outstations - Montgarrie Road, Alford; Castleton Place, Braemar; Ellon; New Byth and Bellabeg,Strathdon.

Mercedes-Benz	258	259	292	293	294	295		
Dart	519	520	521	522				
Leopard	143							
Tiger	422	423	424	425	427	430	431	461
	463	467						
Interurban	528	588	639	640				
B10M Coach	545	546	547					
B10M PS	589	590	591	592	593			
Olympian	038	046	047	051	052	053	062	065
	066	085	086	088	089	091		

Ballater (Golf Road) - Bluebird Buses

Mercedes-Benz	306		
Dart	503		
Tiger	442	446	
Interurban	586	587	
Olympian	044	061	064

Elgin (Pinefield) - Bluebird Buses

Outstation - March Road, Buckie; North Road, Forres

Mercedes-Benz	224	256	260	274	275	276	277	278
	282	289	290	291	302	303	315	316
	317	318	319					
Leopard	134	136	137	139	140	163	164	216
Tiger	433	434	450					
Interurban	527	534	536	544	579	580	581	584
B10M Coach	554	555	556	557				
Bristol VR	111	114	117	125				
Olympian	034	035	039	040	043	054	055	087

Fyvie (Schoolhill) - Bluebird Buses

Leopard	142					
Tiger	443	444	445	447	448	453

Tain is the setting for this picture of 446, TSV722, a Leyland Tiger with Alexander TC-type bodywork which was new to Bluebird as B332LSA. The vehicle is now based at Aberdeen depot, and provides interesting comparison to the TE model on page 26. *Murdoch Currie*

Inverurie ( ) - Bluebird Buses

Mercedes-Benz	227	285	305
B10M Coach	549	551	558
Olympian	008	009	010	011

Inverness (Burnett Road) - Inverness Traction

Outstation - Kiltarlity

Mercedes-Benz	257	283	284	304	308	314	341	342
	343	344	345	346	347	348	349	351
Dart	501	504	505	506	507	508	509	510
	511	512	513	514	515	516	517	
Tiger	455	456						
Interurban	535	537	538	542	543	585		
B10M Coach	548	550	552	553				
B10M PS	594	595	596	597	598			
Olympian	056	057						

Macduff (Union Road) - Bluebird Buses

Outstation - Aberchirder

Mercedes-Benz	233	234	286	287	288	301	313	
Leopard	144	152	153	154	160			
Tiger	464	465						
Interurban	628	629	630	631	632	633	634	636
Bristol VR	104	109	113	123	124	126		

Perth (Ruthvenfield Road) - Stagecoach - National Express ♣

Outstations - Stirling Road, Crieff; Spittalfield

Mercedes-Benz	309	310	311	312	336	337	338	339
	340							
Volvo B6	491	492	493	494	495	496	497	498
	499							
Leopard	155	156	157	158	167	169	170	171
	172	213	214	215	221	223		
Interurban	529	561	570					
B10M Coach	560	618♣	619♣	620♣	622♣	625♣	626♣	627♣
B10M PS	571	572	573	574	575	576	577	578
Bristol VR	188	190	191	193				
Olympian	012	013	014	017	019	020	021	022
	023	024	025	029	030	031	032	067
	068	069	070	071	101			
Heritage	1112	1115	1117					

Peterhead (St Peter Street) - Bluebird Buses

Outstations - Hanover Street, Fraserburgh; Longside Road, Mintlaw

Mercedes-Benz	261	262	270	271	272	273	279	307
	320	321						
Dart	502	518						
Leopard	141	161	165	166				
Tiger	428	429	449	451	458			
Interurban	530	531	532	533	562	563	564	565
	566	567	568	569	637	638		
B10M Coach	547							
Bristol VR	116							
Olympian	002	003	005	006	036	037	045	048
	058	063	096	097	098	099		

Mercedes-Benz minibuses provide the entire small vehicle requirement for Bluebird Buses though these carry a variety of body styles. In 1998 the StarRiders are expected to be withdrawn leaving the work mostly in the hands of Alexander Sprint-bodied examples like 340, N640VSS which is seen on service in Perth. *Malc McDonald*

Stonehaven (Spurryhillock Ind Est) - Bluebird Buses

Mercedes-Benz	231	235	296	297	298			
Leopard	148							
Tiger	421	426	434	459	460	468		
Interurban	582	583						
Olympian	004	007	015	018	033	041	042	049
	050							

Tain (Scotsburn Road) - Inverness Traction

Outstation - Lairg

Mercedes-Benz	225	236	299	350	352			
Tiger	452	454						
Interurban	539	540	541					
B10M Coach	559							
Olympian	026	027	028	059	060	090	092	100
	102							

Unallocated and reserve

Mercedes-Benz	237	238	239	240	241	242	243	244
	245	246	247	248	249	250	251	252
	254	255						
Bedford	217							
Leopard	131	132	133	135	138	145	146	147
	149	150	151	162				
Tiger	436	437	438	439	440			
Bristol VR	072	074	075	076	077	078	079	103
	105	106	107	108	110	112	115	120
	122	128						
Titan O/T	080	081	082	083	084			
Heritage	1102	1105	1116					
Heritage at SVB Museum	1106	1107	1109	1110	1111	1113	1114	1118

BUSWAYS

Busways Travel Services Ltd, Manors, Newcastle-upon-Tyne, NE1 2EL

66	TBC2X	Leyland Leopard PSU3F/4R	Plaxton Supreme IV Express	C53F	1981	Ex City of Nottingham, 1988
81	L81YBB	Volvo B10M-62	Plaxton Expressliner 2	C44FT	1993	
82	L82YBB	Volvo B10M-62	Plaxton Expressliner 2	C44FT	1993	
83	L83YBB	Volvo B10M-62	Plaxton Expressliner 2	C44FT	1993	
84	L84YBB	Volvo B10M-62	Plaxton Expressliner 2	C44FT	1993	
91	N91RVK	Volvo B10M-62	Plaxton Expressliner 2	C44FT	1996	
92	P92URG	Volvo B10M-62	Plaxton Expressliner 2	C44FT	1996	

101-125

Leyland Lynx LX112L10ZR1S Leyland B49F 1988-89

101	F101HVK	106	F106HVK	111	F111HVK	116	F116HVK	121	F121HVK
102	F102HVK	107	F107HVK	112	F112HVK	117	F117HVK	122	F122HVK
103	F103HVK	108	F108HVK	113	F113HVK	118	F118HVK	123	F123HVK
104	F104HVK	109	F109HVK	114	F114HVK	119	F119HVK	124	F124HVK
105	F105HVK	110	F110HVK	115	F115HVK	120	F120HVK	125	F125HVK

126	H126ACU	Leyland Lynx LX2R11C15Z4S	Leyland	DP47F	1990
127	H127ACU	Leyland Lynx LX2R11C15Z4S	Leyland	DP47F	1990

204-223

Leyland Atlantean AN68A/2R Alexander AL H49/37F 1980

204	EJR104W	208	EJR108W	211	EJR111W	215	EJR115W	219	EJR119W
205	EJR105W	209	EJR109W	212	EJR112W	217	EJR117W	222	EJR122W
207	EJR107W	210	EJR110W	214	EJR114W	218	EJR118W	223	EJR123W

248-303

Leyland Atlantean AN68A/2R Alexander AL H49/37F 1978

248	SCN248S	267u	SCN267S	279u	SCN279S	289u	UVK289T	300	UVK300T
251	SCN251S	268	SCN268S	282u	SCN282S	290	UVK290T	302u	VCU302T
254	SCN254S	270	SCN270S	283	SCN283S	295u	UVK295T	303	VCU303T
259	SCN259S	277	SCN277S	287	UVK287T	299	UVK299T		

314-363

Leyland Atlantean AN68A/2R Alexander AL H49/37F 1980

314	AVK134V	319	AVK139V	330	AVK150V	339u	AVK159V	351	AVK171V
315	AVK135V	321	AVK141V	334	AVK154V	340	AVK160V	360	AVK180V
316	AVK136V	326	AVK146V	336	AVK156V	341u	AVK161V	363	AVK183V
318	AVK138V	329	AVK149V	338	AVK158V	350	AVK170V		

Busways undertake several duties for National Express for which a fleet of Volvo coaches are operated. These are now in Flightlink livery as illustrated by 91, N91RVK pictured at Milton Keynes while heading south to Gatwick airport.
Phillip Stephenson

421-430

Scania N113DRB — Alexander RH — H47/29F — 1990

421	H421BNL	423	H423BNL	425	H425BNL	427	H427BNL	429	H429BNL
422	H422BNL	424	H424BNL	426	H426BNL	428	H428BNL	430	H430BNL

500u	MVK500R	Leyland Atlantean AN68A/2R	Alexander AL	H48/35F	1976
532u	MVK532R	Leyland Atlantean AN68A/2R	Alexander AL	H48/31F	1976
544	MVK544R	Leyland Atlantean AN68A/2R	Alexander AL	H48/31F	1977
551	MVK551R	Leyland Atlantean AN68A/2R	Alexander AL	H48/33F	1977

601-665

Leyland Olympian ONLXB/1R — Alexander RH — H45/31F — 1985-86

601	C601LFT	615	C615LFT	628	C628LFT	641	C641LFT	654	C654LFT
602	C602LFT	616	C616LFT	629	C629LFT	642	C642LFT	655	C655LFT
603	C603LFT	617	C617LFT	630	C630LFT	643	C643LFT	656	C656LFT
604	C604LFT	618	C618LFT	631	C631LFT	644	C644LFT	657	C657LFT
605	C605LFT	619	C619LFT	632	C632LFT	645	C645LFT	658	C658LFT
606	C606LFT	620	C620LFT	633	C633LFT	646	C646LFT	659	C659LFT
608	C608LFT	621	C621LFT	634	C634LFT	647	C647LFT	660	C660LFT
609	C609LFT	622	C622LFT	635	C635LFT	648	C648LFT	661	C661LFT
610	C610LFT	623	C623LFT	636	C636LFT	649	C649LFT	662	C662LFT
611	C611LFT	624	C624LFT	637	C637LFT	650	C650LFT	663	C663LFT
612	C612LFT	625	C625LFT	638	C638LFT	651	C651LFT	664	C664LFT
613	C613LFT	626	C626LFT	639	C639LFT	652	C652LFT	665	C665LFT
614	C614LFT	627	C627LFT	640	C640LFT	653	C653LFT		

667-676

Leyland Olympian ON2R50C13Z4 — Northern Counties Palatine — H47/30F — 1990-91

667	H667BNL	669	H669BNL	671	H671BNL	673	H673BNL	675	H675BNL
668	H668BNL	670	H670BNL	672	H672BNL	674	H674BNL	676	H676BNL

677-697

Leyland Olympian ONLXB/1RH — Northern Counties — H43/30F — 1988 — Ex London Buses, 1991

677	E901KYR	682	E909KYR	686	E914KYR	690	E919KYR	694	E923KYR
678	E905KYR	683	E910KYR	687	E915KYR	691	E920KYR	695	E924KYR
679	E906KYR	684	E911KYR	688	E917KYR	692	E921KYR	696	E925KYR
680	E907KYR	685	E912KYR	689	E918KYR	693	E922KYR	697	E927KYR
681	E908KYR								

701-740

Volvo Olympian YN2RV18Z4 — Alexander RL — H47/28F — 1995

701	N701LTN	709	N709LTN	717	N717LTN	725	N725LTN	733	N733LTN
702	N702LTN	710	N710LTN	718	N718LTN	726	N726LTN	734	N734LTN
703	N703LTN	711	N711LTN	719	N719LTN	727	N727LTN	735	N735LTN
704	N704LTN	712	N712LTN	720	N720LTN	728	N728LTN	736	N736LTN
705	N705LTN	713	N713LTN	721	N721LTN	729	N729LTN	737	N737LTN
706	N706LTN	714	N714LTN	722	N722LTN	730	N730LTN	738	N738LTN
707	N707LTN	715	N715LTN	723	N723LTN	731	N731LTN	739	N739LTN
708	N708LTN	716	N716LTN	724	N724LTN	732	N732LTN	740	N740LTN

815-838

Leyland Fleetline FE30AGR — Alexander AL — H44/30F — 1977

815w	OCU815R	819	OCU819R	821w	OCU821R	833u	RCU833S	837	RCU837S
816	OCU816R	820	OCU820R	822	OCU822R	834	RCU834S	838	RCU838S
818	OCU818R								

901-920

Scania N113CRB — Alexander PS — B51F* — 1989 — *901-5 are B48F; 906 is B49F

901	F901JRG	905	F905JRG	909	F909JRG	913	F913JRG	917	F917JRG
902	F902JRG	906	F906JRG	910	F910JRG	914	F914JRG	918	F918JRG
903	F903JRG	907	F907JRG	911	F911JRG	915	F915JRG	919	F919JRG
904	F904JRG	908	F908JRG	912	F912JRG	916	F916JRG	920	F920JRG

921-926

Scania N113CRB — Alexander PS — B51F* — 1989-90 — *926 is B49F

921	G921TCU	923	G923TCU	924	G924TCU	925	G925TCU	926	G926TCU
922	G922TCU							

927	G113SKX	Scania N113CRB	Alexander PS	B49F	1989	Ex Scania demonstrator, 1991

928-937

Scania N113CRB — Alexander PS — B51F — 1991

928	H428EFT	930	H430EFT	932	H432EFT	934	H434EFT	936	H436EFT
929	H429EFT	931	H431EFT	933	H433EFT	935	H435EFT	937	H437EFT

938	G108CEH	Scania N113CRB	Alexander PS	B49F	1990	Ex Stevensons, 1993

951	M951DRG	Scania L113CRL	Northern Counties Paladin	B49F	1994
952	M952DRG	Scania L113CRL	Northern Counties Paladin	DP49F	1994
953	M953DRG	Scania L113CRL	Alexander Strider	B51F	1994
954	M954DRG	Scania L113CRL	Alexander Strider	B51F	1994

1101-1128

Dennis Dart SLF — Alexander ALX200 — B37F — 1997-98

1101	R101KRG	1108	R108KRG	1114	R114KRG	1119	R119KRG	1124	R124KRG
1102	R102KRG	1109	R109KRG	1115	R115KRG	1120	R120KRG	1125	R125KRG
1103	R103KRG	1110	R110KRG	1116	R116KRG	1121	R121KRG	1126	R126KRG
1104	R104KRG	1112	R112KRG	1117	R117KRG	1122	R122KRG	1127	R127KRG
1105	R105KRG	1113	R113KRG	1118	R118KRG	1123	R123KRG	1128	R128KRG
1107	R107KRG								

1201	M201DRG	Dennis Lance 11SDA3113	Plaxton Verde	B49F	1994
1202	M202DRG	Dennis Lance 11SDA3113	Plaxton Verde	B49F	1994
1203	M203DRG	Dennis Lance 11SDA3113	Plaxton Verde	B49F	1994
1204	M204DRG	Dennis Lance 11SDA3113	Optare Sigma	B47F	1994
1218u	KBB118D	Leyland Atlantean PDR1/1R	MCW	O44/34F	1966
1227	SVK627G	Leyland Atlantean PDR1A/1R	Alexander J	O44/30F	1969

1401-1459

Mercedes-Benz 709D — Reeve Burgess Beaver — B19F* — 1987-88 *1431/49/51/3 are B23F
1426/9/35/40/2/3/5/50/4-9 are B20F

1401u	D401TFT	1425	E425AFT	1432	E432AFT	1443u	E443AFT	1453	E453AFT
1402	D402TFT	1426	E426AFT	1433	E433AFT	1445	E445AFT	1454	E454AFT
1415	D415TFT	1427	E427AFT	1434	E434AFT	1447	E447AFT	1455	E455AFT
1419	D419TFT	1428	E428AFT	1435u	E435AFT	1449	E449AFT	1456	E456AFT
1421	E421AFT	1429	E429AFT	1437	E437AFT	1450	E450AFT	1457	E457AFT
1422u	E422AFT	1430	E430AFT	1440u	E440AFT	1451	E451AFT	1458	E458AFT
1423	E423AFT	1431	E431AFT	1442u	E442AFT	1452	E452AFT	1459	E459AFT
1424	E424AFT								

1461-1500

Mercedes-Benz 709D — Alexander Sprint — B23F — 1996

1461	N461RVK	1469	N469RVK	1477	N477RVK	1485	N485RVK	1493	N493RVK
1462	N462RVK	1470	N470RVK	1478	N478RVK	1486	N486RVK	1494	N494RVK
1463	N463RVK	1471	N471RVK	1479	N479RVK	1487	N487RVK	1495	N495RVK
1464	N464RVK	1472	N472RVK	1480	N480RVK	1488	N488RVK	1496	N496RVK
1465	N465RVK	1473	N473RVK	1481	N481RVK	1489	N489RVK	1497	N497RVK
1466	N466RVK	1474	N474RVK	1482	N482RVK	1490	N490RVK	1498	N498RVK
1467	N467RVK	1475	N475RVK	1483	N483RVK	1491	N491RVK	1499	N499RVK
1468	N468RVK	1476	N476RVK	1484	N484RVK	1492	N492RVK	1500	N501RVK

1635	E635BVK	Renault-Dodge S56	Alexander AM	B25F	1987
1637	E637BVK	Renault-Dodge S56	Alexander AM	B25F	1987

1679-1693

Optare MetroRider — Optare — B29F — 1991-92 Ex Welcome, 1993

1679	J371BNW	1682	J374BNW	1685	J377BNW	1688u	J380BNW	1691	K164FYG
1680	J372BNW	1683	J375BNW	1686	J378BNW	1689	K162FYG	1692	K165FYG
1681	J373BNW	1684	J376BNW	1687	J379BNW	1690	K163FYG	1693	K166FYG

1701	J701KCU	Dennis Dart 9.8SDL3017	Plaxton Pointer	B40F	1992
1702	J702KCU	Dennis Dart 9.8SDL3017	Plaxton Pointer	B40F	1992

Opposite: -**Busways provide the main services in The city of Newcastle, Sunderland as their surrounding areas. Apart from some Atlanteans and Fleetlines the Busways fleet has now been re-liveried into corporate colours. The Favourite and some of the Blue Bus unit's also retain their former colours, though a start has been made to bring the Blue Bus vehicles into livery. Pictured here are Scania 953, M953DRG and Volvo B10M with Alexander PS bodywork, 2225, P125XCN. In January 1997, several of the batch were diverted to Ribble where they were placed in service at Bolton.**
Richard Godfrey

1703-1743

Dennis Dart 9.8SDL3017* Alexander Dash B40F 1992-93 *1723-28 are 9.8SDL3025; *1729-43 are 9.8SDL3035

1703 K703PCN	1711 K711PCN	1721 K721PCN	1729 L729VNL	1737 L737VNL
1704 K704PCN	1712 K712PCN	1722 K722PCN	1730 L730VNL	1738 L738VNL
1705 K705PCN	1713 K713PCN	1723 K723PNL	1731 L731VNL	1739 L739VNL
1706 K706PCN	1714 K714PCN	1724 K724PNL	1732 L732VNL	1740 L740VNL
1707 K707PCN	1715 K715PCN	1725 K725PNL	1733 L733VNL	1741 L741VNL
1708 K708PCN	1717 K717PCN	1726 K726PNL	1734 L734VNL	1742 L742VNL
1709 K709PCN	1718 K718PCN	1727 K727PNL	1735 L735VNL	1743 L743VNL
1710 K710PCN	1720 K720PCN	1728 K728PNL	1736 L736VNL	

1744-1759

Dennis Dart 9.8SDL3035 Plaxton Pointer B40F 1993

1744u L744VNL	1748 L748VNL	1751 L751VNL	1754 L754VNL	1757 L757VNL
1745 L745VNL	1749 L749VNL	1752 L752VNL	1755 L755VNL	1758 L758VNL
1746 L746VNL	1750 L750VNL	1753 L753VNL	1756 L756VNL	1759 L759VNL

1760-1765

Dennis Dart 9.8SDL3040 Alexander Dash B40F 1994

1760 L760ARG	1762 L762ARG	1763 L763ARG	1764 L764ARG	1765 L765ARG
1761 L761ARG				

1766-1771

Dennis Dart 9.8SDL3040 Plaxton Pointer B40F 1994

1766 M766DRG	1768 M768DRG	1769 M769DRG	1770 M770DRG	1771 M771DRG
1767 M767DRG				

1772-1785

Dennis Dart Alexander Dash B40F 1996

1772 N772RVK	1775 N775RVK	1778 N779RVK	1781 P781WCN	1784 P784WCN
1773 N773RVK	1776 N776RVK	1779 N780RVK	1782 P782WCN	1785 P785WCN
1774 N774RVK	1777 N778RVK	1780 P780WCN	1783 P783WCN	

1786-1793

Dennis Dart Alexander Dash B40F 1996-97

1786 P786WVK	1788 P788WVK	1790 P790WVK	1792 P792WVK	1793 P793WVK
1787 P787WVK	1789 P789WVK	1791 P791WVK		

1832	LBN201P	Leyland Leopard PSU3C/4R	Plaxton Elite III Express	C51F	1976 Ex Southend, 1987
1833	LBN202P	Leyland Leopard PSU3C/4R	Plaxton Elite III Express	C51F	1976 Ex Southend, 1988
1863	ESU263	Leyland Tiger TRCTL11/3R	Plaxton Paramount 3500	C49FT	1984 Ex Armchair, Brentford, 1992
1901	M901DRG	Volvo B10B	Alexander Strider	B51F	1994
1902	M902DRG	Volvo B10B	Alexander Strider	B51F	1994

2201-2217

Volvo B10M-55 Alexander PS B49F 1995

2201 N201LTN	2205 N205LTN	2209 N209LTN	2212 N212LTN	2215 N215LTN
2202 N202LTN	2206 N206LTN	2210 N210LTN	2213 N213LTN	2216 N216LTN
2203 N203LTN	2207 N207LTN	2211 N211LTN	2214 N214LTN	2217 N217LTN
2204 N204LTN	2208 N208LTN			

2218-2235

Volvo B10M-55 Alexander PS B49F 1996

2218 P118XCN	2220 P120XCN	2222 P122XCN	2224 P124XCN	2226 P126XCN
2219 P119XCN	2221 P121XCN	2223 P123XCN	2225 P125XCN	2235 P135XCN

2236-2257

Volvo B10BLE Alexander ALX300 B44F 1997-98

2236 R236KRG	2241 R241KRG	2246 R246KRG	2250 R250KRG	2254 R254KRG
2237 R237KRG	2242 R242KRG	2247 R247KRG	2251 R251KRG	2255 R255KRG
2238 R238KRG	2243 R243KRG	2248 R248KRG	2252 R252KRG	2256 R256KRG
2239 R239KRG	2244 R244KRG	2249 R249KRG	2253 R253KRG	2257 R257KRG
2240 R240KRG	2245 R245KRG			

Special event vehicles - traditional liveries

B140	LCU112	Daimler CCG6	Roe	H35/28R	1964
B141	WBR248	Atkinson PM746HL	Marshall	B45D	1964 Ex Preservation, 1986
B141	FBR53D	Leyland Panther PSUR1/1	Strachan	B47D	1966 Ex Preservation, 1986

1997 saw the end of the Bristol RE in service with Busways as the last were replaced on Blue Bus services by Dennis Darts. Pictured in Newcastle is Plaxton-bodied Dart 1750, L750VNL, illustrating the application of Blue Bus services name. *Richard Godfrey*

Ancilliary vehicles:-

DT18	D298YTY	Dodge Commando G10	Wadham Stringer Vanguard B-F	1987	Ex MoD, 1997
DT19	D305YTY	Dodge Commando G10	Wadham Stringer Vanguard B-F	1987	Ex MoD, 1997
DT20	B866JVK	Dodge Commando G10	Wadham Stringer Vanguard B-F	1985	Ex MoD, 1997
DT21	D918KPT	Dodge Commando G10	Wadham Stringer Vanguard B-F	1986	Ex MoD, 1997

Previous registrations:

ESU263	A829PPP

Allocations:-

Byker (Shields Road) - Blue Bus Services - Flightlink ✈

Volvo B10M	81✈	82✈	83✈	84✈	91✈	92✈		
Tiger	66	1832	1833					
Mercedes-Benz	1402	1415	1419	1424	1425	1437	1447	1452
	1483	1484	1485	1486				
MetroRider	1689	1690	1691					
Dart	1701	1702	1713	1718	1720	1722	1723	1724
	1745	1746	1750	1751	1752	1753		
Atlantean	204	205	207	208	268	277	303	326
	338	340	544					

Byker (Shields Road) - Busways Newcastle - Magic Bus ♠

Mercedes-Benz	1421	1423	1426	1427	1428	1429	1430	1432
	1433	1434	1461	1462	1463	1464	1465	1466
	1467	1468	1469					
Scania SD	906	928	929	933	934	935	936	937
	951	952	953	954				
Volvo B10BLE	2236							
Atlantean	209♠	210♠	211♠	212♠	214♠	217♠	218♠	219♠
	251♠	254♠	259♠	300♠	314♠	315♠	316♠	318 29Mi
	321♠	329♠	336♠	350♠	351♠	360♠	363♠	
Olympian	602	603	604	605	606	608	609	610
	611	612	613	614	615	616	617	618
	619	625	663	684♠	685♠	686♠	687♠	688♠
	689♠	690♠	692♠	694♠	701	702	703	704
	705	706	707	708	709	710	711	712
	713	714	715	716	717	718	719	720
	721	722	723	724	725	726	727	728
	729	730						
Scania DD	421	422	423	424	425	426	427	428
	429	430						

Slatyford (Slatyford Lane) - Busways Newcastle

Mercedes-Benz	1470	1471	1472	1473	1474	1475	1476	1477
	1478	1479	1480	1481	1482			
Scania SD	901	902	903	904	905	907	908	909
	910	911	912	913	914	915	916	917
	918	919	920	921	922	923	924	925
	926	927	930	931	932	938		
Volvo B10M	2201	2202	2203	2204	2205	2206	2207	2208
	2218	2219	2220	2221	2222	2223	2224	2225
	2226	2235						
Olympian	601	620	621	622	623	624	626	627
	628	629	630	631	632	633	634	635
	636	637	638	639	640	641	642	643
	644	645	646	647	648	649	662	664
	665	677	678	679	680	681	682	683
	691	693	695	696	697			

South Shields (Dean Road) - Busways South Shields - Economic ♦

Mercedes-Benz	1431	1449	1450	1451	1453	1454	1456	1457
	1458	1459	1487	1488	1489	1490	1491	1492
	1493	1494	1495	1496				
Dart	1703	1704	1705	1706	1707	1708	1709	1710
	1711	1712	1740	1741	1742	1743	1749♦	1754
	1755	1756	1757	1758	1759	1766	1767	1768
	1769	1783	1784	1785	1790	1791♦	1792♦	1793♦
Lynx	101	108	115	116	117	118♦	119	120
	121	122	123	124	125	126	127♦	
Atlantean	215	222	248	270	283	287	290	299
	1227♦							
Olympian	675♦	676♦	731♦	732♦	733♦	734♦	735♦	736♦
	737♦	738♦	739♦	740♦				

Sunderland (North Bridge Street) - Busways Sunderland - Favourite♥

Mercedes-Benz	1435	1440	1442	1443	1445	1455	1497♥	1498♥
	1499♥	1500♥						
MetroRiders	1679	1680	1681	1682	1683	1684	1685	1686
	1687	1692	1693					
Renault Dodge	1635	1637						
Dart	1714♥	1715♥	1717♥	1721♥	1725	1726	1727	1728
	1729	1730	1731	1732	1733	1734	1735	1736
	1737	1738	1739	1748♥	1760	1761	1762	1763
	1764	1765	1770♥	1771♥	1772	1773	1774	1775
	1776	1777	1778	1779	1780	1781	1782	1786
	1787	1788	1789	1790				
Dart SLF	1101	1102	1103	1104	1105	1107	1108	1109
	1110	1112	1113	1114				
Lynx	102	103♥	104	105	106	107	109	110
	111	112	113	114				
Lance	1201	1202	1203	1204				
Tiger	1863♥							
Volvo B10	1901	1902	2209	2210	2211	2212	2213	2214
	2215	2216	2217					
Atlantean	223♥	319♥	330♥	334♥				
Fleetline	816	818	819	820	822	834	837	838
Olympian	650	651	652	653	654	655	656	657
	658	659	660	661	667	668	669	670
	671	672	673	674				

Unallocated

Mercedes-Benz	1401	1422	1455					
MetroRider	1688							
Dart	1744							
Atlantean	267	279	282	289	295	302	339	341
	500	532	1218					
Fleetline	815	821	833					

Busways are currently taking delivery of the first Alexander ALX300 buses for the Group with a batch of twenty-three on Volvo B10BLE chassis. Representing an earlier large intake from the 1980s is Leyland Olympian 631, C631LFT. The vehicle carries a standard version of Alexander's bodywork.
Richard Godfrey

CAMBUS

Cambus Ltd, 100 Cowley Road, Cambridge CB4 4DN
Viscount Bus & Coach Co Ltd, 351 Lincoln Road, Peterborough, PE1 2PG

| 81 | GAZ4381 | Optare MetroRider MR17 | Optare | B29F | 1999 | CNG Powered |
| 82 | GAZ4382 | Optare MetroRider MR17 | Optare | B29F | 1999 | CNG Powered |

155-169

Volvo B6-9M — Marshall C32 — B32F — 1993

155	L655MFL	158	L658MFL	161	L661MFL	164	L664MFL	168	L668MFL
156	L656MFL	159	L659MFL	162	L662MFL	165	L665MFL	169	L669MFL
157	L657MFL	160	L660MFL	163	L663MFL	167	L667MFL		

200-211

Mercedes-Benz 709D — Alexander Sprint — B25F — 1996 — Ex Western, 1996

200	N614VSS	203	N619VSS	206	N616VSS	208	N620VSS	210	N643VSS
201	N615VSS	204	N641VSS	207	N618VSS	209	N642VSS	211	N644VSS
202	N617VSS	205	N613VSS						

310	F167SMT	Leyland Lynx LX112L10ZR1S	Leyland Lynx	B49F	1989	Ex Miller, Foxton, 1992
311	F168SMT	Leyland Lynx LX112L10ZR1S	Leyland Lynx	B49F	1989	Ex Miller, Foxton, 1992
312	F171SMT	Leyland Lynx LX112L10ZR1S	Leyland Lynx	B49F	1989	Ex Miller, Foxton, 1992

315-319

Volvo B10M-55 — Alexander PS — B49F — 1996

| 315 | P315EFL | 316 | P316EFL | 317 | P317EFL | 318 | P318EFL | 319 | P319EFL |

320	P320EFL	Volvo B6-9.9M	Alexander ALX200	B35F	1997	
321	P321EFL	Volvo B6-9.9M	Alexander ALX200	B35F	1997	
322	P322EFL	Dennis Dart SLF	Alexander ALX200	B39F	1997	
323	P323EFL	Dennis Dart SLF	Alexander ALX200	B39F	1997	
324	P324EFL	Dennis Dart SLF	Alexander ALX200	B39F	1997	
350	N350YFL	Dennis Dart	Alexander Dash	B40F	1996	
351	N351YFL	Dennis Dart	Alexander Dash	B40F	1996	
352	N352YFL	Dennis Dart	Alexander Dash	B40F	1996	
353	R353LER	Dennis Dart	Alexander ALX200	B39F	1997	
354	R354LER	Dennis Dart SLF	Alexander ALX200	B39F	1997	
355	R355LER	Dennis Dart SLF	Alexander ALX200	B39F	1997	
356	R356LER	Dennis Dart SLF	Alexander ALX200	B39F	1997	
364	P364APM	Dennis Dart SLF	Plaxton Pointer	B39F	1996	Ex demonstrator, 1997
365	R365JVA	Dennis Dart SLF	Alexander ALX200	B39F	1997	
366	R366JVA	Dennis Dart SLF	Alexander ALX200	B39F	1997	
407	H407GAV	Volvo B10M-60	Plaxton Paramount 3500 III	C53F	1991	
408	J408TEW	Volvo B10M-60	Plaxton Paramount 3500 III	C53F	1992	
409	J409TEW	Volvo B10M-60	Plaxton Paramount 3500 III	C49FT	1992	
421	K911RGE	Volvo B10M-60	Jonckheere Deauville P599	C49FT	1993	Ex Park's, 1994
422	K912RGE	Volvo B10M-60	Jonckheere Deauville P599	C49FT	1993	Ex Park's, 1994

431-435

Volvo B10M-60 — Plaxton Paramount 3500 III — C48FT* — 1991 — Ex Wallace Arnold, 1994
*431 is C49FT

| 431 | H649UWR | 432 | H642UWR | 433 | H643UWR | 434 | H652UWR | 435 | H653UWR |

439-444

Volvo B10M-60 — Plaxton Première 350 — C48FT — 1992 — Ex Wallace Arnold, 1994

| 439 | J739CWT | 441 | J741CWT | 442 | J742CWT | 443 | J743CWT | 444 | J744CWT |
| 440 | J740CWT | | | | | | | | |

Cambus operate services from, and around Cambridge while the vehicles at Peterborough carry the Viscount name. During the company's time as an independent, a number of Optare MetroRiders were placed in service. Pictured in Peterborough is 987, J807DWW. *Les Peters*

445-456

Volvo B10M-62 — Plaxton Expressliner 2 — C49FT — 1995-97

445	N445XVA	**448**	N448XVA	**451**	N451XVA	**453**	R453RCE	**455**	R455RCE
446	N446XVA	**449**	N449XVA	**452**	N452XVA	**454**	R454RCE	**456**	R456RCE
447	N447XVA	**450**	N450XVA						

481	A681KDV	Leyland Olympian ONLXB/1R	Eastern Coach Works	H45/32F	1983	Ex North Devon, 1996
482	A561KWY	Leyland Olympian ONLXB/1R	Eastern Coach Works	H45/32F	1983	Ex Selby & District, 1996
483	A683KDV	Leyland Olympian ONLXB/1R	Eastern Coach Works	H45/32F	1983	Ex North Devon, 1996
500	E500LFL	Leyland Olympian ONLXCT/1RH	Optare	DPH43/27F	1988	
501	E501LFL	Leyland Olympian ONLXCT/1RH	Optare	DPH43/27F	1988	
502	E502LFL	Leyland Olympian ONLXCT/1RH	Optare	DPH43/27F	1988	
503	UWW3X	Leyland Olympian ONLXB/1R	Roe	H47/29F	1982	Ex West Yorkshire PTE, 1987
504	UWW4X	Leyland Olympian ONLXB/1R	Roe	H47/29F	1982	Ex West Yorkshire PTE, 1987
505	UWW8X	Leyland Olympian ONLXB/1R	Roe	H47/29F	1982	Ex West Yorkshire PTE, 1987

506-517

Leyland Olympian ONLXB/1RZ — Northern Counties — H45/30F — 1989

506	F506NJE	**509**	F509NJE	**512**	F512NJE	**514**	F514NJE	**516**	F516NJE
507	F507NJE	**510**	F510NJE	**513**	F513NJE	**515**	F515NJE	**517**	F517NJE
508	F508NJE	**511**	F511NJE						

518	N518XER	Volvo Olympian YN2RV18Z4	Northern Counties Palatine	DPH45/31F	1995
519	N519XER	Volvo Olympian YN2RV18Z4	Northern Counties Palatine	DPH45/31F	1995
520	N520XER	Volvo Olympian YN2RV18Z4	Northern Counties Palatine	DPH45/31F	1995
523	H473CEG	Leyland Olympian ON2R50G13Z4	Leyland	H47/31F	1990
524	H474CEG	Leyland Olympian ON2R50G13Z4	Leyland	H47/31F	1990
525	H475CEG	Leyland Olympian ON2R50G13Z4	Leyland	H47/31F	1990

526-579 — Volvo Olympian YN2RV18V3 — Northern Counties Palatine — H49/33F — 1996

526	P526EFL	537	P537EFL	548	P548EFL	559	P559EFL	570	P570EFL
527	P527EFL	538	P538EFL	549	P549EFL	561	P561EFL	571	P571EFL
528	P528EFL	539	P539EFL	550	P550EFL	562	P562EFL	572	P572EFL
529	P529EFL	540	P540EFL	551	P551EFL	563	P563EFL	573	P573EFL
530	P530EFL	541	P541EFL	552	P552EFL	564	P564EFL	574	P574EFL
531	P531EFL	542	P542EFL	553	P5534FL	565	P565EFL	575	P575EFL
532	P532EFL	543	P543EFL	554	P554EFL	566	P566EFL	576	P576EFL
533	P533EFL	544	P544EFL	556	P556EFL	567	P567EFL	577	P577EFL
534	P534EFL	545	P545EFL	557	P557EFL	568	P568EFL	578	P578EFL
535	P535EFL	546	P546EFL	558	P558EFL	569	P569EFL	579	P579EFL
536	P536EFL	547	P547EFL						

580-586 — Volvo Olympian — Alexander RL — H45/27F — 1998

580	R580JVA	582	R582JVA	584	R584JVA	585	R585JVA	586	R586JVA
581	R581JVA	583	R583JVA					

735	PWY37W	Bristol VRT/SL3/6LXB	Eastern Coach Works	H43/31F	1981	Ex York City & District, 1990
737	SUB795W	Bristol VRT/SL3/6LXB	Eastern Coach Works	H43/31F	1981	Ex York City & District, 1990
739	URP943W	Bristol VRT/SL3/501	Eastern Coach Works	H43/31F	1981	Ex Buckinghamshire Road Car, 1994

742-746 — Bristol VRT/SL3/6LXB — Eastern Coach Works — H43/31F — 1980-81

742	VEX295X	743	VEX300X	744	VEX296X	745	VEX303X	746	VEX304X

747	STW24W	Bristol VRT/SL3/6LXB	Eastern Coach Works	H39/31F	1981	Ex Green, Kirkintilloch, 1991
751	VEX298X	Bristol VRT/SL3/6LXB	Eastern Coach Works	H43/31F	1981	
753	VEX289X	Bristol VRT/SL3/6LXB	Eastern Coach Works	H43/31F	1981	
754	KVF245V	Bristol VRT/SL3/6LXB	Eastern Coach Works	H43/31F	1980	
755	VEX293X	Bristol VRT/SL3/6LXB	Eastern Coach Works	H43/31F	1981	
760	KVF250V	Bristol VRT/SL3/6LXB	Eastern Coach Works	H43/31F	1980	
770	SUB790W	Bristol VRT/SL3/6LXB	Eastern Coach Works	H43/31F	1981	Ex Keighley & District, 1990
772	SUB792W	Bristol VRT/SL3/6LXB	Eastern Coach Works	H43/31F	1981	Ex York City & District, 1990
773	SUB793W	Bristol VRT/SL3/6LXB	Eastern Coach Works	H43/31F	1981	Ex York City & District, 1990
775	PWY45W	Bristol VRT/SL3/6LXB	Eastern Coach Works	H43/31F	1981	Ex Keighley & District, 1990
777	PWY47W	Bristol VRT/SL3/6LXB	Eastern Coach Works	H43/31F	1981	Ex Keighley & District, 1990
779	PWY49W	Bristol VRT/SL3/6LXB	Eastern Coach Works	H43/31F	1981	Ex Keighley & District, 1990
780	PWY50W	Bristol VRT/SL3/6LXB	Eastern Coach Works	H43/31F	1981	Ex Keighley & District, 1990
781	VEX301X	Bristol VRT/SL3/6LXB	Eastern Coach Works	H43/31F	1981	
782	VEX299X	Bristol VRT/SL3/6LXB	Eastern Coach Works	H43/31F	1981	
784	RAH264W	Bristol VRT/SL3/6LXB	Eastern Coach Works	H43/31F	1980	
788	VAH278X	Bristol VRT/SL3/6LXB	Eastern Coach Works	H43/31F	1981	
789	VAH279X	Bristol VRT/SL3/6LXB	Eastern Coach Works	H43/31F	1981	
790	VAH280X	Bristol VRT/SL3/6LXB	Eastern Coach Works	H43/31F	1981	
791	VEX291X	Bristol VRT/SL3/6LXB	Eastern Coach Works	H43/31F	1981	
796	KVF246V	Bristol VRT/SL3/6LXB	Eastern Coach Works	H43/31F	1980	

952-957 — Iveco TurboDaily 59-12 — Marshall C31 — B25F — 1992

951	K171CAV	953	K173CAV	955	K175CAV	956	K176CAV	957	K177CAV
952	K172CAV	954	K174CAV					

960-974 — Optare MetroRider — Optare — B29F — 1992-93

960	J960DWX	963	K963HUB	966	K966HUB	969	K969HUB	972	K972HUB
961	J961DWX	964	K964HUB	967	K967HUB	970	K970HUB	973	K973HUB
962	J962DWX	965	K965HUB	968	K968HUB	971	K971HUB	974	K974HUB

975-979 — Optare MetroRider MR17 — Optare — B29F — 1995

975	M975WWR	976	M976WWR	977	M977WWR	978	M978WWR	979	M979VWY

Opposite:- **When Stagecoach acquired Cambus the fleet contained considerable numbers of Bristol VRs that were nearing the end of their economic life. In order to reduce the engineering costs a major investment in new buses was needed, and these arrived in the form of Northern Counties-bodied Volvo Olympians. Fifty two arrived in 1996 and a further seven - with Alexander bodywork - are expected shortly. Pictured in service with Viscount names is 572, P572EFL. Seven Iveco minibuses were placed in service in 1992, three of which operate from Cambridge and four from Peterborough. Representing the batch is 974, K174CAV. The bodywork on this batch is by local coachbuilder, Marshall.** *Les Peters/Richard Godfrey*

While the number of original Leyland Nationals continues to decline across the group there has been an increase in 1997 in the number of National 2s being transferred between fleets. Typical of these and earlier moves is 391, LFR860X, which came to Gloucester in 1995 from Ribble. *Mike Willis*

Circle-Line:

1022	HEU122N	Leyland National 11351/1R		B52F	1975	Ex Stagecoach Midland Red, 1997
1026	G26XBK	Iveco Daily 49.10	Phoenix	B25F	1990	Ex Stagecoach Midland Red, 1997
1055	F55RFS	MCW MetroRider MF150/98	MCW	B25F	1988	Ex Fife Scottish, 1996
1056	F56RFS	MCW MetroRider MF150/98	MCW	B25F	1988	Ex Fife Scottish, 1997
1057	F57RFS	MCW MetroRider MF150/98	MCW	B25F	1988	Ex Fife Scottish, 1996
1058	F58RFS	MCW MetroRider MF150/98	MCW	B25F	1988	Ex Fife Scottish, 1996
1060	F60RFS	MCW MetroRider MF150/98	MCW	B25F	1988	Ex Fife Scottish, 1996
1071	F871UAC	Iveco Daily 49.10	Robin Hood City Nippy	B25F	1989	Ex Stagecoach Midland Red, 1997
1113	EJR113W	Leyland Atlantean AN68A/2R	Alexander AL	H49/37F	1980	Ex Busways, 1996
1118	F118YVP	MCW MetroRider MF158/16	MCW	B28F	1988	Ex Western Buses, 1997
1122	KHT122P	Leyland National 11351/1R		B52F	1976	Ex Stagecoach Midland Red, 1997
1137	AKV137V	Leyland Atlantean AN68A/2R	Alexander AL	H49/37F	1980	Ex Busways, 1996
1214	A214MCK	Leyland Atlantean AN68D/2R	East Lancashire	H50/36F	1984	Ex Ribble, 1997
1250	SCN250S	Leyland Atlantean AN68A/2R	Alexander AL	H49/37F	1978	Ex Busways, 1996
1237	HAH237V	Bristol VRT/SL3/6LXB	Eastern Coach Works	H43/31F	1979	Ex Cambus (Viscount), 1997
1249	KVF249V	Bristol VRT/SL3/6LXB	Eastern Coach Works	H43/31F	1980	Ex Cambus (Viscount), 1997
1255	SCN255S	Leyland Atlantean AN68A/2R	Alexander AL	H49/37F	1978	Ex Busways, 1996
1256	SCN256S	Leyland Atlantean AN68A/2R	Alexander AL	H49/37F	1978	Ex Busways, 1996
1264	SCN264S	Leyland Atlantean AN68A/2R	Alexander AL	H49/37F	1978	Ex Busways, 1996
1350	DHW350W	Bristol VRT/SL3/680 (6LXB)	Eastern Coach Works	H43/31F	1981	
1352	DHW352W	Bristol VRT/SL3/680 (6LXB)	Eastern Coach Works	H43/31F	1981	
1364	RIW3364	Leyland Tiger TRCTL11/3R	Plaxton Paramount 3200	C53F	1983	Ex Stagecoach Manchester, 1996
1397	WAO397Y	Leyland National 2 NL116HLXB/1R		B52F	1982	Ex Busways, 1996
1467	467WYA	Leyland National 11351A/1R(DAF)		B52F	1978	
1469	A469TUV	Leyland Cub CU335	Wadham Stringer Vanguard	B21FL	1984	Ex LB of Wandsworth, 1992
1482	TRN482V	Leyland Atlantean AN68A/1R	Eastern Coach Works	H43/31F	1980	Ex Ribble, 1997
1502	VAE502T	Leyland National 10351B/1R		B44F	1979	Ex Stagecoach Midland Red, 1997

The 1998 Stagecoach Bus Handbook

The Cumberland operations were acquired by Stagecoach in 1987. The new owners quickly recast the Carlisle city network and introduced crew-operated Routemasters to that city. However, these have now been replaced with a mixture of new Alexander-bodied Volvo B10Ms and the longer version of the Olympian. Pictured at the northern-bound bus layby is 1009, F809FAO. *Gerry Mead*

789	N789VRM	Volvo B10M-55	Alexander PS	DP48F	1995	
790	N790VRM	Volvo B10M-55	Alexander PS	DP48F	1995	
791	R791PAO	Volvo B10M-62	Plaxton Premier Interurban	DP51F	1997	
792	R792PAO	Volvo B10M-62	Plaxton Premier Interurban	DP51F	1997	
793	R793URM	Volvo B10M-55	Alexander PS	B49F	1998	
794	R794URM	Volvo B10M-55	Alexander PS	B49F	1998	
795	R795URM	Volvo B10M-55	Alexander PS	B49F	1998	
810u	TRN810V	Leyland National 10351B/1R		B44F	1979	Ex Ribble, 1986
884u	RHG884X	Leyland National 2 NL116AL11/1R		B52F	1982	Ex Ribble, 1997
888u	ARN888Y	Leyland National 2 NL116HLXB/1R		B52F	1983	Ex Ribble, 1997
896u	CEO721W	Leyland National 2 NL116L11/1R		B49F	1980	Ex Ribble, 1997
900	B900WRN	Leyland Tiger TRCTL11/1R	Duple Dominant	B49F	1984	Ex Ribble, 1997
1001	URM801Y	Leyland Olympian ONLXB/1R	Eastern Coach Works	DPH45/30F	1982	
1002	URM802Y	Leyland Olympian ONLXB/1R	Eastern Coach Works	H45/32F	1982	

1003-1011

Leyland Olympian ONLXB/2RZ   Alexander RL   H51/36F   1988

| 1003 | F803FAO | 1005 | F805FAO | 1007 | F807FAO | 1009 | F809FAO | 1011 | F811FAO |
| 1004 | F804FAO | 1006 | F806FAO | 1008 | F808FAO | 1010 | F810FAO | | |

1012-1019

Leyland Olympian ON2R56G13Z4 Alexander RL   H51/34F   1990

| 1012 | H112SAO | 1014 | H114SAO | 1016 | H116SAO | 1018 | H118SAO | 1019 | H119SAO |
| 1013 | H113SAO | 1015 | H115SAO | 1017 | H117SAO | | | | |

1020-1027

Leyland Olympian ON2R56G13Z4 Alexander RL   DPH47/27F   1991

| 1020 | J120AAO | 1022 | J122AAO | 1024 | J124XHH | 1026 | J126XHH | 1027 | J127XHH |
| 1021 | J121AAO | 1023 | J123XHH | 1025 | J125XHH | | | | |

1028-1035

Leyland Olympian ON2R50G13Z4 Alexander RL   DPH43/27F 1992

1028	K128DAO	1030	K130DAO	1032	K132DAO	1034	K134DAO	1035	K135DAO
1029	K129DAO	1031	K131DAO	1033	K133DAO				

1090	C382SAO	Leyland Olympian ONLXB/1RV	Alexander RL	H47/30F	1986	Ex Bluebird, 1991
1091	C383SAO	Leyland Olympian ONLXB/1RV	Alexander RL	H47/30F	1986	Ex Bluebird, 1991
1092	D384XAO	Leyland Olympian ONLXB/1RV	Alexander RL	H47/30F	1987	Ex Bluebird, 1991
1093	D380XRS	Leyland Olympian ONLXB/1RV	Alexander RL	H47/30F	1987	Ex Bluebird, 1992
1094	D381XRS	Leyland Olympian ONLXB/1RV	Alexander RL	H47/30F	1987	Ex Bluebird, 1992
1103	KRN103T	Leyland Leopard PSU3E/4R	Duple Dominant II	C47F	1978	Ex Ribble, 1989
1105	KRN105T	Leyland Leopard PSU3E/4R	Duple Dominant II	C47F	1978	Ex Ribble, 1989
1113	KRN113T	Leyland Leopard PSU3E/4R	Duple Dominant II	C47F	1979	Ex Ribble, 1989
1119	KRN119T	Leyland Leopard PSU3E/4R	Duple Dominant II	C47F	1979	Ex Ribble, 1986
1120	G520LWU	Volvo B10M-60	Plaxton Paramount 3500 III	C49FT	1990	Ex Cambus (Premier), 1997
1125	GRM625V	Leyland Leopard PSU3F/4R	Duple Dominant II	C49F	1980	
1149	PSU788	Leyland Tiger TRCTL11/3RZ	Duple Caribbean 2	C48FT	1985	Ex Ribble, 1997
1151	B151WRN	Leyland Tiger TRCTL11/2RH	Duple Laser 2	C49F	1985	Ex Ribble, 1991
1153	B153WRN	Leyland Tiger TRCTL11/2RH	Duple Laser 2	C49F	1985	Ex Ribble, 1991
1154	B154WRN	Leyland Tiger TRCTL11/2RH	Duple Laser 2	C49F	1985	Ex Ribble, 1991
1155	B43MAO	Leyland Tiger TRCTL11/3RH	Duple Laser 2	C53F	1985	Ex Ribble, 1991
1160	L160BFV	Dennis Javelin 11SDL2133	Plaxton Premiére Interurban	DP47F	1993	Ex Ribble, 1997
1162	WLT380	Volvo B10M-61	Plaxton Paramount 3500 II	C48F	1986	Ex Ribble, 1994
1175	MRJ275W	Leyland Leopard PSU5D/4R	Plaxton Supreme IV	C50F	1981	Ex Ribble, 1989
1199	FDV799V	Leyland Leopard PSU3E/4R	Plaxton Supreme IV Express	C49F	1980	Ex Ribble, 1989
1201	F201FHH	Leyland Olympian ONLXCT/3RZ	Alexander RL	DPH55/41F	1989	
1202	F202FHH	Leyland Olympian ONLXCT/3RZ	Alexander RL	DPH55/41F	1989	
1253	HNE253V	Leyland Leopard PSU5C/4R	Duple Dominant II	C53F	1980	Ex Ribble, 1989
2002	CBV2S	Bristol VRT/SL3/501 (6LXB)	Eastern Coach Works	O43/31F	1977	Ex Ribble, 1986
2024	DBV24W	Bristol VRT/SL3/6LXB	Eastern Coach Works	H43/31F	1980	Ex Ribble, 1986
2032	DBV32W	Bristol VRT/SL3/6LXB	Eastern Coach Works	H43/31F	1980	Ex Ribble, 1986
2035	UWV610S	Bristol VRT/SL3/6LXB	Eastern Coach Works	O43/31F	1977	Ex Southdown, 1990
2036	UWV612S	Bristol VRT/SL3/6LXB	Eastern Coach Works	O43/31F	1977	Ex Southdown, 1990
2037	UWV618S	Bristol VRT/SL3/6LXB	Eastern Coach Works	O43/31F	1978	Ex Southdown, 1990
2038	UWV620S	Bristol VRT/SL3/6LXB	Eastern Coach Works	O43/31F	1978	Ex Southdown, 1990
2075	XRR175S	Bristol VRT/SL3/6LXB	Eastern Coach Works	O43/27F	1980	Ex Ribble, 1995
2076	UWV622S	Bristol VRT/SL3/6LXB	Eastern Coach Works	O43/31F	1980	Ex Ribble, 1996
2100	DBV100W	Leyland Olympian B45.02	Eastern Coach Works	H45/33F	1980	Ex Ribble, 1997
2102	JFR2W	Leyland Olympian ONLXB/1R	Eastern Coach Works	O45/32F	1981	Ex Ribble, 1997
2116	OFV16X	Leyland Olympian ONLXB/1R	Eastern Coach Works	H45/32F	1982	Ex Ribble, 1997
2117	OFV17X	Leyland Olympian ONLXB/1R	Eastern Coach Works	H45/32F	1982	Ex Ribble, 1997
2129	VRN829Y	Leyland Olympian ONLXBT/1R	Eastern Coach Works	O45/32F	1982	Ex Ribble, 1997
2134	DBV134Y	Leyland Olympian ONLXB/1R	Eastern Coach Works	H45/32F	1983	Ex Ribble, 1997
2138	A138MRN	Leyland Olympian ONLXB/1R	Eastern Coach Works	H45/32F	1984	Ex Ribble, 1997
2170	C170ECK	Leyland Olympian ONLXB/1R	Eastern Coach Works	DPH42/30F	1985	Ex Ribble, 1997
2174	C174ECK	Leyland Olympian ONLXB/1R	Eastern Coach Works	DPH42/30F	1985	Ex Ribble, 1997
2175	C175ECK	Leyland Olympian ONLXB/1R	Eastern Coach Works	DPH42/30F	1985	Ex Ribble, 1989
2176	C176ECK	Leyland Olympian ONLXB/1R	Eastern Coach Works	DPH42/30F	1985	Ex Ribble, 1989
2177	C177ECK	Leyland Olympian ONLXB/1R	Eastern Coach Works	DPH42/30F	1986	Ex Ribble, 1989
2179	C179ECK	Leyland Olympian ONLXB/1R	Eastern Coach Works	DPH41/26F	1985	Ex Ribble, 1997

2180-2189

Leyland Olympian ON2R50G16Z4 Alexander RL   DPH51/31F 1989 Ex Ribble, 1997

2180	G180JHG	2182	G182JHG	2184	G184JHG	2186	G186JHG	2189	G189JHG
2181	G181JHG	2183	G183JHG	2185	G185JHG				

2191	H191WFR	Leyland Olympian ON2R50G16Z4 Alexander RL	H47/30F	1990	Ex Ribble, 1997
2192	H192WFR	Leyland Olympian ON2R50G16Z4 Alexander RL	H47/30F	1990	Ex Ribble, 1997
2194	H194WFR	Leyland Olympian ON2R50G16Z4 Alexander RL	H47/30F	1990	Ex Ribble, 1997

Opposite, top: - **Much kudos has been gained by Stagecoach fas a result of their services within the English Lakes. Many of the tourist services are operated with open-top buses, and Mercedes 709s and Volvo B6s based at Kendal. The fleet was augmented in 1997 with the arrival of an accident-damaged Olympian and this was joined for the 1998 season by a further example. Continuing to use the Ribble fleetnumber is 2002, JFR2W, which was seen working the main 599 service shortly after entering service.**
Opposite, bottom: - **In 1992 the majority of the initial order for 100 Volvo B10 buses were placed in service with Cumberland and these became the fore-runner of the subsequent deliveries. Pictured in Carlisle is 717, K717DAO.** *Gerry Mead*

The attractive village of Hawkshead is the location for this picture of Volvo B6 282L282JAO, which is lettered for The Coniston Rambler, a service which connects Hawkshead and Coniston with Windermere and Ambleside. In summer, Cumberland publish a comprehensive timetable of the services which is available from the many tourist information points. *British Bus Publishing*

2199-2210

Leyland Olympian ON2R56G13Z4 Alexander RL   DPH43/27F* 1991   Ex Ribble, 1997
*2204-6/10 are DPH47/27F

2199	J199HFR	2203	J203HFR	2205	J205HFR	2207	J207HFR	2209	J209HFR
2201	J201HFR	2204	J204HFR	2206	J206HFR	2208	J208HFR	2210	J210HFR
2202	J202HFR								

2211-2223

Leyland Olympian ONLXB/1R   Alexander RL   H45/32F   1984-85 Ex Ribble, 1997

2211	A975OST	2216	B892UAS	2217	B893UAS	2219	B895UAS	2223	B899UAS

Previous Registrations:

109DRM	A101DAO	LJC800	From new
B43MAO	B155WRN, PCK335	LJY145	D205LWX
C382SAO	C473SSO, GSO3V	PSU787	C495LJV
C383SAO	C474SSO, GSO4V	PSU788	B146ACK
D384XAO	D375XRS, GSO5V	TCK841	B107HAO
D560RCK	D561RCK	VRR447	B180RLJ
DSV943	D203LWX	WLT380	C105DWR
JPU817	D207LWX	WLT706	C109OHH
K449YCW	K300LCT	WLT824	C110OHH
K450YCW	K200LCT	YDG616	D206LWX

Allocations:-

Barrow (Walney Road) - Cumberland - National Express ♥

Outstations - Millom; Coniston; Ulverston; Askam and Haverthwaite

Mercedes-Benz	1	2	3	4	5	16	17	18
	19	20	21	22	23	36	44	45
	53	54	55	56	68	70	71	72
	87	88	89					

In 1997 the Lancaster and Morecambe operations of Ribble Buses were separated to form Stagecoach Lancaster, another unit within Stagecoach (North West) Ltd, but one now administered by Cumberland. The vehicles then based at the depots were transferred over with minimal renumbering taking place. Pictured with the new names is 459, M459VCW seen here on rail replacement work. *Nick Coleman.*

Volvo PS	754	755	756	757	758	759	760	761
	762	763	764	765	766			
Tiger	101							
Volvo Coach	125♥	126♥	127♥	158	1120			
Bristol VR	421							
Olympian	1001	1002	1003	1005	1090	1091	1092	1093
	1094	1201	1202	2177				

Carlisle (Willowholme Ind Est)

Outstation - Penrith

Mercedes-Benz	76	77	78	79	80	81	82	83
	84	528	560					
Volvo PS	706	707	708	709	710	711	712	713
	714	715	716	717	718	719	720	721
	722	723	724	725	726	727	728	729
	730	731	732	733	734	735	736	737
	738	739	741	745	772	773	781	783
	784	785	786	789	790	791	792	
Leopard	505	569	1103	1125	1175	1253		
Tiger	102	106	107	156	1153	1154		
Volvo B6	270	283						
Volvo Coach	160							
Bristol VR	422	423	432	434	2024	2032	2076	
Olympian	1006	1009	1010	1011	1028	1029	1030	1031
	1032	1033						

Kendal (Station Road)

Outstations - Ambleside; Appleby; Grange and Orton

Bristol VR	433	435	436	437	2035	2036	2037	2038
Olympian	1019	1020	1021	1022	1023	1024	1025	1026
	1027	2102	2129	2175				
Volvo PS	705							
Tiger	103	105	162	1151	1155			
Leopard	1105	1113	1119	1199				
Volvo B6	275	276	282					
Mercedes-Benz	6	7	8	9	10	11	12	13
	14	15	47	48	49	50	51	65
	529	559						
Volvo Coach	153	161						

Morecambe (Heysham Road)

Outstations - Garstang; Ingleton; Kirby Lonsdale and Lancaster

Olympian	1004	1007	2100	2116	2117	2138	2170	2174
	2179	2180	2181	2182	2183	2184	2185	2186
	2189	2191	2192	2194	2199	2201	2202	2203
	2204	2205	2206	2207	2208	2209	2210	2211
	2216	2217	2219	2223				
Volvo PS	455	456	457	458	459	460	461	462
	463	699	700	701	702	703	704	742
	743	744	793	794	795			
Tiger	109	645	900	1149				
Javelin	135	136	137	152	154	1160		
MetroRider	449	450						
Mercedes-Benz	565	566	567	592	597	602	604	607
	615	625						

Workington (Lillyhall) - Cumberland - National Express ♥

Bristol VR	425	426	427	428	431			
Olympian	1008	1012	1013	1014	1015	1016	1017	1018
	1034	1035	2134	2176				
Volvo PS	746	748	749	750	751	752	753	767
	768	769	770	771	774	775	776	777
	778	779	780	787	788			
Mercedes-Benz	24	25	26	27	28	29	30	31
	32	33	52	57	58	59	60	61
	62	63	64	66	67	73	74	75
	85	86	533					
Tiger	110	111	114					
Volvo Coach	120♥	121♥	128♥	129♥	130♥	131♥	132♥	159
	1162							

Unallocated and stored

National	373	398	810	879	884	888	896
Bristol VR	420	424					

DEVON

Devon General Ltd, Belgrave Road, Exeter, EX1 2AJ
Bayline Ltd, Regents Close, Torquay, Devon TQ2 5NA

201-215

						Ford Transit VE6			Mellor			B16F		1987-88	

201	D110PTT	204	D113PTT	207w	D117PTT	211	D131PTT	214	E825ATT
202w	D111PTT	205	D114PTT	210w	D125PTT	212w	D134PTT	215w	E827ATT
203w	D112PTT	206	D116PTT						

217-227

Ford Transit VE6 — Mellor — B16F — 1988

217	E200BDV	219	E209BDV	221	E211BDV	225w	F750FDV	227	F755FDV
218	E205BDV	220	E210BDV	223	E216BDV				

229-240

Ford Transit VE6 — Mellor — B16F — 1987

229	D654NOD	234	D647NOD	236w	D649NOD	237w	D650NOD	240w	D656NOD
230	D639NOD	235	D648NOD						

242-269

Ford Transit VE6 — Mellor — B16F — 1987-88

242w	F772FDV	248w	D781NDV	254	D792NDV	260w	D799NDV	265w	E810WDV
244w	D777NDV	249w	D784NDV	257	D796NDV	261w	E800WDV	266	E815WDV
245	D778NDV	250	D785NDV	258	D797NDV	263w	E802WDV	267w	E816WDV
246w	D779NDV	251	D786NDV	259w	D798NDV	264	E806WDV	269w	E822WDV
247	D780NDV	252	D787NDV						

300-314

Iveco Daily 59.12 — Mellor Duet — B21D — 1994

300	L929CTT	303	L932CTT	306	L935CTT	309	L938CTT	312	L941CTT
301	L930CTT	304	L933CTT	307	L936CTT	310	L939CTT	313	L942CTT
302	L931CTT	305	L934CTT	308	L937CTT	311	L940CTT	314	L943CTT

315-333

Iveco Daily 59.12 — WS Wessex II — B21D — 1994

315	M638HDV	319	M639HDV	323	M625HDV	327	M630HDV	331	M194HTT
316	M640HDV	320	M629HDV	324	M628HDV	328	M193HTT	332	M191HTT
317	M637HDV	321	M624HDV	325	M626HDV	329	M627HDV	333	M641HDV
318	M636HDV	322	M623HDV	326	M192HTT	330	M622HDV		

Three Leyland Titans and many Bristol VRs now operate with Stagecoach Devon where the company have re-introduced double-deck operation to several routes and contracts since acquiring the operation in 1996. Pictured in Exeter is 950, KYN282X which was latterly with Stagecoach Selkent.
Mark Bailey

While the original Devon minibus operation was based on Ford Transits many of these were replaced, first with second generation VE6s and then with Mercedes-Benz 709s. In 1998 35 joined the fleet and these featured high-back seating and were used on the more rural services rather then Exeter City routes. From that batch is 423, F741FDV which is seen here in Sidmouth. *Paul Wigan*

334-364 — Iveco Daily 59.12 — Mellor Duet — B29F — 1993

334 K702UTT	341 K721UTT	347 K730UTT	353 K927VDV	359 K822WFJ
335 K711UTT	342 K722UTT	348 K731UTT	354 K824WFJ	360 K805WFJ
336 K713UTT	343 K913VDV	349 K732UTT	355 K823WFJ	361 K804WFJ
337 K714UTT	344 K725UTT	350 K724UTT	356 K821WFJ	362 K806WFJ
338 K717UTT	345 K726UTT	351 K924VDV	357 K803WFJ	363 K816WFJ
339 K719UTT	346 K727UTT	352 K926VDV	358 K925VDV	364 K620XOD
340 K720UTT				

365-377 — Iveco Daily 59.12 — Marshall C31 — B29F — 1994

365 L193FDV	368 L197FDV	371 L204FDV	374 L210FDV	376 L212FDV
366 L194FDV	369 L201FDV	372 L208FDV	375 L211FDV	377 L214FDV
367 L195FDV	370 L203FDV	373 L209FDV		

No.	Reg	Type	Body	Seats	Year	Notes
378	N182CMJ	Iveco TurboDaily 59.12	Alexander	B29F	1996	Ex Stagecoach Midland Red, 1997
380	F958HTO	Iveco Daily 49.10	Robin Hood City Nippy	B23F	1988	Ex Red & White, 1996
381	G912KWF	Iveco Daily 49.10	Reeve Burgess Beaver	B25F	1989	Ex Red & White, 1996
382	G919KWF	Iveco Daily 49.10	Reeve Burgess Beaver	B25F	1989	Ex Red & White, 1996
383	G920KWF	Iveco Daily 49.10	Reeve Burgess Beaver	B25F	1989	Ex Red & White, 1996
384	G924KWF	Iveco Daily 49.10	Reeve Burgess Beaver	B25F	1989	Ex Red & White, 1996
385	H370PNY	Iveco Daily 49-10	Carlyle Dailybus 2	B25F	1991	Ex Red & White, 1996
386	L950EOD	Iveco TurboDaily 59-12	Mellor Duet	B26D	1993	Ex Stagecoach Oxford, 1997
387	L946EOD	Iveco TurboDaily 59-12	Mellor Duet	B29F	1993	Ex Stagecoach Oxford, 1997
388	L318BOD	Iveco TurboDaily 59-12	Mellor Duet	B26D	1993	Ex Stagecoach Oxford, 1997
389	L945EOD	Iveco TurboDaily 59-12	Mellor Duet	B26D	1994	Ex Stagecoach Oxford, 1997
390	K718UTT	Iveco TurboDaily 59-12	Mellor Duet	B26D	1993	Ex Stagecoach Oxford, 1997
391	L947EOD	Iveco TurboDaily 59-12	Mellor Duet	B26D	1994	Ex Stagecoach Oxford, 1997
392	L948EOD	Iveco TurboDaily 59-12	Mellor Duet	B26D	1994	Ex Stagecoach Oxford, 1997
393	L949EOD	Iveco TurboDaily 59-12	Mellor Duet	B26D	1994	Ex Stagecoach Oxford, 1997

Pictured heading for Whimple, N599DWY is seen in all-over red livery with Stagecoach names. The bus has since been numbered 750 and previously operated for the East Devon fleet which has ceased trading. Another similar vehicle, L547CDV, also joined the fleet in 1997 and this is provided by South Devon Council for services recently won by Stagecoach. *Mark Bailey*

400-434

| | | | | | | | | | | Mercedes-Benz 709D | Reeve Burgess Beaver | DP25F | 1988 |

400	F748FDV	407	F719FDV	414	F730FDV	421	F738FDV	428	F756FDV
401	E830ATT	408	F720FDV	415	F731FDV	422	F740FDV	429	F757FDV
402	F714FDV	409	F722FDV	416	F732FDV	423	F741FDV	430	F758FDV
403	F715FDV	410	F723FDV	417	F733FDV	424	F742FDV	431	F759FDV
404	F716FDV	411	F726FDV	418	F735FDV	425	F743FDV	432	F760FDV
405	F717FDV	412	F728FDV	419	F736FDV	426	F744FDV	433	F762FDV
406	F718FDV	413	F729FDV	420	F737FDV	427	F745FDV	434	F763FDV

435-443

Mercedes-Benz 709D — Reeve Burgess Beaver — DP25F — 1989

435	F404KOD	437	F406KOD	439	F408KOD	441	F411KOD	443	F413KOD
436	F405KOD	438	F407KOD	440	F410KOD	442	F412KOD		

444-468

Mercedes-Benz 709D — Marshall C19 — B21D — 1995

444	M226UTM	449	M231UTM	454	M236UTM	459	M241UTM	464	M246UTM
445	M227UTM	450	M232UTM	455	M237UTM	460	M242UTM	465	M247UTM
446	M228UTM	451	M233UTM	456	M238UTM	461	M243UTM	466	M248UTM
447	M229UTM	452	M234UTM	457	M239UTM	462	M244UTM	467	M249UTM
448	M230UTM	453	M235UTM	458	M240UTM	463	M245UTM	468	M250UTM

470-487

Mercedes-Benz 709D — Alexander Sprint — B23F — 1996

470	N978NAP	474	N982NAP	478	N509BJA	482	N513BJA	485	N516BJA
471	N979NAP	475	N506BJA	479	N510BJA	483	N514BJA	486	N517BJA
472	N980NAP	476	N507BJA	480	N511BJA	484	N515BJA	487	N518BJA
473	N981NAP	477	N508BJA	481	N512BJA				

488-505 Mercedes-Benz 709D Reeve Burgess Beaver B20F* 1986-87 Ex Busways, 1996
*495 is B24F

488	D404TFT	**492**	D409TFT	**496**	D417TFT	**500**	E438AFT	**503**	D413TFT
489	D405TFT	**493**	D412TFT	**497**	D418TFT	**501**	E439AFT	**504**	D420TFT
490	D407TFT	**494**	D414TFT	**498**	E448AFT	**502**	E446AFT	**505**	E441AFT
491	D408TFT	**495**	D416TFT	**499**	E436AFT				

589-598 Mercedes-Benz 811D Alexander Sprint B28F 1988 Ex Stagecoach Selkent, 1996-97
597/8 ex Bluebird, 1996

589	F614XMS	**591**	F619XMS	**593**	F631XMS	**595**	F641XMS	**597**	F609XMS
590	F615XMS	**592**	F620XMS	**594**	F616XMS	**596**	F630XMS	**598**	F617XMS

599	H889NFS	Mercedes-Benz 814D	PMT Ami	DP33F	1990	Ex Bluebird, 1996

701-714 Volvo B6LE Alexander ALX200 B35F 1997

701	P701BTA	**704**	P704BTA	**707**	P707BTA	**710**	P710BTA	**713**	P713BTA
702	P702BTA	**705**	P705BTA	**708**	P708BTA	**711**	P711BTA	**714**	P714BTA
703	P703BTA	**706**	P706BTA	**709**	P709BTA	**712**	P712BTA		

750	N599DWY	Dennis Dart 9.8SDL3054	Plaxton Pointer	B40F	1995	Ex East Devon, Aylesbeare, 1997
751	R751BDV	Dennis Dart	Alexander ALX200	B40F	1997	
752	L547CDV	Dennis Dart 8.5SDL	Wright Handybus	B28FL	1993	Owned by South Devon Council
771	G28TGW	Dennis Dart 8.5SDL3003	Carlyle Dartline	DP30F	1990	Ex Stagecoach Selkent, 1997
772	G30TGW	Dennis Dart 8.5SDL3003	Carlyle Dartline	DP30F	1990	Ex Stagecoach Selkent, 1997
773	G35TGW	Dennis Dart 8.5SDL3003	Carlyle Dartline	DP30F	1990	Ex Stagecoach Selkent, 1997
774	G34TGW	Dennis Dart 8.5SDL3003	Carlyle Dartline	DP30F	1990	Ex Stagecoach Docklands, 1997
775	G37TGW	Dennis Dart 8.5SDL3003	Carlyle Dartline	DP30F	1990	Ex Stagecoach Docklands, 1997
776	G36TGW	Dennis Dart 8.5SDL3003	Carlyle Dartline	B28F	1990	Ex Stagecoach Docklands, 1997
790	WUH166T	Leyland National 11351A/1R		B52F	1978	Ex Red & White, 1997
791	BUH211V	Leyland National 11351A/1R		B49F	1979	Ex Red & White, 1997
792	DDW433V	Leyland National 10351A/1R		B41F	1979	Ex Red & White, 1997

801-806 Volvo B10M-62 Plaxton Premiére Interurban DP51F 1996

801	P801XTA	**803**	P803XTA	**804**	P804XTA	**805**	P805XTA	**806**	P806XTA
802	P802XTA								

898	AKG214A	Leyland Tiger TRCTL11/3R	Duple Laser	C49FT	1984	Ex Red & White, 1997
899	AKG197A	Leyland Tiger TRCTL11/3R	Duple Laser	C49FT	1984	Ex Red & White, 1997
901	R901FDV	Volvo Olympian	Alexander RL	H45/27F	1997	
935	VDV135S	Bristol VRT/SL3/6LXB	Eastern Coach Works	CO43/31F	1977	Ex Western National, 1983
936	UWV604S	Bristol VRT/SL3/6LXB	Eastern Coach Works	CO43/31F	1977	Ex Stagecoach South, 1996
937	UWV614S	Bristol VRT/SL3/6LXB	Eastern Coach Works	CO43/31F	1978	Ex Stagecoach South, 1996
938	RAH265W	Bristol VRT/SL3/6LXB	Eastern Coach Works	H43/31F	1980	Ex Cambus, 1997
939	RAH268W	Bristol VRT/SL3/6LXB	Eastern Coach Works	H43/31F	1980	Ex Cambus, 1997
941	LWU468V	Bristol VRT/SL3/6LXB	Eastern Coach Works	H43/31F	1980	Ex Cambus, 1997
942	PWY40W	Bristol VRT/SL3/6LXB	Eastern Coach Works	H43/31F	1981	Ex Cambus (Viscount), 1997
943	PWY48W	Bristol VRT/SL3/6LXB	Eastern Coach Works	H43/31F	1981	Ex Cambus, 1997
944	NUM341V	Bristol VRT/SL3/6LXB	Eastern Coach Works	H43/31F	1980	Ex Cambus, 1997
945	LWU470V	Bristol VRT/SL3/6LXB	Eastern Coach Works	H43/31F	1980	Ex Cambus (Viscount), 1997
946	JUB650V	Bristol VRT/SL3/6LXB	Eastern Coach Works	H43/31F	1980	Ex Cambus, 1997
950	KYN282X	Leyland Titan TNLXB2RR	Leyland	H44/27F	1981	Ex Stagecoach Selkent, 1997
951	OHV738Y	Leyland Titan TNLXB2RR	Leyland	H44/27F	1983	Ex Stagecoach East London, 1997
952	OHV729Y	Leyland Titan TNLXB2RR	Leyland	H44/27F	1983	Ex Stagecoach East London, 1997

Previous Registrations:

AKG197A	A225VWO	AKG214A	A227VWO	G28TGW	G28TGW, 49CLT

Named vehicles: 935 Ark Royal; 936 Illustrious; 937 Invincible.

Opposite, top: - **Stagecoach Devon took delivery of fourteen Volvo B6BLEs from the 1997 order and these have been supplemented by Dennis Darts brought in from other operations. Pictured here is Volvo 712, P712BTA which is lettered to advise passengers of the low floor facility.** *Mark Bailey*
Opposite, bottom:- **Ten of the longer Alexander Sprint minibuses now operate with Staecoach Devon, these being displaced from Selkent in 1996 with two operating for a time with Bluebird Buses. The index marks were obtained by Alexanders for the order delivered new to London Buses.** *Les Peters*

Allocations:-

Exeter (Belgrave Road)

Iveco	300	301	302	303	304	305	306	307
	308	309	310	311	312	313	314	315
	316	317	318	319	320	321	322	323
	324	325	326	327	328	329	330	331
	332	333	334	342	343	347	348	359
	378	380	381	382	383	384	385	
Mercedes-Benz	400	401	402	403	404	405	407	408
	409	410	412	413	415	416	417	418
	419	420	421	422	423	425	426	428
	430	431	432	433	434	440	441	442
	443	444	445	446	447	448	449	450
	451	452	453	454	455	456	457	458
	459	460	461	462	463	464	465	466
	467	468	471	473	477	479	481	483
	484	485	486	487	488	489	490	491
	492	493	496	497	498	499	500	501
	502	503	504	505	589	590	591	592
	593	594	595	596	597	598	599	
Dart	750	751	752	771	773			
Volvo B6	801	802	803	804	805	806		
National	790	791	792					
Tiger	898	899						
Volvo B10M	807							
Bristol VR	938	939	943	944	945	946		
Olympian	601							

Torquay (Regent Close)

Transit	201	204	205	206	211	214	217	218
	219	220	221	223	227	229	234	235
	244	247	250	251	252	254	257	258
	264	266						
Iveco	335	336	337	338	339	340	341	344
	345	346	349	350	351	352	353	354
	355	356	357	358	360	361	362	363
	364	365	366	367	368	369	370	371
	372	373	374	375	376	377	386	387
	388	389	390	391	392	393		
Mercedes-Benz	406	411	414	424	427	429	435	436
	437	438	439	470	472	474	475	476
	478	480	482	494	495			
Volvo B6	701	702	703	704	705	706	707	708
	709	710	711	712	713	714		
Bristol VR	935	936	937	941	942			
Titan	950	951	952					

Unallocated:-

Transit	202	203	207	210	212	215	225	230
	236	237	240	242	245	246	248	249
	259	260	261	263	265	267	269	
Dart	770	772	774	775	776			

EAST LONDON

East London Bus & Coach Company Ltd, 2-4 Clements Road, Ilford, Essex, IG1 1BA

DA10	G684KNW	DAF SB220LC550		Optare Delta		B36D	1989		

DA11-35

DAF SB220LC550 — Optare Delta — B40D — 1992-93

11	J711CYG	16	J716CYG	21	J721CYG	26	J726CYG	31	K631HWX
12	J712CYG	17	J717CYG	22	J722CYG	27	J727CYG	32	K632HWX
13	472YMF	18	J718CYG	23	J723CYG	28	J728CYG	33	K633HWX
14	J714CYG	19	J719CYG	24	J724CYG	29	J729CYG	34	K634HWX
15	YLJ332	20	J720CYG	25	J725CYG	30	K630HWX	35	K635HWX

DAL1-27

Dennis Dart 9.8SDL3054 — Alexander Dash — B36F — 1995

1	N301AMC	7	N307AMC	13	N313AMC	18	N318AMC	23	N323AMC
2	N302AMC	8	N308AMC	14	N314AMC	19	N319AMC	24	N324AMC
3	N303AMC	9	N309AMC	15	N315AMC	20	N320AMC	25	N325AMC
4	N304AMC	10	N310AMC	16	N316AMC	21	N321AMC	26	N326AMC
5	N305AMC	11	N311AMC	17	N317AMC	22	N322AMC	27	N327AMC
6	N306AMC	12	N312AMC						

DAL715-722

Dennis Dart 9.8SDL3035 — Plaxton Pointer — B37D — 1994 — Ex Stagecoach Oxford, 1997

715	L715JUD	717	L717JUD	719	L719JUD	721	L721JUD	722	L722JUD
716	L716JUD	718	L718JUD	720	L720JUD				

DAL1716	NFX667	Dennis Dart 9.8SDL3017	Alexander Dash	DP32F	1992
DAL1719	XYK976	Dennis Dart 9.8SDL3017	Alexander Dash	DP32F	1992

DRL109-138

Dennis Dart 9SDL3024 — Plaxton Pointer — B34F — 1993

109	K109SRH	116	K116SRH	125	K125SRH	131	K131SRH	135	K135SRH
111	K211SRH	119	K119SRH	126	K126SRH	132	K132SRH	136	L136VRH
113	K113SRH	121	K121SRH	128	K128SRH	133	K133SRH	137	L137VRH
114	K114SRH	122	K122SRH	129	K129SRH	134	K134SRH	138	L138VRH
115	K115SRH	124	K124SRH	130	K130SRH				

Barking station is the location for this picture of East London's DAL3, N303AMC. During 1998 dual-doored buses are being transferred from Stagecoach Oxford where they have been displaced by single-door examples. When the Darts arrive in London they will carry fleetnumbers in the PD class matching the numbers in the index mark.
Tony Wilson

DRL139-146

Dennis Dart 9SDL3034 — Plaxton Pointer — B34F — 1993

139	L139VRH	141	L141VRH	143	L143VRH	145	L145VRH	146	L146VRH
140	L140VRH	142	L142VRH	144	L144VRH				

DWL15-26

Dennis Dart 9SDL3016 — Wright Handy-bus — B35F — 1993

15	NDZ3015	18	NDZ3018	21	NDZ3021	23	NDZ3023	25	NDZ3025
16	NDZ3016	19	NDZ3019	22	NDZ3022	24	NDZ3024	26	NDZ3026
17	NDZ3017	20	NDZ3020						

DW133-159

Dennis Dart 8.5SDL3015 — Wright Handy-bus — B29F — 1993

133	NDZ3133	139	NDZ3139	145	NDZ3145	150	NDZ3150	155	NDZ3155
134	NDZ3134	140	NDZ3140	146	NDZ3146	151	NDZ3151	156	NDZ3156
135	NDZ3135	141	NDZ3141	147	NDZ3147	152	NDZ3152	157	NDZ3157
136	NDZ3136	142	NDZ3142	148	NDZ3148	153	NDZ3153	158	NDZ3158
137	NDZ3137	143	NDZ3143	149	NDZ3149	154	NDZ3154	159	NDZ3159
138	NDZ3138	144	NDZ3144						

LCY1-9

Dennis Dart SLF — Alexander ALX200 — B29F — 1997

1	P801NJN	3	P803NJN	5	P805NJN	7	P807NJN	9	R209XNO
2	P802NJN	4	P804NJN	6	P806NJN	8	R208XNO		

MRL144-176

Optare MetroRider MR03 — Optare — B26F — 1990-91 Ex Stagecoach Selkent, 1996-97

144	H144UUA	150	H150UUA	162	H162WWT	171	H171WWT	176	H176WWT
148	H148UUA	160	H160WWT	170	H170WWT	174	H174WWT		

PD1-18

Dennis Dart — Plaxton Pointer — B37D — 1997

1	R701YWC	5	R705YWC	9	R709YWC	13	R713YWC	16	R716YWC
2	R702YWC	6	R706YWC	10	R710YWC	14	R714YWC	17	R717YWC
3	R703YWC	7	R707YWC	11	R711YWC	15	R715YWC	18	R718YWC
4	R704YWC	8	R708YWC	12	R712YWC				

PD410-427

Dennis Dart 9.8SDL3054 — Plaxton Pointer — B40F — 1996 — Ex Docklands Transit, 1997

410	N410MBW	414	N414MBW	418	N418MBW	422	N422MBW	425	N425MBW
411	N411MBW	415	N415MBW	419	N419MBW	423	N423MBW	426	N426MBW
412	N412MBW	416	N416MBW	420	N420MBW	424	N424MBW	427	N427MBW
413	N413MBW	417	N417MBW	421	N421MBW				

RM613	WLT613	AEC Routemaster R2RH	Park Royal	H36/28R	1960	
RML886	WLT886	AEC Routemaster R2RH1	Park Royal	H36/28R	1961	Cummins engine
RML890	XFF814	AEC Routemaster R2RH1	Park Royal	H40/32R	1961	Cummins engine
RML898	XFF813	AEC Routemaster R2RH1	Park Royal	H40/32R	1961	Iveco engine
RM980	USK625	AEC Routemaster R2RH	Park Royal	H36/28R	1961	Ex Bluebird, 1997
RM1289	XSL596A	AEC Routemaster 2R2RH	Park Royal	H36/28R	1962	Ex Bluebird, 1997
RMC1456	LFF875	AEC Routemaster R2RH	Park Royal	H32/25RD	1962	
RMC1461	461CLT	AEC Routemaster R2RH	Park Royal	H32/25RD	1962	
RMC1485	485CLT	AEC Routemaster R2RH	Park Royal	H32/25RD	1962	
RM1527	527CLT	AEC Routemaster 2R2RH	Park Royal	H36/28R	1963	
RM1599	YTS820A	AEC Routemaster 2R2RH	Park Royal	H36/28R	1963	Ex Bluebird, 1997

RML2272-2592

AEC Routemaster R2RH1 — Park Royal — H40/32R — 1965-66

2272/86/311/445/56/95-7/541/50/65/81 have Cummins engines; all others have Iveco engines

2272	CUV272C	2399	JJD399D	2444	JJD444D	2470	JJD470D	2497	JJD497D
2286	CUV286C	2402	JJD402D	2445	JJD445D	2481	JJD481D	2541	JJD541D
2300	CUV300C	2415	JJD415D	2450	JJD450D	2488	JJD488D	2550	JJD550D
2303	CUV303C	2429	JJD429D	2451	JJD451D	2493	JJD493D	2565	JJD565D
2311	CUV311C	2435	JJD435D	2456	JJD456D	2495	JJD495D	2581	JJD581D
2392	JJD392D	2437	JJD437D	2462	JJD462D	2496	JJD496D	2592	JJD592D

Opposite, top: - **An interesting vehicle in the East London fleet is open-top Titan T512, KYV512X. East London are currently converting a further ten of the model for transfer to the Scottish fleets where they will displace the varied models currently in use.** *Malc McDonald*
Opposite, bottom:- **The latest double-deck arrivals for East London are long-wheelbase Volvo Olympians with Alexander bodywork, represented here by VA54, R154VPU photographed working service 26 towards Waterloo Station.** *Malc McDonald*

RML2607-2760

AEC Routemaster R2RH1   Park Royal   H40/32R   1967-68
2610/6/39-42/61/70/1/96/705/23/43/8 have Cummins engines;
2665 has Scania engine; all others except 2760 have Iveco engines

2607	NML607E	**2641**	NML641E	**2665**	SMK665F	**2705**	SMK705F	**2743**	SMK743F
2610	NML610E	**2642**	NML642E	**2670**	SMK670F	**2709**	SMK709F	**2748**	SMK748F
2616	NML616E	**2657**	NML657E	**2671**	SMK671F	**2723**	SMK723F	**2749**	SMK749F
2624	NML624E	**2661**	SMK661F	**2696**	SMK696F	**2738**	SMK738F	**2760**	SMK760F
2639	NML639E								

S22-29

Scania N113DRB   Alexander RH   H47/31F   1991

22	J822HMC	**24**	J824HMC	**26**	J826HMC	**28**	J828HMC	**29**	J829HMC
23	J823HMC	**25**	J825HMC	**27**	J827HMC				

S30	J230XKY	Scania N113DRB	Northern Counties Palatine	H47/33F	1991
S31	J231XKY	Scania N113DRB	Northern Counties Palatine	H47/33F	1991

S32-71

Scania N113DRB   Northern Counties Palatine   H41/25D   1991-92

32	J132HMT	**40**	J140HMT	**48**	K848LMK	**56**	K856LMK	**64**	K864LMK
33	J133HMT	**41**	J141HMT	**49**	K849LMK	**57**	K857LMK	**65**	K865LMK
34	J134HMT	**42**	J142HMT	**50**	K850LMK	**58**	K858LMK	**66**	K866LMK
35	J135HMT	**43**	J143HMT	**51**	K851LMK	**59**	K859LMK	**67**	K867LMK
36	J136HMT	**44**	J144HMT	**52**	K852LMK	**60**	K860LMK	**68**	K868LMK
37	J137HMT	**45**	J145HMT	**53**	K853LMK	**61**	K861LMK	**69**	K869LMK
38	J138HMT	**46**	K846LMK	**54**	K854LMK	**62**	K862LMK	**70**	K870LMK
39	J139HMT	**47**	K847LMK	**55**	K855LMK	**63**	K863LMK	**71**	K871LMK

SLD1-9

Dennis Dart SLF   Alexander ALX200   B40F   1996

1	P21HMF	**3**	P23HMF	**5**	P25HMF	**7**	P27HMF	**9**	P29HMF
2	P31HMF	**4**	P24HMF	**6**	P26HMF	**8**	P28HMF		

SLD10-19

Dennis Dart SLF   Alexander ALX200   B40F   1997

10	P610SEV	**12**	R712XAR	**14**	R114VPU	**16**	R116VPU	**18**	R118VPU
11	P611SEV	**13**	P613SEV	**15**	R115VPU	**17**	R117VPU	**19**	R119VPU

SLD30-50

Dennis Dart SLF   Alexander ALX200   B40F   On order

30		**35**		**39**		**43**		**47**	
31		**36**		**40**		**44**		**48**	
32		**37**		**41**		**45**		**49**	
33		**38**		**42**		**46**		**50**	
34									

SLW15-30

Scania N113CRL   Wright Pathfinder 320   B37D   1994

15	RDZ6115	**19**	RDZ6119	**22**	RDZ6122	**25**	RDZ6125	**28**	RDZ6128
16	RDZ6116	**20**	RDZ6120	**23**	RDZ6123	**26**	RDZ6126	**29**	RDZ6129
17	RDZ6117	**21**	RDZ6121	**24**	RDZ6124	**27**	RDZ6127	**30**	RDZ6130
18	RDZ6118								

SR1	E155CGJ	Mercedes-Benz 811D	Optare StarRider	B26F	1988
SR2	E712LYU	Mercedes-Benz 811D	Optare StarRider	B26F	1988

SR12-119

Mercedes-Benz 811D   Optare StarRider   B26F   1988-89

12	F912YWY	**60**	F160FWY	**72**	F172FWY	**76**	F176FWY	**105**	G105KUB
13	F913YWY	**65**	F165FWY	**73**	F173FWY	**78**	F178FWY	**106**	G106KUB
32	F32CWY	**66**	F166FWY	**74**	F174FWY	**79**	F179FWY	**107**	G107KUB
50	F50CWY	**70**	F170FWY	**75**	F175FWY	**91**	G91KUB	**119**	G119KUB
56	F156FWY	**71**	F171FWY						

T1-163

Leyland Titan TNLXB2RRSp Park Royal H44/26D* 1978-80 *63/80 are DPH44/26F, many H44/22D

1	THX401S	11	WYV11T	18	WYV18T	28	WYV28T	35	WYV35T
2	THX402S	12	WYV12T	21	WYV21T	30	WYV30T	36	WYV36T
3	WYV3T	13	WYV13T	22	WYV22T	31	WYV31T	39	WYV39T
4	WYV4T	14	WYV14T	23	WYV23T	32	WYV32T	63	WYV63T
6	WYV6T	15	WYV15T	24	WYV24T	33	WYV33T	80	CUL80V
7	WYV7T	16	WYV16T	25	WYV25T	34	WYV34T	163	CUL163V
8	WYV8T								

T261	GYE261W	Leyland Titan TNTL112RR	Park Royal/Leyland	H44/26D	1981

T264-549

Leyland Titan TNLXB2RR Leyland H44/24D* 1981-82
266/85, 311/20/31 are H44/26D; 512 is O44/24D; 501/2 ex Stagecoach Selkent 1997

264	GYE264W	379	KYV379X	458	KYV458X	497	KYV497X	527	KYV527X
266	GYE266W	380	KYV380X	460	KYV460X	500	KYV500X	529	KYV529X
268	GYE268W	386	KYV386X	461	KYV461X	501	KYV501X	531	KYV531X
272	GYE272W	387	KYV387X	462	KYV462X	502	KYV502X	532	KYV532X
285	KYN285X	394	KYV394X	465	KYV465X	503	KYV503X	533	KYV533X
286	KYN286X	395	KYV395X	466	KYV466X	505	KYV505X	535	KYV535X
298	KYN298X	406	KYV406X	467	KYV467X	506	KYV506X	536	KYV536X
306	KYN306X	428	KYV428X	469	KYV469X	508	KYV508X	537	KYV537X
311	KYV311X	434	KYV434X	470	KYV470X	512	KYV512X	539	KYV539X
318	KYV318X	437	KYV439X	471	KYV471X	513	KYV513X	540	KYV540X
320	KYV320X	441	KYV441X	473	KYV473X	514	KYV514X	541	KYV541X
326	KYV326X	444	KYV444X	476	KYV476X	515	KYV515X	543	KYV543X
331	KYV331X	445	KYV445X	480	KYV480X	517	KYV517X	544	KYV544X
334	KYV334X	446	KYV446X	486	KYV486X	521	KYV521X	545	KYV545X
340	KYV340X	448	KYV448X	488	KYV488X	522	KYV522X	546	KYV546X
360	KYV360X	453	KYV453X	490	KYV490X	525	KYV525X	548	KYV548X
366	KYV366X	454	KYV454X	492	KYV492X	526	KYV526X	549	KYV549X
378	KYV378X	456	KYV456X	495	KYV495X				

T550-675

Leyland Titan TNLXB2RR Leyland H44/24D 1982-83

550	NUW550Y	569	NUW569Y	595	NUW595Y	622	NUW622Y	640	NUW640Y
551	NUW551Y	573	NUW573Y	597	NUW597Y	623	NUW623Y	641	NUW641Y
552	NUW552Y	576	NUW576Y	598	NUW598Y	624	NUW624Y	644	NUW644Y
553	NUW553Y	578	NUW578Y	600	NUW600Y	625	NUW625Y	650	NUW650Y
554	NUW554Y	579	NUW579Y	602	NUW602Y	627	NUW627Y	652	NUW652Y
556	NUW556Y	580	NUW580Y	603	NUW603Y	629	NUW629Y	653	NUW653Y
557	NUW557Y	581	NUW581Y	605	NUW605Y	630	NUW630Y	657	NUW657Y
559	NUW559Y	583	NUW582Y	608	NUW608Y	631	NUW631Y	658	NUW658Y
562	NUW562Y	584	NUW584Y	609	NUW609Y	632	NUW632Y	660	NUW660Y
563	NUW563Y	585	NUW585Y	610	NUW610Y	633	NUW633Y	662	NUW662Y
564	NUW564Y	588	NUW588Y	613	NUW613Y	636	NUW636Y	665	NUW665Y
565	NUW565Y	589	NUW589Y	614	NUW614Y	637	NUW637Y	666	NUW666Y
566	NUW566Y	590	NUW590Y	617	NUW617Y	639	NUW639Y	669	NUW669Y
568	NUW568Y	592	NUW592Y	621	NUW621Y				

East London was allocated many of the Scania N113 double-decks purchased by London Buses and, like the later Volvo Olympians, featured bodywork by both Alexander and Northern Counties. Pictured at Shoreditch is S67, K867LMK. As shown in the allocation table, the majority of the Scanias are based at Upton Park.
Gerry Mead

VN40, P540HMP, is shown here to compare and contrast the differences to bodywork on Volvo Olympians with the colour picture on page 71. The vehicle carries Northern Counties dual-door bodywork and is seen in Romford working service 86. *Gerry Mead*

T686-996					Leyland Titan TNLXB2RR		Leyland		H44/24D*		1983-84		*802-970 are H44/26D
											855, 874 and 996 ex Selkent, 1997		
686	OHV686Y	751	OHV751Y	867	A867SUL	922	A922SYE	953	A953SYE
691	OHV691Y	789	OHV789Y	873	A873SUL	935	A935SYE	960	A960SYE
699	OHV699Y	802	OHV802Y	874	A874SUL	944	A944SYE	965	A965SYE
700	OHV700Y	819	RYK819Y	902	A902SYE	945	A945SYE	971	A971SYE
749	OHV749Y	855	A855SUL	921	A921SYE	949	A949SYE	996	A996SYE

T1050	A650THV	Leyland Titan TNLXB2RR	Leyland	H44/24D	1984
T1128	630DYE	Leyland Titan TNLXB1RF	Park Royal	DPH43/29F	1979

VN1-26					Volvo Olympian YN2RV18Z4		Northern Counties Palatine		H49/31F		1996
1	P801GMU	7	P807GMU	12	P812GMU	17	P817GMU	22	P822GMU
2	P802GMU	8	P808GMU	13	P813GMU	18	P818GMU	23	P823GMU
3	P803GMU	9	P809GMU	14	P814GMU	19	P819GMU	24	P824GMU
4	P804GMU	10	P810GMU	15	P815GMU	20	P820GMU	25	P825GMU
5	P805GMU	11	P811GMU	16	P816GMU	21	P821GMU	26	P826GMU
6	P806GMU								

Opposite, top:- The Optare-bodied DAF single-deck, known as the Delta, is operated by only two Stagecoach subsidiaries. East London now use twenty-six of which two are on extended loan to Stagecoach South, the only other user of the type, where they provide connections with South West Trains' London services. Pictured here is DA17, J717CYG. *Gerry Mead*

Opposite, bottom:- The Leyland Titan was purchased by London Buses in similar quantities to the MCW Metrobus, though the Titan is proving to have been the better option. The early models were built at Park Royal with running units supplied from Leyland. When that facility closed thirteen were hand-built in Lillyhall (in the building now a Stagecoach Cumberland depot) before production re-commenced in part of the Leyland National assembly plant in Cumbria. Seen here is T394, KYV394X.

The 1998 Stagecoach Bus Handbook

AEC Routemasters are contracted to operate certain services on behalf of London Buses. The original fleet East London received from London Buses has been increased following the transfer of three from Bluebird Buses who used them on Perth City services until the delivery of low-floor B6s at the end of 1996. Special gold fleet names are displayed on this class as shown in this view of RML2303, CUV303C. As we go to press we have learnt that the two RMA-class Routemasters are to be transferred for use with Stagecoach Portugal. *Malc McDonald*

VN27-43

Volvo Olympian YN2RV18Z4   Northern Counties Palatine   H49/27D   1996-97

27	P527HMP	31	P531HMP	35	P535HMP	38	P538HMP	41	P541HMP
28	P528HMP	32	P532HMP	36	P536HMP	39	P539HMP	42	P542HMP
29	P529HMP	33	P533HMP	37	P537HMP	40	P540HMP	43	P543HMP
30	P530HMP	34	P534HMP						

VN44-81

Volvo Olympian   Alexander RL   H51/28D   1997

44	P644SEV	52	R152VPU	60	R160VPU	68	R168VPU	75	R175VPU
45	P645SEV	53	R153VPU	61	R161VPU	69	R169VPU	76	R176VPU
46	P646SEV	54	R154VPU	62	R162VPU	70	R170VPU	77	R177VPU
47	R747XAR	55	R155VPU	63	R163VPU	71	R171VPU	78	R178VPU
48	R148VPU	56	R156VPU	64	R164VPU	72	R172VPU	79	R179VPU
49	R149VPU	57	R157VPU	65	R165VPU	73	R173VPU	80	R180VPU
50	R150VPU	58	R158VPU	66	R166VPU	74	R174VPU	81	R181VPU
51	R151VPU	59	R159VPU	67	R167VPU					

VN111-121

Volvo Olympian   Northern Counties Palatine   H--/--D   On order

111	114	116	118	120
112	115	117	119	121
113				

VN122-148

Volvo Olympian   Alexander RL   H--/--D   On order

122	128	134	139	144
123	129	135	140	145
124	130	136	141	146
125	131	137	142	147
126	132	138	143	148
127	133			

The 1998 Stagecoach Bus Handbook

VN149-164   Volvo Olympian   Northern Counties Palatine   H--/--D   On order

149	153	156	159	162
150	154	157	160	163
151	155	158	161	164
152				

VP4	H654UWR	Volvo B10M-60	Plaxton Paramount 3500 III	C49FT	1991	Ex Wallace Arnold, 1995
VP5	H655UWR	Volvo B10M-60	Plaxton Paramount 3500 III	C49FT	1991	Ex Wallace Arnold, 1995
VP7	H657UWR	Volvo B10M-60	Plaxton Paramount 3500 III	C51F	1991	Ex Wallace Arnold, 1995

Previous Registrations:

461CLT	From new	E155CGJ	E711LYU, WLT461	XFF813	WLT898
472YMF	J713CYG	LFF875	456CLT	XFF814	WLT890
485CLT	From new	NFX667	K716PCN	XYK976	K719PCN
527CLT	From new	WLT613	From new	YLJ332	J715CYG
630DYE	WDA3T, 486CLT	WLT886	From new		

Liveries: Red; green (1962 Green Line); yellow (East London Line): red and silver (East London Coaches); blue (London City Airport); Corporate.

Note: All vehicles were formerly London Buses, 1994 unless shown otherwise or acquired later. DA13/5, 1716/9 are on loan to Stagecoach South for South West Trains feeder contracts.

Allocations:-

Barking (Longbridge Road) - East London

Delta	DA10	DA11	DA12	DA14	DA16	DA17	DA18	DA19
	DA20	DA20	DA22	DA23	DA24	DA25	DA26	DA27
	DA28	DA29	DA30	DA31	DA32	DA33	DA34	DA35
Dart	DAL12	DAL13	DAL14	DAL15	DAL16	DAL17	DAL18	DAL19
	DAL20	DAL21	DAL22	DAL23	DAL24	DAL25	DAL26	DAL27
	DRL111	DRL113	DRL119	DRL121	DW159	PD410	PD411	PD412
	PD413	PD414	PD415	PD416	PD417	PD418	PD419	PD420
	PD421	PD422	PD423	PD424	PD425	PD426	PD427	SLD10
	SLD11	SLD12	SLD13	SLD14	SLD15	SLD16	SLD17	SLD18
	SLD19							
Titan	T434	T454	T465	T476	T500	T510	T502	T503
	T508	T514	T517	T522	T525	T526	T531	T532
	T537	T539	T549	T550	T551	T552	T563	T564
	T568	T573	T578	T580	T581	T583	T585	T589
	T592	T597	T598	T600	T603	T609	T613	T614
	T624	T625	T627	T629	T630	T631	T632	T633
	T637	T641	T644	T650	T652	T653	T657	T658
	T660	T669	T855					

Bow (Fairfield Road) - East London

Routemaster	RML898	RML2300	RML2303	RML2392	RML2399	RML2402	RML2415	RML2429
	RML2435	RML2437	RML2444	RML2450	RML2451	RML2462	RML2470	RML2481
	RML2488	RML2493	RML2592	RML2607	RML2624	RML2657	RML2665	RML2696
	RML2709	RML2738	RML2749					
Titan	T268	T272	T285	T286	T311	T340	T366	T380
	T386	T387	T395	T406	T441	T445	T448	T456
	T458	T488	T495	T496	T548	T562	T622	T623
	T666	T996						
Olympian	VA44	VA45	VA46	VA47	VA48	VA49	VA50	VA51
	VA52	VA53	VA54	VA55	VA56	VA57	VA58	VA59
	VA60	VA61	VA62	VA63	VA64	VA65	VA66	VA67
	VA68	VA69	VA70	VA71	VA72	VA73	VA74	VA75
	VA76	VA77	VA78	VA79	VA80	VA81	VN35	VN36
	VN37	VN38	VN39	VN40	VN41	VN42	VN43	

Leyton (High Road) - East London

| Dart | DRL109 | SLD1 | SLD2 | SLD3 | SLD4 | SLD5 | SLD6 | SLD7 |
| | SLD8 | SLD9 | | | | | | |

Scania N113	S62	S63	S64	S65	S66	S67	S68	S69
	S70	S71						
Titan	T261	T264	T266	T298	T318	T320	T326	T334
	T360	T378	T394	T428	T437	T466	T467	T469
	T473	T497	T505	T513	T515	T521	T527	T533
	T535	T541	T553	T554	T556	T557	T559	T565
	T569	T576	T579	T584	T588	T590	T595	T602
	T605	T608	T610	T617	T621	T636	T639	T640
	T662	T665	T686	T691	T699	T702	T749	T751
	T789	T802	T819	T832	T867	T873	T874	T902
	T921	T922	T935	T944	T945	T1050		

Romford (North Street) - East London - East London Coaches ♦

Dart	DAL1	DAL2	DAL3	DAL4	DAL5	DAL6	DAL7	DAL8
	DAL9	DAL10	DAL11					
Volvo Coach	VP4♦	VP5♦	VP7♦					
Titan	T1	T2	T3	T4	T6	T7	T8	T11
	T12	T13	T14	T15	T16	T18	T21	T22
	T23	T24	T25	T28	T30	T31	T32	T33
	T34	T35	T36	T39	T63♦	T80♦	T163	T306
	T331	T379	T444	T446	T453	T460	T461	T462
	T470	T480	T486	T490	T506	T529	T536	T540
	T543	T545	T546	T1128♦				
Olympian	VN1	VN2	VN3	VN4	VN5	VN6	VN7	VN8
	VN9	VN27	VN28	VN29	VN30	VN31	VN32	VN33
	VN34							

Stratford (Waterden Road) - East London - East London Line ♥ - London City Airport ♠

Dart	DRL125	DRL126	DRL128	DRL129	DRL130	DRL131	DRL132	DRL133
	DRL134	DRL135	DW133	DW134	DW135	DW136	DW137	DW138
	DW139	DW140	DW141	DW142	DW143	DW144	DW145	DW146
	DW147	DW148	DW149	DW150	DW151	DW152	DW153	DW154
	DW155	DW156	DW157	DW158	DWL15	DWL16	DWL17	DWL18
	DWL19	DWL20	DWL21	DWL22	DWL23	DWL24	DWL25	DWL26
	LCY1♠	LCY2♠	LCY3♠	LCY4♠	LCY5♠	LCY6♠	LCY7♠♦	LCY8♠
	LCY9♠	PD1	PD2	PD3	PD4	PD5	PD6	PD7
	PD8	PD9	PD10	PD11	PD12	PD13	PD14	PD15
	PD16	PD17	PD18					
MetroRider	MRL144♥	MRL148	MRL150	MRL160	MRL162	MRL170	MRL171	MRL174
	MRL176							
StarRider	SR1	SR2	SR12♥	SR13♥	SR32♥	SR50♥	SR56♥	SR60♥
	SR65	SR66	SR70♥	SR71	SR72♥	SR73♥	SR74♥	SR75♥
	SR76♥	SR78	SR79	SR91♥	SR105♥	SR106♥	SR107♥	SR119♥

Upton Park (Redclyffe Road) - East London

Dart	DRL114	DRL115	DRL116	DRL122	DRL124	DRL136	DRL137	DRL138
	DRL139	DRL140	DRL141	DRL142	DRL143	DRL144	DRL145	DRL146
Routemaster	RM613	RML886	RML890	RM980	RM1289	RM1456	RM1461	RM1485
	RM1527	RM1599	RM2272	RM2286	RM2311	RM2445	RM2456	RM2495
	RM2496	RM2496	RM2497	RM2541	RM2550	RM2565	RM2581	RM2610
	RM2616	RM2639	RM2641	RM2642	RM2661	RM2670	RM2671	RM2705
	RM2723	RM2734	RM2748	RM2760				
Scania N113 DD	S22	S23	S24	S25	S26	S27	S28	S29
	S30	S21	S32	S33	S34	S35	S36	S37
	S38	S39	S40	S41	S42	S43	S44	S45
	S46	S47	S48	S49	S50	S51	S52	S53
	S54	S55	S56	S57	S58	S59	S60	S61
Scania N113 SD	SLW15	SLW16	SLW17	SLW18	SLW19	SLW20	SLW21	SLW22
	SLW23	SLW24	SLW25	SLW26	SLW27	SLW28	SLW29	SLW30
Titan	T512	T949	T953	T960	T965	T971		
Olympian	VN10	VN11	VN12	VN13	VN14	VN15	VN16	VN17
	VN18	VN19	VN20	VN21	VN22	VN23	VN24	VN25
	VN26							

The 1998 Stagecoach Bus Handbook

EAST MIDLAND

East Midland Motor Services Ltd, Grimsby Cleethorpes Transport Ltd,
Chesterfield Transport Ltd, New Street, Chesterfield, Derbyshire, S40 2LQ

1-9			Dennis Lance 11SDA3106*		East Lancashire EL2000		B45F	1993	1-7 ex Grimsby Cleethorpes, 1993
									*5-9 are type 11SDA3111
1	K701NDO	3	K703NDO	5	L705HFU	7	L707HFU	9	L709HFU
2	K702NDO	4	K704NDO	6	L706HFU	8	L708HFU		

12-19			Mercedes-Benz 811D		Alexander Sprint		B31F	1992	Ex Chesterfield, 1995
12	J213AET	15	J215AET	17	J217AET	18	J218AET	19	J219AET
14	J214AET	16	J216AET						

21	EKY21V	Leyland National 2 NL116L11/1R		B52F	1980	Ex Chesterfield, 1995
22	EKY22V	Leyland National 2 NL116L11/1R		B52F	1980	Ex Chesterfield, 1995
23	EKY23V	Leyland National 2 NL116L11/1R		B52F	1981	Ex Chesterfield, 1995

| **24-29** | | | Leyland National 2 NL106L11/1R | | | | B44F | 1980 | Ex Chesterfield, 1995 |
| 24 | EKY24V | 25 | EKY25V | 27 | EKY27V | 28 | EKY28V | 29 | EKY29V |

| **30-34** | | | Leyland National 2 NL116AL11/1R | | | | B52F | 1981 | Ex Chesterfield, 1995 |
| 30 | OWB30X | 31 | OWB31X | 32 | OWB32X | 33 | OWB33X | 34 | OWB34X |

35	SKY31Y	Leyland Tiger TRCTL11/3R	Eastern Coach Works B51	C51F	1983	
36	SKY32Y	Leyland Tiger TRCTL11/3R	Eastern Coach Works B51	C51F	1983	
37	PJI4316	Leyland Tiger TRCTL11/2R	Duple Dominant IV	C47F	1983	
39	A39XHE	Leyland Tiger TRCTL11/2R	Alexander TE	DP45F	1983	
41	A41XHE	Leyland Tiger TRCTL11/2R	Alexander TE	DP45F	1984	
42	A42XHE	Leyland Tiger TRCTL11/2R	Alexander TE	DP49F	1984	
44	A44XHE	Leyland Tiger TRCTL11/2R	Alexander TE	DP49F	1984	
48	B54DWJ	Leyland Tiger TRCTL11/2RH	Alexander TE	DP49F	1985	

50-55			Leyland National 2 NL116HLXCT/1R				B52F	1984	Ex Chesterfield, 1995
50	B150DHL	52	B152DHL	53	B153DHL	54	B154DHL	55	B155DHL
51	B151DHL								

59	B52DWE	Leyland Tiger TRCTL11/2RH	Alexander TE	DP49F	1984	
60	B53DWJ	Leyland Tiger TRCTL11/2RH	Alexander TE	DP49F	1985	
64	E60WDT	Leyland Lynx LX112TL11ZR1	Leyland Lynx	DP49F	1988	Ex Chesterfield, 1995
65	E61WDT	Leyland Lynx LX112TL11ZR1	Leyland Lynx	DP49F	1988	Ex Chesterfield, 1995
71	A71GEE	Leyland Olympian ONTL11/1R	Eastern Coach Works	H45/31F	1983	Ex Grimsby Cleethorpes, 1993
72	A72GEE	Leyland Olympian ONTL11/1R	Eastern Coach Works	H45/31F	1983	Ex Grimsby Cleethorpes, 1993
73	A73GEE	Leyland Olympian ONTL11/1R	Eastern Coach Works	H47/28D	1983	Ex Grimsby Cleethorpes, 1993
74	A74GEE	Leyland Olympian ONTL11/1R	Eastern Coach Works	H47/28D	1983	Ex Grimsby Cleethorpes, 1993
75	F75TFU	Dennis Dominator DDA1021	Alexander RH	H45/33F	1989	Ex Grimsby Cleethorpes, 1993
76	F76TFU	Dennis Dominator DDA1021	Alexander RH	H45/33F	1989	Ex Grimsby Cleethorpes, 1993
77	F77TFU	Dennis Dominator DDA1021	Alexander RH	H45/33F	1989	Ex Grimsby Cleethorpes, 1993
78	F78TFU	Dennis Dominator DDA1022	Alexander RH	H45/33F	1989	Ex Grimsby Cleethorpes, 1993
79	G79VFW	Dennis Dominator DDA1028	Alexander RH	H45/33F	1990	Ex Grimsby Cleethorpes, 1993
80	G80VFW	Dennis Dominator DDA1028	Alexander RH	H45/33F	1990	Ex Grimsby Cleethorpes, 1993
81	G81VFW	Dennis Dominator DDA1029	Alexander RH	H45/33F	1990	Ex Grimsby Cleethorpes, 1993

82-89			Dennis Dominator DDA1034*		East Lancashire		H45/33F	1991-92	Ex Grimsby Cleethorpes, 1993
									*86-9 are DDA1036
82	H482BEE	84	H484BEE	86	J91DJV	88	J93DJV	89	J94DJV
83	H483BEE	85	H485BEE	87	J92DJV				

In July 1995 Stagecoach confirmed the acquisition of ailing Chesterfield Transport following an Extraordinary General Meeting at which over 99% of Chesterfield's employees voted in favour of the take over. Chesterfield was thus placed under East Midlands control. Many of the Leyland Nationals that remain with East Midlands are those which entered the fleet at that time. Seen in Sheffield is former Chesterfield 52, B152DHL. *Tony Wilson*

90-98

| | | | | | | | | | Mercedes-Benz 709D | | Alexander Sprint | | B25F* | | 1988 | Ex Chesterfield, 1995 *97/8 are DP25F |

90	E90YWB	92	E92YWB	94	E94YWB	96	E96YWB	98	E98YWB
91	E91YWB	93	E93YWB	95	E95YWB	97	E97YWB		

99	H257THL	Mercedes-Benz 709D	Reeve Burgess Beaver	B25F	1991	Ex Chesterfield, 1995

101-109

Volvo Olympian YN2RV18Z4 — Northern Counties Palatine — H47/29F — 1993

101	K101JWJ	103	K103JWJ	105	K105JWJ	107	K107JWJ	109	L109LHL
102	K102JWJ	104	K104JWJ	106	K106JWJ	108	L108LHL		

113	MBE613R	Leyland Fleetline FE30AGR	Roe	O45/29D	1976	Ex Grimsby Cleethorpes, 1993
114	BJV103L	Daimler Fleetline CRG6LX	Roe	O45/29D	1973	Ex Grimsby Cleethorpes, 1993

130-144

Volvo Olympian YN2RV18Z4 — Alexander RL — H47/32F — 1995

130	N130AET	133	N133AET	136	N136AET	139	N139AET	142	N142AET
131	N131AET	134	N134AET	137	N137AET	140	N140AET	143	N143AET
132	N132AET	135	N135AET	138	N138AET	141	N141AET	144	N144AET

145-160

Volvo Olympian — Alexander RL — H51/35F — 1996-97

145	P145KWJ	149	P149KWJ	152	P152KWJ	156	P156KWJ	159	P159KAK
146	P146KWJ	150	P150KWJ	153	P153KWJ	157	P157KWJ	160	P160KAK
148	P148KWJ	151	P151KWJ	154	P154KWJ	158	P158KWJ		

172	XGS736S	Leyland Leopard PSU3E/4R	Plaxton Supreme III	C53F	1978	Ex Grimsby Cleethorpes, 1993
173	BHO441V	Leyland Leopard PSU5C/4R	Duple Dominant II	C55F	1980	Ex Grimsby Cleethorpes, 1993
174	MRJ270W	Leyland Leopard PSU5C/4R	Plaxton Supreme IV	C41DL	1980	Ex Grimsby Cleethorpes, 1993
175	EFU935Y	Leyland Leopard PSU5C/4R	Duple Dominant I	C53F	1983	Ex Grimsby Cleethorpes, 1993
176	OJL823Y	Leyland Leopard PSU5C/4R	Duple Dominant III	C53F	1983	Ex Grimsby Cleethorpes, 1993
177	OJL822Y	Leyland Leopard PSU5C/4R	Duple Dominant III	C49F	1983	Ex Grimsby Cleethorpes, 1993

Most of the fleet based at Grimsby depot carry the Grimsby Cleethorpes operating name though, as shown in the allocation listing, many of the coaches carry Peter Sheffield names. Photographed opposite the depot is open-top 113, MBE613R, a dual-doored Roe-bodied Leyland Fleetline.
Tony Wilson

183	PJI4314	Leyland Tiger TRCTL11/2R	Plaxton Paramount 3200 E	C47F	1983	
187	PYE841Y	Leyland Tiger TRCTL11/3R	Duple Laser	C53F	1983	Ex Grimsby Cleethorpes, 1993
188	PYE842Y	Leyland Tiger TRCTL11/3R	Duple Laser	C53F	1983	Ex Grimsby Cleethorpes, 1993
189	PSU764	Leyland Tiger TRCTL11/3R	Duple Laser	C53F	1983	Ex Grimsby Cleethorpes, 1993
190	PSU443	Leyland Tiger TRCTL11/3R	Duple Laser	C53F	1983	Ex Grimsby Cleethorpes, 1993
191	A243YGF	Leyland Tiger TRCTL11/3RH	Duple Laser	C57F	1984	Ex Grimsby Cleethorpes, 1993
192	PS2743	Leyland Tiger TRCTL11/3RH	Duple Laser	C57F	1984	Ex Grimsby Cleethorpes, 1993

209-224

Bristol VRT/SL3/6LXB*   Eastern Coach Works   H43/31F   1980-81 *218 is type 6LXC

209	EWE203V	211	JAK211W	218	KWA218W	223	KWA223W	224	KWA224W
210	EWE206V	214	KWA214W	221	KWA221W				

231	EJV31Y	Dennis Falcon H SDA411	Wadham Stringer Vanguard	B42F	1983	Ex Grimsby Cleethorpes, 1993
232	EJV32Y	Dennis Falcon H SDA411	Wadham Stringer Vanguard	B42F	1983	Ex Grimsby Cleethorpes, 1993
233	EJV33Y	Dennis Falcon H SDA411	Wadham Stringer Vanguard	B42F	1983	Ex Grimsby Cleethorpes, 1993
234	EJV34Y	Dennis Falcon H SDA411	Wadham Stringer Vanguard	B42F	1983	Ex Grimsby Cleethorpes, 1993
259	BFW136W	Ford R1114	Plaxton Supreme IV	C53F	1981	Ex Grimsby Cleethorpes, 1993
260u	UWA150S	Leyland Fleetline FE30AGR	Roe	H42/29D	1978	Ex Chesterfield, 1995
261u	UWA151S	Leyland Fleetline FE30AGR	Roe	H42/29D	1978	Ex Chesterfield, 1995
299	TWF201Y	Leyland Olympian ONLXB/1R	Roe	H47/29F	1982	Ex Chesterfield, 1995
300	TWF202Y	Leyland Olympian ONLXB/1R	Roe	H47/29F	1982	Ex Chesterfield, 1995

301-325

Leyland Olympian ONLXB/1R   Eastern Coach Works   H45/32F   1981-84

301	NHL301X	306	SHE306Y	311	SHE311Y	316	A316XWG	321	A321YWJ
302	NHL302X	307	SHE307Y	312	UDT312Y	317	A317XWG	322	A322AKU
303	NHL303X	308	SHE308Y	313	UDT313Y	318	A318XWG	323	A323AKU
304	NHL304X	309	SHE309Y	314	A314XWG	319	A319YWJ	324	A324AKU
305	NHL305X	310	SHE310Y	315	A315XWG	320	A320YWJ	325	A325AKU

326-330

Leyland Olympian ONLXB/1R   Eastern Coach Works   CH40/32F   1985

326	C326HWJ	327	C327HWJ	328	C328HWJ	329	C329HWJ	330	C330HWJ

331-336 — Leyland Olympian ONLXB/1R — Eastern Coach Works — H45/32F — 1986

331	C331HWJ	333	C333HWJ	334	C334HWJ	335	C335HWJ	336	C336HWJ
332	C332HWJ								

337	GSO8V	Leyland Olympian ONLXB/1RV	Alexander RL	H45/32F	1987	Ex United Counties, 1992

339-343 — Leyland Olympian ON6LXB/2RZ — Alexander RL — DPH51/31F — 1989

339	G339KKW	340	G340KKW	341	G341KKW	342	G342KKW	343	G343KKW

344-353 — Leyland Olympian ON25R6G13Z4 — Alexander RL — DPH51/31F* — 1990-91 — *349-353 are DPH47/27F

344	H344SWA	346	H346SWA	348	H348SWA	350	J350XET	352	J352XET
345	H345SWA	347	H347SWA	349	J349XET	351	J351XET	353	J353XET

354-358 — Leyland Olympian ON2R50G13Z4 — Northern Counties Palatine — H47/29F — 1992

354	K354DWJ	355	K355DWJ	356	K356DWJ	357	K357DWJ	358	K358DWJ

359-363 — Leyland Olympian ON2R54G13Z4 — Alexander RL — DPH43/27F — 1992

359	K359DWJ	360	K360DWJ	361	K361DWJ	362	K362DWJ	363	K363DWJ

No.	Reg	Chassis	Body	Layout	Year	Notes
412	DWF22V	Leyland Leopard PSU3E/4R	Duple Dominant(1985)	B55F	1979	
413	DWF23V	Leyland Leopard PSU3E/4R	Duple Dominant(1985)	B51F	1979	
414	DWF24V	Leyland Leopard PSU3E/4R	Alexander P(1985)	B52F	1979	
416	DWF26V	Leyland Leopard PSU3E/4R	Duple Dominant(1985)	B55F	1980	
418	P418KWF	Dennis Dart SFD4	Alexander Dash	B41F	1996	
419	P419KWF	Dennis Dart SFD4	Alexander Dash	B41F	1996	
420	P420KWF	Dennis Dart SFD4	Alexander Dash	B41F	1996	
421	E927PBE	Leyland Tiger TRBLXCT/2RH	Alexander P	B51F	1987	Ex Grimsby Cleethorpes, 1993
422	E928PBE	Leyland Tiger TRBLXCT/2RH	Alexander P	DP51F	1987	Ex Grimsby Cleethorpes, 1993
423	E929PBE	Leyland Tiger TRBLXCT/2RH	Alexander P	DP51F	1987	Ex Grimsby Cleethorpes, 1993
424	E930PBE	Leyland Tiger TRBLXCT/2RH	Alexander P	DP51F	1987	Ex Grimsby Cleethorpes, 1993

425-433 — Leyland Tiger TRCTL11/2RH — Alexander P — B52F — 1985

425	B625DWF	427	B627DWF	429	B629DWF	431	B631DWF	433	B633DWF
426	B626DWF	428	B628DWF	430	B630DWF	432	B632DWF		

435-453 — Volvo B6-9.9M — Alexander Dash — B40F — 1993

435	L435LWA	439	L439LWA	443	L443LWA	448	L448LWA	451	L451LWA
436	L436LWA	440	L440LWA	445	L445LWA	449	L449LWA	452	L452LWA
437	L437LWA	441	L441LWA	446	L446LWA	450	L450LWA	453	L453LHL
438	L438LWA	442	L442LWA	447	L447LWA				

591-600 — Volvo B10M-55 — Alexander PS — DP48F — 1994 — Ex Ribble, 1995

591	L341KCK	593	L343KCK	595	L339KCK	597	M411RRN	599	M413RRN
592	L342KCK	594	L344KCK	596	L340KCK	598	M412RRN	600	M414RRN

601-609 — Volvo B10M-55 — Alexander PS — DP48F — 1995

601	M601VHE	603	M603VHE	605	M605VHE	607	M607VHE	609	M609WET
602	M602VHE	604	M604VHE	606	M606VHE	608	M608WET		

614	EKW614V	Leyland National 2 NL106L11/1R		B44F	1980
615	EKW615V	Leyland National 2 NL106L11/1R		B44F	1980
616	EKW616V	Leyland National 2 NL106L11/1R		B44F	1980

Opposite, top:- **Two batches of Alexander-bodied Volvo Olympians have entered East Midlands fleet. The first arrived in 1995 and are exclusivly located at Grimsby while the 1996 batch comprises the longer version - identified by the additional small window in the centre - are all at Chesterfield where 151, P151KWJ was seen when pictured.** *Tony Wilson.*

Opposite, bottom:- **During the period of NBC ownership East Midland was given dispensation to acquire a batch of Alexander-bodied Leyland Tigers in preference to the then standard National. These arrived in 1985 and illustrating the batch is 433, B633DWF.** *Tony Wilson*

617-621

Leyland National 2 NL116L11/1R B49F 1980

617	GWE617V	618	GWE618V	619	GWE619V	620	HWJ620W	621w	HWJ621W

622	MWG622X	Leyland National 2 NL116AL11/1R		B49F	1981	
623	MWG623X	Leyland National 2 NL116AL11/1R		B49F	1981	
624	MWG624X	Leyland National 2 NL116AL11/1R		B49F	1981	
625	LAG188V	Leyland National 2 NL116L11/1R		B49F	1980	Ex East Yorkshire, 1988
626	LAG189V	Leyland National 2 NL116L11/1R		B49F	1980	Ex East Yorkshire, 1988
627	NRP580V	Leyland National 2 NL116L11/1R		B49F	1980	Ex United Counties, 1992
628	SVV586W	Leyland National 2 NL116L11/1R		B49F	1981	Ex United Counties, 1992
634	VWA34Y	Leyland National 2 NL116HLXB/1R		DP47F	1983	
635	VWA35Y	Leyland National 2 NL116HLXB/1R		DP47F	1983	
636	VWA36Y	Leyland National 2 NL116HLXB/1R		DP47F	1983	

637-643

Volvo B10M-62 Plaxton Premiére Interurban DP51F 1993

637	L637LDT	639	L639LDT	641	L641LDT	642	L642LDT	643	L643LDT
638	L638LDT	640	L640LDT						

652	HSV194	Volvo B10M-61	Plaxton Paramount 3500 III	C53F	1987	Ex Cambus (Premier), 1996
653	HSV195	Volvo B10M-61	Plaxton Paramount 3500 III	C50F	1988	Ex Cambus (Premier), 1996
654	HSV196	Volvo B10M-61	Plaxton Paramount 3500 III	C50F	1988	Ex Cambus (Premier), 1996
655	H402DEG	Volvo B10M-60	Plaxton Paramount 3500 III	C53F	1990	Ex Cambus (Premier), 1996
656	M942TSX	Volvo B10M-60	Plaxton Premiére Interurban	DP51F	1994	Ex Fife Scottish, 1997
657	M943TSX	Volvo B10M-60	Plaxton Premiére Interurban	DP51F	1994	Ex Fife Scottish, 1997
658	K575DFS	Volvo B10M-60	Plaxton Premiére Interurban	DP51F	1993	Ex Western Buses, 1997
660	KSU463	Volvo B10M-60	Plaxton Excalibur	C44FT	1992	Ex Busways, 1997
662	M808JTY	Volvo B10M-62	Plaxton Expressliner 2	C44FT	1995	Ex Busways, 1997
663	R663TKU	Volvo B10M-62	Plaxton Expressliner 2	C44FT	1997	
664	R664TKU	Volvo B10M-62	Plaxton Expressliner 2	C44FT	1997	

720-727

Mercedes-Benz 811D Reeve Burgess Beaver B31F 1989-90

720	G820KWF	722	G822KWF	724	G824KWF	726	G826KWF	727	G827KWF
721	G821KWF	723	G823KWF	725	G825KWF				

728	E721BVO	Mercedes-Benz 811D	Optare StarRider	B33F	1988	Ex Maun, Mansfield, 1990
729	E880DRA	Mercedes-Benz 811D	Optare StarRider	B33F	1988	Ex Maun, Mansfield, 1990

731-751

Mercedes-Benz 709D Alexander Sprint B25F 1993

731	L731LWA	735	L735LWA	739	L739LWA	743	L743LWA	748	L748LWA
732	L732LWA	736	L736LWA	740	L740LWA	744	L744LWA	749	L749LWA
733	L733LWA	737	L737LWA	741	L741LWA	745	L745LWA	750	L750LWA
734	L734LWA	738	L738LWA	742	L742LWA	746	L746LWA	751	L751LHL

752-776

Mercedes-Benz 709D Alexander Sprint B25F 1995-96

752	N752CKU	757	N757CKU	762	N762EWG	767	N767EWG	772	N772EWG
753	N753CKU	758	N758CKU	763	N763EWG	768	N768EWG	773	N773EWG
754	N754CKU	759	N759CKU	764	N764EWG	769	N769EWG	774	N774EWG
755	N755CKU	760	N760CKU	765	N765EWG	770	N770EWG	775	N775EWG
756	N756CKU	761	N761CKU	766	N766EWG	771	N771EWG	776	N776EWG

902-906

MCW MetroRider MF150/94 MCW B23F 1988 Ex Grimsby Cleethorpes, 1993

902	E47HFE	903	E48HFE	904	E49HFE	905	E50HFE	906	E51HFE

907	E56HFE	MCW MetroRider MF150/94	MCW	DP23F	1988	Ex Grimsby Cleethorpes, 1993
908	E57HFE	MCW MetroRider MF150/94	MCW	DP23F	1988	Ex Grimsby Cleethorpes, 1993
909	E58HFE	MCW MetroRider MF150/94	MCW	DP23F	1988	Ex Grimsby Cleethorpes, 1993

Previous Registrations:

A243YGF	A601HVT, PS2045	OJL823Y	EJV419Y, PS2743
GSO8V	D378XRS	PJI4314	UWJ33Y
HSV194	E904UNW	PJI4316	UHE37Y
HSV195	E905UNW	PS2743	A602HVT
HSV196	E315OEG	PSU443	A844SYR
KSU463	J422HDS	PSU764	PYE843Y
OJL822Y	SSG321Y, PS2945		

Pictured in Vicar Lane, Chesterfield is East Midland 606, M606VHE which is from the only batch of Alexander-bodied Volvo B10Ms delivered new to the company. Ten further examples were supplied from Ribble in 1995 and were placed on Chesterfield services at that time. *Tony Wilson*

Allocations:-

Chesterfield (Stonegravels)

Mercedes-Benz	15	16	17	18	19	90	91	92
	93	94	95	96	97	99	720	721
	722	723	725	726	727	728	729	744
	745	746	748	749	750	751	752	753
	754	755	756	757	758	759	760	761
	762	763	764	765	766			
Coaches	638	641	654	655				
Dart	418	419	420					
Lynx	64	65						
National 2	31	32	33	34	51	52	53	54
	616	617	618	619	620	623		
Tiger	39	183	425	426	427	428	429	430
	431	432	433					
Volvo PS	591	592	593	594	595	596	597	598
	599							
Bristol VR	209							
Olympian	145	146	148	149	150	151	152	153
	154	156	157	158	159	160	299	300
	305	306	307	310	312	316	317	318
	322	324	327	329	334	339	341	342
	347	348	349	350				

Calver (Flinthouse Garage)

Mercedes-Benz	12	14						
National 2	21	22	23	24	25	27	28	29
	30	50						

Grimsby (Victoria Street) - Grimsby-Cleethorpes - Peter Sheffield ♥

Mercedes-Benz	767	768	769	770	771	772	773	774
	775	776						
Dennis Lance	1	2	3	4	5	6	7	8
	9							
Dennis Falcon	232	233	234					
Leopard	172♥	173♥	174♥	175♥	176♥			
Ford	259♥							
Tiger	35♥	37♥	59♥	60♥	187♥	188♥	189♥	190
	191♥	192♥	421	422	423	424	✔	
Interurban	639	640	643					
Volvo B10M Coach	652	653						
Dominator	75	76	77	78	79	80	81	82
	83	84	85	86	87	88	89	
Olympian	71	72	73	74	130	131	132	133
	134	135	136	137	138	139	140	141
	142	143	144	303♥				

Mansfield (Sutton Road)

Bristol VR	210	211	214	218	221	223	224	
Olympian	101	102	103	104	105	106	107	108
	109	311	313	325	331	332	335	336
	337	340	343	344	345	346	351	352
	353	354	355	356	357	358		
National 2	615	627						
Tiger	42							
Volvo B6	435	436	437	438	439	440	441	442
	443	445	446	447	448	449	450	451
	452	453						
Volvo PS	601	602	603	604	605	606	607	608
	609							
Interurban	637	642	656	657				
MetroRider	902	903	904	905	906	907	908	909
Volvo B10M Coach	660	662	663	664				

Worksop (Hardy Street)

Olympian	301	302	304	308	309	314	315	319
	320	321	323	326	328	330	333	359
	360	361	362	363				
Falcon	231							
Leopard	412	413	414	416				
Volvo PS	600							
Interurban	658							
National 2	55	614	624	625	626	628	634	635
	636							
Mercedes-Benz	98	724	731	732	733	734	735	736
	737	738	739	740	741	742	743	

Unallocated and stored

National	621	
Fleetline	260	261

FIFE SCOTTISH

Fife Scottish Omnibuses Ltd, Esplanade, Kirkcaldy, Fife, KY1 1SP

1-5		Mercedes-Benz 811D		Carlyle		B31F*	1990	Ex Stagecoach Selkent, 1996 *4/5 are DP28F	
1	F286KGK	2	H882LOX	3	H883LOX	4	H509AGC	5	H885LOX

70-76		Mercedes-Benz 709D		Alexander Sprint		B25F	1994		
70	M770TFS	72	M772TFS	74	M774TFS	75	M775TFS	76	M776TFS
71	M771TFS	73	M773TFS						

77	VLT77	Mercedes-Benz 811D	Reeve Burgess Beaver	B33F	1989	Ex Stagecoach Selkent, 1994
78	M778TFS	Mercedes-Benz 709D	Alexander Sprint	B25F	1994	
79	M779TFS	Mercedes-Benz 709D	Alexander Sprint	B25F	1994	
80	G280TSL	Mercedes-Benz 709D	Alexander Sprint	B23F	1990	Ex Bluebird, 1992
81	G281TSL	Mercedes-Benz 709D	Alexander Sprint	B23F	1990	Ex Bluebird, 1992
82	M780TFS	Mercedes-Benz 709D	Alexander Sprint	B25F	1994	

85-94		Mercedes-Benz 709D		Alexander Sprint		B25F	1993		
85	K485FFS	87	K487FFS	89	K489FFS	91	K491FFS	93	K493FFS
86	K486FFS	88	K488FFS	90	K490FFS	92	K492FFS	94	K494FFS

95	N95ALS	Mercedes-Benz 709D	Alexander Sprint	B25F	1996
96	N96ALS	Mercedes-Benz 709D	Alexander Sprint	B25F	1996
97	N97ALS	Mercedes-Benz 709D	Alexander Sprint	B25F	1996
141	WFS141W	Leyland Leopard PSU3F/4R	Alexander AYS	B53F	1980
159	CSF159W	Leyland Leopard PSU3G/4R	Alexander AYS	B53F	1981
160	CSF160W	Leyland Leopard PSU3G/4R	Alexander AYS	B53F	1981

180-189		Leyland Leopard PSU3G/4R		Alexander AYS		B53F	1982		
180	PSX180Y	182	PSX182Y	185	PSX185Y	187	PSX187Y	189	PSX189Y
181	PSX181Y	183	PSX183Y	186	PSX186Y	188	PSX188Y		

261	CSF161W	Leyland Leopard PSU3G/4R	Alexander AYS	DP49F	1981
262	CSF162W	Leyland Leopard PSU3G/4R	Alexander AYS	DP47F	1981

The first delivery of Alexander PSs for Fife Scottish were delivered in 1994 and from this batch 302, L302PSC is seen at Dunfermline. On the right of the vehicle is the letter C indicating the allocation to Cowdenbeath, a feature which is only used by Fife within Stagecoach.

British Bus Publishing

264-269 Leyland Leopard PSU3F/4R Alexander AYS DP49F 1981

264	CSF164W	266	CSF166W	267	CSF167W	268	CSF168W	269	CSF169W
265	CSF165W								

270-279 Leyland Leopard PSU3G/4R Alexander AT DP49F 1982

270	NFS170Y	272	NFS172Y	274	NFS174Y	276	NFS176Y	278	NFS178Y
271	NFS171Y	273	NFS173Y	275	NFS175Y	277	NFS177Y	279	NFS179Y

290	RSC190Y	Leyland Leopard PSU3G/4R	Alexander AT	DP49F	1982
291	RSC191Y	Leyland Leopard PSU3G/4R	Alexander AT	DP49F	1982
292	RSC192Y	Leyland Leopard PSU3G/4R	Alexander AT	DP49F	1982
294	RSC194Y	Leyland Leopard PSU3G/4R	Alexander AT	DP49F	1982

301-310 Volvo B10M-55 Alexander PS B49F 1994

301	L301PSC	303	L303PSC	305	L305PSC	307	L307PSC	309	L309PSC
302	L302PSC	304	L304PSC	306	L306PSC	308	L308PSC	310	L310PSC

314-329 Volvo B10M-55 Alexander PS B49F* 1995-96 *314/5 are DP48F

314	M314PKS	318	N318VMS	321	N321VMS	324	N324VMS	327	N327VMS
315	M315PKS	319	N319VMS	322	N322VMS	325	N325VMS	328	N328VMS
316	N316VMS	320	N320VMS	323	N323VMS	326	N326VMS	329	N329VMS
317	N317VMS								

330-342 Volvo B10M-55 Alexander PS B49F 1998

330	R330HFS	334	R334HFS	337	R337HFS	339	R339HFS	341	R341HFS
331	R331HFS	335	R335HFS	338	R338HFS	340	R340HFS	342	R342HFS
332	R332HFS	336	R336HFS						

412-419 Leyland Tiger TRCTL11/3RH Alexander P B61F 1986-87

412	D512CSF	414	D614ASG	416	D516DSX	418	D518DSX	419	D519DSX
413	D713CSC	415	D615ASG	417	D517DSX				

420-424 Leyland Tiger TRBTL11/2RH Alexander P B57F 1987

420	D520DSX	421	D521DSX	422	D522DSX	423	D523DSX	424	D524DSX

441	GSU341	Leyland Tiger TRCTL11/2RH	Alexander TC	DP49F	1985
442	GSU342	Leyland Tiger TRCTL11/2RH	Alexander TC	DP49F	1985
444	GSU344	Leyland Tiger TRCTL11/2RH	Alexander TC	C47F	1985
445	MSU345	Leyland Tiger TRCTL11/2RH	Alexander TC	C47F	1985

466-470 Leyland Tiger TRBTL11/2R Alexander TE DP49F 1983 Ex Kelvin Central, 1989

466	MNS6Y	467	MNS7Y	468	MNS8Y	469	MNS9Y	470	MNS10Y

477	D277FAS	Leyland Tiger TRCTL11/3RH	Alexander TE	DP53F	1987	Ex Highland Scottish, 1987
478	D278FAS	Leyland Tiger TRCTL11/3RH	Alexander TE	DP53F	1987	Ex Highland Scottish, 1987
479	D279FAS	Leyland Tiger TRCTL11/3RH	Alexander TE	DP53F	1987	Ex Highland Scottish, 1987
503	GSU343	Volvo B10M-61	Van Hool Alizée	C46FT	1983	Ex Ribble (Hyndburn), 1996
504	IIL3504	Volvo B10M-61	Van Hool Alizée	C49FT	1988	Ex Rainworth Travel, 1993
506	IIL3506	Volvo B10M-61	Van Hool Alizée	C49FT	1988	Ex Rainworth Travel, 1993
512	M102CCD	Dennis Javelin 11SDL2133	Plaxton Premiere Interurban	DP47F	1994	Ex Stagecoach South, 1995
513	M103CCD	Dennis Javelin 11SDL2133	Plaxton Premiere Interurban	DP47F	1995	Ex Stagecoach South, 1995
514	M104CCD	Dennis Javelin 11SDL2133	Plaxton Premiere Interurban	DP47F	1995	Ex Stagecoach South, 1995
539	R539GSF	Volvo B10M-62	Plaxton Premiére Interurban	DP51F	1997	
541	R541GSF	Volvo B10M-62	Plaxton Premiére Interurban	DP51F	1997	
542	R542GSF	Volvo B10M-62	Plaxton Premiére Interurban	DP51F	1997	
543	R543GSF	Volvo B10M-62	Plaxton Premiére Interurban	DP51F	1997	

Opposite:- **The upper picture shows 504, IIL3504 which is one of three Van Hool Alizée coaches within the Fife Scottish fleet. This body type has not been supplied new to the company though a few second-hand models are owned. The lower picture shows one of the two Jonckheere Mistral 35 articulated coaches used on Stagecoach Express services to Glasgow. During 1997 those articulated coaches based in England were transferred to Scotland as competition in Glasgow increased. For 1998 a further delivery of twenty-five - all built by Jonckheere - are to be supplied with many expected to be based once again in England. Experience gained from the model has shown quite a potential for operation in this country.** *Gerry Mead/Tony Wilson*

Based at St. Andrews when photographed arriving in Stirling during the summer of 1997, Fife Scottish 441, GSU341, has since been withdrawn from service, though sister vehicles 442-4 remain. The body style is the Alexander TC-type, a style less common than the then stage equivalents. *Richard Godfrey*

544-556

		Volvo B10M-62			Plaxton Premiére Interurban		DP51F	1994	
544	M944TSX	**547**	M947TSX	**550**	M950TSX	**553**	M953TSX	**555**	M955TSX
545	M945TSX	**548**	M948TSX	**551**	M951TSX	**554**	M954TSX	**556**	M956TSX
546	M946TSX	**549**	M949TSX	**552**	M952TSX				

561	N561SJF	Volvo B10MA-55	Jonckheere Mistral 35	AC72F	1996	
562	N562SJF	Volvo B10MA-55	Jonckheere Mistral 35	AC72F	1996	
563	P563MSX	Volvo B10MA-55	Plaxton Premiére Interurban	AC71F	1996	
564	P564MSX	Volvo B10MA-55	Plaxton Premiére Interurban	AC71F	1996	

565-569

		Volvo B10M-62			Plaxton Premiére Interurban		DP51F	1996	
565	P565MSX	566	P566MSX	567	P567MSX	568	P568MSX	569	P569MSX

570	P670EWB	Volvo B10MA-55	Plaxton Premiére Interurban	AC71F	1996	Ex East Midland, 1997
571	P671EWB	Volvo B10MA-55	Plaxton Premiére Interurban	AC71F	1996	
573	P973UBV	Volvo B10MA-55	Plaxton Premiére Interurban	AC71F	1996	Ex Ribble, 1997
574	P974UBV	Volvo B10MA-55	Plaxton Premiére Interurban	AC71F	1996	Ex Ribble, 1997
575	P975UBV	Volvo B10MA-55	Plaxton Premiére Interurban	AC71F	1996	Ex Ribble, 1997
576	P976UBV	Volvo B10MA-55	Plaxton Premiére Interurban	AC71F	1996	Ex Ribble, 1997

578-590

		Volvo B10M-60			Plaxton Premiére Interurban		DP51F	1993	
578	L578HSG	581	L581HSG	584	L584HSG	587	L587HSG	**589**	L589HSG
579	L579HSG	**582**	L582HSG	**585**	L585HSG	**588**	L588HSG	**590**	L590HSG
580	L580HSG	583	L583HSG	586	L586HSG				

601-605

		Dennis Dart 9.8SDL3017		Alexander Dash		B40F	1992		
601	K601ESH	602	K602ESH	**603**	K603ESH	**604**	K604ESH	**605**	K605ESH

The 1998 Stagecoach Bus Handbook

Stagecoach Express has proved particularly popular with the travelling public as an increased number of routes have been introduced thus providing a network now radiating from Glasgow and Edinburgh. Pictured in Kirkcaldy is Fife Scottish 556, M956TSX one of many Plaxton-bodied Interurban coaches supplied to the Stagecoach Group. *Les Peters*

606-613

		Dennis Dart SFD412		Alexander Dash		B40F	1996		
606	P606CMS	608	P608CMS	610	P610CMS	612	P612CMS	613	P613CMS
607	P607CMS	609	P609CMS	611	P611CMS				

614	R614	Dennis Dart SLF		Alexander ALX200		B37F	1997		

623-628

		Volvo B6-9.9M		Alexander Dash		B40F	1993	Ex Ribble, 1994	
623	L423MVV	625	L425MVV	626	L426MVV	627	L427MVV	628	L428MVV
624	L424MVV								

651-659

		Volvo B6-9.9M		Alexander Dash		B40F	1993-94		
651	L651HKS	653	L653HKS	655	L655HKS	657	L657HKS	659	L659HKS
652	L652HKS	654	L654HKS	656	L656HKS	658	L658HKS		

667	L267CCK	Volvo B6-9.9M	Alexander Dash	B40F	1993	Ex Ribble, 1994
668	L268CCK	Volvo B6-9.9M	Alexander Dash	B40F	1993	Ex Ribble, 1994
669	L269CCK	Volvo B6-9.9M	Alexander Dash	B40F	1993	Ex Ribble, 1994
670	M670SSX	Volvo B6-9.9M	Alexander Dash	B40F	1994	
671	M671SSX	Volvo B6-9.9M	Alexander Dash	B40F	1994	
672	M672SSX	Volvo B6-9.9M	Alexander Dash	B40F	1994	
673	M673SSX	Volvo B6-9.9M	Alexander Dash	B40F	1994	

701-725

		Leyland Olympian ON2R50G13Z4 Alexander RL				H47/32F	1992		
701	J801WFS	704	J804WFS	707	J807WFS	720	K720ASC	723	K723ASC
702	J802WFS	705	J805WFS	718	K718ASC	721	K721ASC	724	K724ASC
703	J803WFS	706	J806WFS	719	K719ASC	722	K722ASC	725	K725ASC

As well as articulated coaches Stagecoach Express operate double-deck buses fitted with high-back seating. The Fife fleet contains several examples based on the Volvo B10M Citybus, including three acquired from Southdown in 1991. One of these, 942, is seen at the Glenrothes terminal of service 43. *Richard Godfrey*

737	G337KKW	Leyland Olympian ON2R56G13Z4	Alexander RL	DPH51/31F	1989	Ex East Midland, 1992
738	G338KKW	Leyland Olympian ON2R56G13Z4	Alexander RL	DPH51/31F	1989	Ex East Midland, 1992
749	OHV749Y	Leyland Titan TNLXB2RR	Leyland	H44/24D	1981	Ex Stagecoach East London, 1998
750	A650THV	Leyland Titan TNLXB2RR	Leyland	H44/24D	1984	Ex Stagecoach East London, 1998
751	OHV751Y	Leyland Titan TNLXB2RR	Leyland	H44/24D	1984	Ex Stagecoach East London, 1998
752	NUW562Y	Leyland Titan TNLXB2RR	Leyland	H44/24D	1984	Ex Stagecoach East London, 1998
753	A613THV	Leyland Titan TNLXB2RR	Leyland	H44/24D	1984	Ex Stagecoach Selkent, 1997
754	NUW554Y	Leyland Titan TNLXB2RR	Leyland	H44/24D	1984	Ex Stagecoach Selkent, 1997
756	NUW566Y	Leyland Titan TNLXB2RR	Leyland	H44/24D	1984	Ex Stagecoach Selkent, 1997
757	NUW558Y	Leyland Titan TNLXB2RR	Leyland	H44/24D	1984	Ex Stagecoach East London, 1998
758	A858SUL	Leyland Titan TNLXB2RR	Leyland	H44/24D	1983	Ex Stagecoach Selkent, 1997
759	RYK819Y	Leyland Titan TNLXB2RR	Leyland	H44/24D	1982	Ex Stagecoach East London, 1998
760	KYV455X	Leyland Titan TNLXB2RR	Leyland	H44/24D	1981	Ex Stagecoach Selkent, 1997
761	RYK820Y	Leyland Titan TNLXB2RR	Leyland	H44/24D	1982	Ex Stagecoach Selkent, 1997
762	OHV801Y	Leyland Titan TNLXB2RR	Leyland	H44/24D	1981	Ex Stagecoach Selkent, 1997
765	A825SUL	Leyland Titan TNLXB2RR	Leyland	H44/24D	1983	Ex Stagecoach Selkent, 1997
766	A66THX	Leyland Titan TNLXB2RR	Leyland	H44/26F	1984	Ex Stagecoach Selkent, 1997
767	A607THV	Leyland Titan TNLXB2RR	Leyland	H44/24D	1984	Ex Stagecoach Selkent, 1997
768	NUW601Y	Leyland Titan TNLXB2RR	Leyland	H44/24D	1984	Ex Stagecoach Selkent, 1997
770	NUW560Y	Leyland Titan TNLXB2RR	Leyland	H44/24D	1984	Ex Stagecoach East London, 1998
771	NUW571Y	Leyland Titan TNLXB2RR	Leyland	H44/24D	1984	Ex Stagecoach Selkent, 1997
772	NUW572Y	Leyland Titan TNLXB2RR	Leyland	H44/24D	1984	Ex Stagecoach Selkent, 1997
773	A873SUL	Leyland Titan TNLXB2RR	Leyland	H44/24D	1983	Ex Stagecoach East London, 1998
775	NUW575Y	Leyland Titan TNLXB2RR	Leyland	H44/24D	1984	Ex Stagecoach Selkent, 1997
776	NUW622Y	Leyland Titan TNLXB2RR	Leyland	H44/24D	1984	Ex Stagecoach East London, 1998
777	NUW577Y	Leyland Titan TNLXB2RR	Leyland	H44/24D	1984	Ex Stagecoach Selkent, 1997
778	NUW623Y	Leyland Titan TNLXB2RR	Leyland	H44/24D	1984	Ex Stagecoach East London, 1998
779	NUW626Y	Leyland Titan TNLXB2RR	Leyland	H44/24D	1984	Ex Stagecoach Selkent, 1997
780	OHV802Y	Leyland Titan TNLXB2RR	Leyland	H44/24D	1981	Ex Stagecoach Selkent, 1997
782	NUW582Y	Leyland Titan TNLXB2RR	Leyland	H44/24D	1984	Ex Stagecoach Selkent, 1997
783	A832SUL	Leyland Titan TNLXB2RR	Leyland	H44/24D	1983	Ex Stagecoach East London, 1998
784	B84WUV	Leyland Titan TNLXB2RR	Leyland	H44/29F	1984	Ex Stagecoach Selkent, 1997

786	NUW586Y	Leyland Titan TNLXB2RR	Leyland	H44/24D	1984	Ex Stagecoach Selkent, 1997
787	NUW587Y	Leyland Titan TNLXB2RR	Leyland	H44/24D	1984	Ex Stagecoach Selkent, 1997
789	OHV789Y	Leyland Titan TNLXB2RR	Leyland	H44/24D	1984	Ex Stagecoach East London, 1998
790	A902SYE	Leyland Titan TNLXB2RR	Leyland	H44/24D	1983	Ex Stagecoach East London, 1998
791	OHV791Y	Leyland Titan TNLXB2RR	Leyland	H44/24D	1984	Ex Stagecoach Selkent, 1997
792	A921SYE	Leyland Titan TNLXB2RR	Leyland	H44/24D	1983	Ex Stagecoach East London, 1998
793	A922SYE	Leyland Titan TNLXB2RR	Leyland	H44/24D	1983	Ex Stagecoach East London, 1998
794	A944SYE	Leyland Titan TNLXB2RR	Leyland	H44/24D	1983	Ex Stagecoach East London, 1998
795	A935SYE	Leyland Titan TNLXB2RR	Leyland	H44/24D	1983	Ex Stagecoach East London, 1998
796	A945SYE	Leyland Titan TNLXB2RR	Leyland	H44/24D	1983	Ex Stagecoach East London, 1998
797	B97WUV	Leyland Titan TNLXB2RR	Leyland	H44/24D	1984	Ex Stagecoach Selkent, 1997
798	A867SUL	Leyland Titan TNLXB2RR	Leyland	H44/24D	1983	Ex Stagecoach East London, 1998
799	B119WUV	Leyland Titan TNLXB2RR	Leyland	H44/24D	1984	Ex Stagecoach Selkent, 1997
816	LSX16P	Ailsa B55-10	Alexander AV	H44/35F	1975	
817	LSX17P	Ailsa B55-10	Alexander AV	H44/35F	1975	
832	LSX32P	Ailsa B55-10	Alexander AV	H44/35F	1975	
834	NSP334R	Ailsa B55-10	Alexander AV	H44/31D	1976	Ex Western Scottish, 1995
836u	NSP336R	Ailsa B55-10	Alexander AV	H44/31D	1976	Ex Western Scottish, 1995

849-866

Ailsa B55-10 MkII — Alexander AV — H44/35F — 1979

849	OSC49V	853	OSC53V	857	OSC57V	862	OSC62V	864	OSC64V
850	OSC50V	854	OSC54V	860	OSC60V	863	OSC63V	866	OSC66V
851	OSC51V	856	OSC56V	861	OSC61V				

867-874

Volvo B55-10 MkIII — Alexander RV — H44/37F* — 1984 — *874 is H44/24F

867	A967YSX	869	A969YSX	871	A971YSX	873	A973YSX	874	A974YSX
868	A968YSX	870	A970YSX	872	A972YSX				

875	UFS875R	Ailsa B55-10	Alexander AV	H44/35F	1977	
876	UFS876R	Ailsa B55-10	Alexander AV	H44/35F	1977	
877	UFS877R	Ailsa B55-10	Alexander AV	H44/35F	1977	
878	UFS878R	Ailsa B55-10	Alexander AV	H44/35F	1977	

901-920

Volvo Citybus B10M-50 — Alexander RV — DPH47/33F* 1985-87 — 908 ex Volvo demonstrator, 1986 / *909/10 are DPH45/35F

901	C801USG	907	C807USG	910	E910KSG	915	C795USG	919	C799USG
905	C805USG	908	B108CCS	914	C794USG	918	C798USG	920	C800USG
906	C806USG	909	E909KSG						

940	F310MYJ	Volvo Citybus B10M-50	Northern Counties	DPH43/33F	1989	Ex Southdown, 1991
941	F311MYJ	Volvo Citybus B10M-50	Northern Counties	DPH43/33F	1989	Ex Southdown, 1991
942	F312MYJ	Volvo Citybus B10M-50	Northern Counties	DPH43/33F	1989	Ex Southdown, 1991

972-997

Volvo Citybus B10M-50 — Alexander RV — H47/37F — 1985-86

972	C802USG	979	B179FFS	984	B184FFS	988	C788USG	992	C792USG
973	C803USG	980	B180FFS	985	B185FFS	989	C789USG	993	C793USG
974	C804USG	981	B181FFS	986	B186FFS	990	C790USG	996	C796USG
977	B177FFS	982	B182FFS	987	C787USG	991	C791USG	997	C797USG
978	B178FFS	983	B183FFS						

1102	ABV669A	Leyland Atlantean PDR1/1	Metro Cammell	O44/31F	1961	Ex Cumberland, 1992
1107	UWV617S	Bristol VRT/SL3/6LXB	Eastern Coach Works	CO43/31F	1978	Ex Stagecoach South, 1994
1125	RVB978S	Bristol VRT/SL3/6LXB	Willowbrook	H43/31F	1978	Ex Stagecoach South, 1994
1136	LEO736Y	Leyland Atlantean AN68D/1R	Northern Counties	H43/32F	1983	Ex Ribble, 1995

Previous Registrations:

ABV669A	927GTA		H509AGC	H884LOX, WLT400
F286KGK	F430BOP, WLT491		IIL3504	E626UNE, GIL2967, E937XSB
GSU342	B208FFS		IIL3506	E624UNE, MIB658, E931XSB
GSU343	PGC522Y, 3402FM, SJI5407		MSU499	D319SGB
GSU344	B210FFS		VLT77	F396DHL

Allocations:-

Aberhill (Methilhaven Road, Methil)

Mercedes-Benz	2	3	5	90	91			
Leopard Bus	189							
Volvo PS	314							
Tiger	466	368	477	478	499			
Volvo coach	503	504	506					
Volvo B10M Artic	561	562	563					
Volvo Interurban	587							
Dart	606	607	608	609	610	611	612	
Titan	753	754	756	777	787	791	799	
Ailsa	836	853	854	855	857	862	863	864
	876	878						
Volvo Citybus	901	905	906	907	908	909	910	914
	915	918	919	940	941	942		

Cowdenbeath (Broad Street)

Mercedes-Benz	71	75	76	80				
Leopard	158	184	264	268	291	292		
Volvo PS	302	303	304	305	306	307	308	309
	310	322	323					
Tiger	415	416	444	467	479			
Javelin	512	513	514					
Dart	614							
Volvo B6	659	667						
Titan	755	758	760	761	762	763	764	
	768	771	772	775	779	782	784	
	786	797						
Ailsa	867							
Volvo Citybus	982	996	997					

Dunfermline (St Leonard's Street)

Leopard	180	181	183	185	262	265	267	272
	274	278	279	290				
Volvo PS	301							
Tiger	412	413	414	417	418	419	422	423
	424	470						
Volvo B10M Artic	564	570	571	573	574	575	576	
Volvo Interurban	543	544	545	546	547	578	580	581
	582	586						
Volvo B6	651	652	653	654	655	656	657	658
	670	671	672	673				
Olypian	706	707	718	719	720	721	722	
	723	724	725					
Volvo Citybus	978	987	990	991	992	993		

Glenrothes (Flemington Road)

Mercedes-Benz	70	78	79	82	85	89	92	93
	94	95	96	97				
Leopard	186	187	269	271	294			
Volvo PS	324	325	326	327	328	329		
Tiger	469							
Volvo Interurban	539	548	549	550	551	552	579	
Ailsa	816	817	832	834	847	849	851	866
	869	873						
Volvo Citybus	974	980	983	984	989			
Atlantean	1136							

Pictured passing through Stirling on service 14 is Fife Scottish 412, D512CSF. Currently allocated to Dunfermline the vehicle is a Volvo B10M with an Alexander P-type body which displays the Alexander name in raised letters on the front panel. *Richard Godfrey*

Kirkcaldy (Esplanade)

Mercedes-Benz	4	72	73	74	81			
Leopard	140	141	150	159	188	261	266	270
	273	276	277					
Volvo PS	316	317	318	319	320	321		
Interurban	542	554	555	556	565	566	567	568
	569	588	589	590				
Dart	601	602	603	604	605	613		
Volvo B6	623	624	625	626	627	628	668	669
Olympian	701	702	703	704	705	737	738	
Titan	769							
Ailsa	850	856	860	871	872	874	877	
Volvo Citybus	972	973	979	981	985	986		

St Andrews (City Road)

Mercedes-Benz	1	77	86	87	88
Leopard	182				
Tiger	420	421	442		
Interurban	541	583	584	585	
Titan	765	766	767		
Ailsa	868	870	875		
Volvo Citybus	920	977	988		

GLASGOW

Stagecoach Glasgow Ltd, Dunblane Street, Glasgow, G4 0HJ

036	R36LSO	Mercedes-Benz Vario O810	Plaxton Beaver 2	B27F	1997		
037	RBZ2621	Mercedes-Benz L608D	Reeve Burgess	B20F	1987	Ex Cumberland, 1997	
051	RBZ4243	Mercedes-Benz L608D	Reeve Burgess	B20F	1986	Ex Cumberland, 1997	

107-120
Volvo B10M-62 — Plaxton Premiére Interurban DP51F — 1997

107	P107FRS	110	P110FRS	114	R114OPS	116	R116OPS	118	R118OPS
108	P108FRS	112	R112OPS	115	R115OPS	117	R117OPS	120	R120OPS
109	P109FRS	113	R113OPS						

166	UWP105	Leyland Tiger TRCTL11/3R	Plaxton Paramount 3200	C50F	1983	Ex Western Buses, 1997	
207	RBZ5497	Mercedes-Benz L608D	Alexander AM	B21F	1986	Ex Bluebird Buses, 1998	

361-386
Volvo B6LE — Alexander ALX200 — DP36F — 1997

361	P361DSA	367	P367DSA	372	P372DSA	377	P377DSA	382	P382DSA
362	P362DSA	368	P368DSA	373	P373DSA	378	P378DSA	383	P383DSA
363	P363DSA	369	P369DSA	374	P374DSA	379	P379DSA	384	P384DSA
364	P364DSA	370	P370DSA	375	P375DSA	380	P380DSA	385	P385DSA
365	P365DSA	371	P371DSA	376	P376DSA	381	P381DSA	386	P386DSA
366	P366DSA								

502-560
Volvo B10M-55 — Alexander PS — B49F — 1997

502	R502KSA	532	P532ESA	539	P539ESA	546	P546ESA	553	P553ESA
504	R504KSA	533	P533ESA	540	P540ESA	547	P547ESA	554	P554ESA
513	R513KSA	534	P534ESA	541	P541ESA	548	P548ESA	556	P556ESA
514	R514KSA	535	P535ESA	542	P542ESA	549	P549ESA	557	P557ESA
515	R515KSA	536	P536ESA	543	P543ESA	550	P550ESA	558	P558ESA
530	P530ESA	537	P537ESA	544	P544ESA	551	P551ESA	559	P559ESA
531	P531ESA	538	P538ESA	545	P545ESA	552	P552ESA	560	P560ESA

955	OHV762Y	Leyland Titan TNLXB2RR	Leyland	H44/27D	1983	Ex Western Buses, 1997	

Previous Registrations:

RBZ2621	D37UAO	RBZ4243	D531RCK	UWP105	XUS535Y

Allocations:-

Glasgow (Blochairn Industrial Estate)

Mercedes-Benz	036	037	051	207				
Interurban	107	108	109	110	112	113	114	115
	116	117	118	120				
Volvo PS	502	504	513	514	515	530	531	532
	533	534	535	536	537	538	539	540
	541	542	543	544	545	546	547	548
	549	550	551	552	553	554	556	557
	558	559	560					

Glasgow (Dunblane Street, Cowcaddens)

Volvo B6BLE	361	362	363	364	365	366	367	368
	369	370	371	372	373	374	375	376
	377	378	379	380	381	382	383	384
	385	386						
Titan	955							

Opposite: - **Stagecoach Glasgow is a separate company to the other Scottish operations though the fleet numbers integrate into the Western Buses fleet. The fleet name of Stagecoach is used shown here on the only Vario in the fleet, number 36, R36LSO, and Volvo B6 385, P385DSA.** *Billy Nicol*

MANCHESTER

Stagecoach Manchester, Daw Bank, Stockport, Cheshire, SK3 0DU

1	ESU913	Scania K92CRB	Van Hool Alizée	C55F	1988	Ex Cambus (Premier), 1996
2	ESU920	Scania K92CRB	Van Hool Alizée	C55F	1988	Ex Cambus (Premier), 1996
7	F947NER	Scania K112CRB	Plaxton Paramount 3500 III	C49F	1988	Ex Cambus (Premier), 1996
8	F948NER	Scania K112CRB	Plaxton Paramount 3500 III	C49F	1988	Ex Cambus (Premier), 1996
10u	C310ENA	Leyland Tiger TRCTL11/3RH	Duple 320	C57F	1986	
240	WBN474T	Leyland National 11351A/1R		B49F	1979	
251	RUF41R	Leyland National 11351A/2R		DP49F	1977	Ex Hogg, Glasgow, 1994
252	JIL8374	Leyland National 1151/1R/0401		B49F	1974	Ex Munro, Uddington, 1994
253	JIL7610	Leyland National 1151/1R/0402		B49F	1973	Ex R & I, Milton Keynes, 1994
255	LIL3317	Leyland National 11351A/1R		B49F	1979	Ex Amberley, Pudsey, 1994
256	SJI2054	Leyland National 11351A/1R		B49F	1979	Ex Amberley, Pudsey, 1994
257	SJI4558	Leyland National 11351A/1R		B49F	1978	Ex Amberley, Pudsey, 1994
258	SJI4559	Leyland National 11351/1R		B49F	1976	Ex Amberley, Pudsey, 1994
259	SJI4560	Leyland National 1151/1R/SC		DP45F	1975	Ex Amberley, Pudsey, 1994
260	JIL5279	Leyland National 1151/1R/0403		B49F	1973	Ex Amberley, Pudsey, 1994
261	TJI2488	Leyland National 11351/1R/SC		DP45F	1975	Ex Golden Coaches, Llantwit Major, 199
264	KDW342P	Leyland National 11351/1R/SC		B49F	1976	Ex Golden Coaches, Llantwit Major, 199
265	WFM801K	Leyland National 1151/2R/0403		B49F	1972	Ex Gatwick Handling, 1994
267	LIL4612	Leyland National 1151/2R/0403		B49F	1972	Ex Gatwick Handling, 1994
269	JIL7609	Leyland National 1151/2R/0403		B49F	1972	Ex Gatwick Handling, 1994
271	JIL7608	Leyland National 1151/2R/0403		B49F	1973	Ex Gatwick Handling, 1994
272	JIL7607	Leyland National 1151/2R/0403		B49F	1973	Ex Gatwick Handling, 1994
273	JIL7606	Leyland National 11351/2R		B49F	1974	Ex Gatwick Handling, 1994

Stagecoach Manchester operate a fleet of Mercedes minibuses that have replaced inherited units that mostly consisted of MCW MetroRiders and Renault-Dodges. The new fleet has batches of 811, 709 and the new Vario. The latter are badged as O810 while there are several options within the model range. 1997 has seen the introduction of minibuses at Glossop, though 535, P535PNE is seen in Altrincham and operates from the minibus unit at Charles Street, Stockport. *Tony Wilson*

301-310   Volvo B6-9.9M   Alexander Dash   B40F   1994 Ex Busways, 1995

301	M741PRS	303	M743PRS	305	M745PRS	307	M847PRS	309	M749PRS
302	M742PRS	304	M744PRS	306	M746PRS	308	M748PRS	310	M750PRS

311-319   Volvo B6-9.9M   Alexander Dash   B40F   1994 Ex East Midland, 1995

311	M461VHE	313	M846HDF	315	M455VHE	317	M457VHE	319	M459VHE
312	M462VHE	314	M454VHE	316	M456VHE	318	M458VHE		

321-357   Volvo B6-9.9M   Alexander ALX200   B40F   1997

321	P321JND	339	P329JND	337	P337JND	344	P344JND	351	P351JND
322	P322JND	330	P330JND	338	P338JND	345	P345JND	352	P352JND
323	P323JND	331	P331JND	339	P339JND	346	P346JND	353	P353JND
324	P324JND	332	P332JND	340	P340JND	347	P347JND	354	P354JND
325	P325JND	334	P334JND	341	P341JND	348	P348JND	355	P355JND
326	P326JND	335	P335JND	342	P342JND	349	P349JND	356	P356JND
327	P327JND	336	P336JND	343	P343JND	350	P350JND	357	P357JND
328	P328JND								

401-430   Mercedes-Benz 811D   Alexander Sprint   B31F   1995-96

401	N401WVR	407	N407WVR	413	N413WVR	419	N419WVR	425	N425WVR
402	N402WVR	408	N408WVR	414	N414WVR	420	N420WVR	426	N426WVR
403	N403WVR	409	N409WVR	415	N415WVR	421	N421WVR	427	N427WVR
404	N404WVR	410	N410WVR	416	N416WVR	422	N422WVR	428	N428WVR
405	N405WVR	411	N411WVR	417	N417WVR	423	N423WVR	429	N429WVR
406	N406WVR	412	N412WVR	418	N418WVR	424	N424WVR	430	N430WVR

501-528   Mercedes-Benz 709D   Alexander Sprint   B25F   1996

501	N645VSS	507	N651VSS	513	N657VSS	519	N663VSS	524	N881AVV
502	N646VSS	508	N652VSS	514	N658VSS	520	N664VSS	525	N882AVV
503	N647VSS	509	N653VSS	515	N659VSS	521	N665VSS	526	N883AVV
504	N648VSS	510	N654VSS	516	N660VSS	522	N879AVV	527	N884AVV
505	N649VSS	511	N655VSS	517	N661VSS	523	N880AVV	528	N885AVV
506	N650VSS	512	N656VSS	518	N662VSS				

530-566   Mercedes-Benz Vario O810   Plaxton Beaver 2   B27F   1997

530	P530PNE	537	P537PNE	544	P544PNE	551	P551PNE	559	P559PNE
531	P531PNE	538	P538PNE	545	P545PNE	552	P552PNE	561	P561PNE
532	P532PNE	539	P539PNE	546	P546PNE	553	P553PNE	562	P562PNE
533	P5332NE	540	P540PNE	547	P547PNE	554	P554PNE	563	P563PNE
534	P534PNE	541	P541PNE	548	P548PNE	556	P556PNE	564	P564PNE
535	P535PNE	542	P542PNE	549	P549PNE	557	P557PNE	565	P565PNE
536	P536PNE	543	P543PNE	550	P550PNE	558	P558PNE	566	P566PNE

601-605   Volvo B10BLE   Northern Counties   B49F   1997

601	P601JBU	602	P602JBU	603	P603JBU	604	P604JBU	605	P605JBU

701-715   Volvo Olympian YN2RC16V3   Alexander RL   H47/32F   1996

701	N325NPN	704	N328NPN	707	N331NPN	710	N334NPN	713	N337NPN
702	N326NPN	705	N329NPN	708	N332NPN	711	N335NPN	714	N338NPN
703	N327NPN	706	N330NPN	709	N333NPN	712	N336NPN	715	N339NPN

716-730   Volvo Olympian   Alexander RL   H51/36F   1996

716	P716GND	719	P719GND	722	P722GND	725	P725GND	728	P728GND
717	P717GND	720	P720GND	723	P723GND	726	P726GND	729	P729GND
718	P718GND	721	P721GND	724	P724GND	727	P727GND	730	P730GND

801-868 — Volvo B10M-55 — Alexander PS — B49F — 1996

801	N801DNE	815	N815DNE	829	P829FVU	843	P843GND	856	P856GND
802	N802DNE	816	N816DNE	830	P830FVU	844	P844GND	857	P857GND
803	N803DNE	817	N817DNE	831	P831FVU	845	P845GND	858	P858GND
804	N804DNE	818	N818DNE	832	P832FVU	846	P846GND	859	P859GND
805	N805DNE	819	P819GNC	833	P833FVU	847	P847GND	860	P860GND
806	N806DNE	820	P820GNC	834	P834FVU	848	P848GND	861	P861GND
807	N807DNE	821	P821FVU	835	P835FVU	849	P849GND	862	P862GND
808	N808DNE	822	P822FVU	836	P836GND	850	P850GND	863	P863GND
809	N809DNE	823	P823FVU	837	P837GND	851	P851GND	864	P864GND
810	N810DNE	824	P824FVU	838	P838GND	852	P852GND	865	P865GND
811	N811DNE	825	P825FVU	839	P839GND	853	P853GND	866	P866GND
812	N812DNE	826	P826FVU	840	P840GND	854	P854GND	867	P867GND
813	N813DNE	827	P827FVU	841	P841GND	855	P855GND	868	P868GND
814	N814DNE	828	P828FVU	842	P842GND				

869-894 — Volvo B10M-55 — Northern Counties Paladin — B49F — 1997

869	P869MNE	874	P874MNE	879	P879MNE	884	P884MNE	890	P890MNE
870	P870MNE	875	P875MNE	880	P880MNE	885	P885MNE	891	P891MNE
871	P871MNE	876	P876MNE	881	P881MNE	886	P886MNE	892	P892MNE
872	P872MNE	877	P877MNE	882	P882MNE	887	P887MNE	893	P893MNE
873	P873MNE	878	P878MNE	883	P883MNE	889	P889MNE	894	P894MNE

895-996 — Volvo B10M-55 — Alexander PS — B49F — 1997-98

895	R895XVM	917	R917XVM	937	R937XVM	957	R957XVM	977	R977XVM
896	R896XVM	918	R918XVM	938	R938XVM	958	R958XVM	978	R978XVM
897	R897XVM	919	R919XVM	939	R939XVM	959	R959XVM	979	R979XVM
898	R898XVM	920	R920XVM	940	R940XVM	960	R960XVM	980	R980XVM
899	R899XVM	921	R921XVM	941	R941XVM	961	R961XVM	981	R981XVM
901	R901XVM	922	R922XVM	942	R942XVM	962	R962XVM	982	R982XVM
902	R902XVM	923	R923XVM	943	R943XVM	963	R963XVM	983	R983XVM
903	R903XVM	924	R924XVM	944	R944XVM	964	R964XVM	984	R984XVM
904	R904XVM	925	R925XVM	945	R945XVM	965	R965XVM	985	R985XVM
905	R905XVM	926	R926XVM	946	R946XVM	966	R966XVM	986	R986XVM
906	R906XVM	927	R927XVM	947	R947XVM	967	R967XVM	987	R987XVM
907	R907XVM	928	R928XVM	948	R948XVM	968	R968XVM	988	R988XVM
908	R908XVM	929	R929XVM	949	R949XVM	969	R969XVM	989	R989XVM
909	R909XVM	930	R930XVM	950	R950XVM	970	R970XVM	990	R990XVM
910	R910XVM	931	R931XVM	951	R951XVM	971	R971XVM	991	R991XVM
912	R912XVM	932	R932XVM	952	R952XVM	972	R972XVM	992	R992XVM
913	R913XVM	933	R933XVM	953	R953XVM	973	R973XVM	993	R993XVM
914	R914XVM	934	R934XVM	954	R954XVM	974	R974XVM	994	R994XVM
915	R915XVM	935	R935XVM	955	R955XVM	975	R975XVM	995	R995XVM
916	R916XVM	936	R936XVM	956	R956XVM	976	R976XVM	996	R996XVM

997	R997DBA	Volvo B10M-55	Alexander PS	B49F	1998
1461	FWH461Y	Scania BR112DH	Northern Counties	H43/32F	1983
1462	FWH462Y	Scania BR112DH	Northern Counties	H43/32F	1983

1463-1467 — Scania N113DRB — Northern Counties — H47/28F — 1991

1463	H463GVM	1464	H464GVM	1465	H465GVM	1466	H466GVM	1467	H467GVM

1721-1728 — Renault-Dodge S75 — Northern Counties — B17FL — 1990-91

1721	H721CNC	1724	H724CNC	1726	H726CNC	1727	H727FNC	1728	H728FNC

Opposite:- **Stagecoach Manchester has received over two-hundred new single-deck buses since Stagecoach acquired the operation in February 1996. In 1997, five Volvo B10BLE chassis were supplied with Northen Counties bodies, though 605 spent some time with Volvo in Sweden. These are normally to be found on service 216 between Ashton and Manchester through Droylesden and Clayton. Seen in Piccadilly is 604, P604JBU. The majority of the Volvo buses carry Alexander PS bodywork, the exception being twenty-five delivered in 1997 with Northern Counties bodywork to the style delivered to other Stagecoach fleets in 1996. All are allocated to Stockport from where 893, P893MNE was working when photographed during the summer.** *Tony Wilson/Richard Godfrey*

Following the reduction in numbers of Atlanteans, MCW Metrobuses are now being withdrawn from service. Only a few of the type have been repainted into corporate livery. One of the few is 5040, MRJ40W, which is seen near the site of Manchester Corporation's Parrs Wood depot. *Cliff Beeton*

2001-2030 — Dennis Dominator DDA1003 — Northern Counties — H43/32F — 1985

2001	B901TVR	2007	B907TVR	2013	B913TVR	2019	B919TVR	2025	B25TVU
2002	B902TVR	2008	B908TVR	2014	B914TVR	2020	B920TVR	2026	B26TVU
2003	B903TVR	2009	B909TVR	2015	B915TVR	2021	B21TVU	2027	B27TVU
2004	B904TVR	2010	B910TVR	2016	B916TVR	2022	B22TVU	2028	B28TVU
2005	B905TVR	2011	B911TVR	2017	B917TVR	2023	B23TVU	2029	B29TVU
2006	B906TVR	2012	B912TVR	2018	B918TVR	2024	B24TVU	2030	B30TVU

2031-2040 — Dennis Dominator DDA2033 — Northern Counties — H43/29F — 1991

2031	H131GVM	2033	H133GVM	2035	H135GVM	2037	H137GVM	2039	H139GVM
2032	H132GVM	2034	H134GVM	2036	H136GVM	2038	H138GVM	2040	H140GVM

3001-3010 — Leyland Olympian ONTL11/1R — Northern Counties — H43/30F — 1982

3001	ANA1Y	3003	ANA3Y	3006	ANA6Y	3008	ANA8Y	3010	ANA10Y
3002	ANA2Y	3004	ANA4Y	3007	ANA7Y	3009	ANA9Y		

3016-3025 — Leyland Olympian ONLXCT/1R — Northern Counties — H43/30F — 1983-84

3016	A581HDB	3018	A583HDB	3020	A585HDB	3022	A22HNC	3024	A24HNC
3017	A582HDB	3019	A584HDB	3021	A21HNC	3023	A23HNC	3025	A25HNC

3026-3035 — Leyland Olympian ONLXB/1R — Northern Counties — H43/30F — 1984

3026	A26ORJ	3028	A28ORJ	3030	A30ORJ	3032	A32ORJ	3034	B34PJA
3027	A27ORJ	3029	A29ORJ	3031	A31ORJ	3033	A33ORJ	3035	B35PJA

3036-3236

Leyland Olympian ONLXB/1R   Northern Counties   H43/30F*   1984-86 *3139/98 and 3213/14 are DPH43/26F

3036	B36PJA	3086	B86SJA	3133	B133WNB	3166	C166YBA	3197	C197YBA
3039	B39PJA	3087	B87SJA	3135	B135WNB	3167	C167YBA	3198	C198YBA
3049	B49PJA	3088	B88SJA	3137	B137WNB	3169	C169YBA	3199	C199YBA
3053	B53PJA	3089	B89SJA	3138	B138WNB	3170	C170YBA	3205	C205CBU
3055	B55PJA	3091	B91SJA	3139	B139WNB	3172	C172YBA	3207	C207CBU
3056	B56PJA	3094	B94SJA	3143	B143WNB	3173	C173YBA	3208	C208CBU
3057	B57PJA	3095	B95SJA	3145	B145WNB	3174	C174YBA	3210	C210CBU
3058	B58PJA	3110	B110SJA	3146	B146XNA	3175	C175YBA	3212	C212CBU
3060	B60PJA	3114	B114SJA	3147	B147XNA	3176	C176YBA	3213	C213CBU
3065	B65PJA	3117	B117TVU	3149	B149XNA	3178	C178YBA	3214	C214CBU
3067	B67PJA	3118	B118TVU	3150	B150XNA	3179	C179YBA	3215	C215CBU
3069	B69PJA	3119	B119TVU	3153	B153XNA	3181	C181YBA	3216	C216CBU
3070	B70PJA	3121	B121TVU	3154	B154XNA	3184	C184YBA	3221	C221CBU
3072	B72PJA	3122	B122TVU	3155	B155XNA	3185	C185YBA	3224	C224CBU
3074	B74PJA	3124	B124TVU	3156	C156YBA	3191	C191YBA	3226	C226ENE
3077	B77PJA	3125	B125TVU	3158	C158YBA	3193	C193YBA	3230	C230ENE
3080	B80PJA	3126	B126WNB	3164	C164YBA	3195	C195YBA	3234	C234ENE
3082	B82PJA	3132	B132WNB	3165	C165YBA	3196	C196YBA	3236	C236EVU
3084	B84PJA							

3255-3277

Leyland Olympian ONLXB/1R   Northern Counties   DPH43/26F   1986-87

3255	C255FRJ	3268	D268JVR	3269	D269JVR	3272	D272JVR	3277	D277JVR
3260	D260JVR							

3282-3304

Leyland Olympian ONLXB/1RZ   Northern Counties   H43/30F*   1988-89 *3291 is DPH43/25F

3282	F282DRJ	3289	F289DRJ	3295	F295DRJ	3298	F298DRJ	3301	F301DRJ
3283	F283DRJ	3291	F291DRJ	3296	F296DRJ	3300	F300DRJ	3304	F304DRJ
3285	F285DRJ	3294	F294DRJ	3297	F297DRJ				

4639-4693

Leyland Atlantean AN68D/1R   Northern Counties   H43/32F   1983-84

4639	ANA639Y	4660	A660HNB	4671	A671HNB	4679	A679HNB	4690	A690HNB
4657	A657HNB	4668	A668HNB	4678	A678HNB	4683	A683HNB	4693	A693HNB

4705-4764

Leyland Atlantean AN68D/1R   Northern Counties   H43/32F*   1984 *4620 is H39/32F

4705	A705LNC	4730	A730LNC	4747	A747NNA	4757	A757NNA	4762	·A762NNA
4725	A725LNC	4743	A743NNA	4749	A749NNA	4761	A761NNA	4764	A764NNA
4726	A726LNC	4745	A745NNA	4751	A751NNA				

5017-5029

MCW Metrobus DR102/10   MCW   H43/30F   1980

5017	GBU17V	5020	GBU20V	5024w	GBU24V	5027w	GBU27V	5029	GBU29V
5019w	MNC495W	5022	GBU22V	5026	MNC498W	5028	GBU28V		

5037-5110

MCW Metrobus DR102/21   MCW   H43/30F   1981

5037	MRJ37W	5047	MRJ47W	5071w	MRJ71W	5080	ORJ80W	5098w	ORJ98W
5038w	MRJ38W	5048	MRJ48W	5072	ORJ72W	5081	ORJ81W	5100	ORJ100W
5040	MRJ40W	5052	MRJ51W	5074	ORJ74W	5091	ORJ91W	5106	SND106X
5041	MRJ41W	5053	MRJ52W	5075	ORJ75W	5092	ORJ92W	5107	SND107X
5042	MRJ42W	5054	MRJ53W	5076	ORJ76W	5093	ORJ93W	5108	SND108X
5043	MRJ43W	5055	MRJ54W	5077	ORJ77W	5094w	ORJ94W	5109w	SND109X
5044	MRJ44W	5066w	MRJ66W	5078	ORJ78W	5095w	ORJ95W	5110	SND110X
5045	MRJ45W	5067	MRJ67W	5079	ORJ79W				

5111-5190

MCW Metrobus DR102/23   MCW   H43/30F   1981-83

5111	SND111X	5121	SND121X	5144	SND144X	5160	ANA160Y	5170	ANA170Y
5116	SND116X	5124	SND124X	5145	SND145X	5162	ANA162Y	5173	ANA173Y
5118	SND118X	5125	SND125X	5153	ANA153Y	5163	ANA163Y	5179	ANA179Y
5119	SND119X	5141	SND141X	5154w	ANA154Y	5164	ANA164Y	5180	ANA180Y
5120	SND120X	5143	SND143X	5158	ANA158Y	5165	ANA165Y	5190	ANA190Y

| 7032 | VNB132L | Leyland Atlantean AN68/1R | Park Royal | O43/32F | 1972 |
| 7729 | RJA729R | Leyland Atlantean AN68A/1R | Northern Counties | H43/32F | 1977 |

Note: All vehicles were formerly GM Buses in 1993, then GMS Buses 1994 unless shown otherwise or new later.

Ancilliary Vehicles

TV1	SND451X	Leyland Atlantean AN68A/1R	Northern Counties	H43/32F	1982	
TV2	SND452X	Leyland Atlantean AN68A/1R	Northern Counties	H43/32F	1982	
TV3	SND455X	Leyland Atlantean AN68A/1R	Northern Counties	H43/32F	1982	
TV4	SND472X	Leyland Atlantean AN68A/1R	Northern Counties	H43/32F	1982	
TV05	LIB1182	Leyland Leopard PSU3F/4R	Plaxton Supreme IV Express	C53F	1981	Ex Evans Tours, Tregaron, 1995
TV06	ETC310W	Leyland Leopard PSU3F/5R	Plaxton Supreme IV Express	C53F	1981	Ex Miller, Calderbank, 1995
TV07	GSU859T	Leyland Leopard PSU3E/2R	Alexander AYS	B53F	1979	Ex Graham, Perth, 1997
TV08	GLJ490N	Bristol LH6L	Eastern Coach Works	B43F	1975	Ex Town & Country SoM 1997
TV09	VDV105S	Bristol LH6L	Eastern Coach Works	B43F	1978	Ex United (Teeside), 1997
TV10	REU316S	Bristol LH6L	Eastern Coach Works	B43F	1978	Ex United (Teeside), 1997
TV11	YAE516V	Bristol LH6L	Eastern Coach Works	B43F	1979	Ex United (Teeside), 1997
A035	D35UAO	Mercedes-Benz L608D	Reeve Burgess	B20F	1986	Ex Cumberland, 1997

Previous Registrations:

ESU913	F951NER	JIL7609	WFM817L	SJI2054	FNS161T
ESU920	F950NER	JIL7610	NRD140M, RIB5086, DBY717M	SJI4558	CFM352S
JIL5279	JHU861L	JIL8374	NTC622M, RIB7003, DBY718M	SJI4559	LPR937P
JIL7606	GFJ663N	LIL3317	EUM900T	SJI4560	HMA657N
JIL7607	JHU868L	LIL4612	WFM806L	TJI2488	KDW347P
JIL7608	XRB416L				

Allocations:-

Glossop (York Street)

Mercedes-Benz	546	547	548	549	550	551	552	553
Olympian	3199	3207	3224	3226	3230	3236	3282	3283
	3285	3291	3294	3295	3296	3297	3301	3304

Manchester (Hyde Road) - Stagecoach Manchester - Magic Bus ⚉

Mercedes-Benz	404	411	414	416	430			
Volvo B6	321	322	323	324	325	326	327	328
	329	330	331	332	334	335	336	337
	338	339	340	341	342	343	344	345
	346	347	348					
Volvo B10M Bus	837	838	839	840	841	842	843	844
	845	846	847	848	895	896	897	898
	899	901	902	903	904	905	906	907
	908	909	910	912	913	914	915	916
	917	918	919	920	921	922	923	924
	925	926	927	928	929	930	931	932
	933	934	935	936	974	975	976	977
	978	979	980	981	982	983	984	
Volvo B10BLE	601	602	603	604	605			
Scania	1461	1462	1463	1464	1465	1466	1467	
Olympian	3001⚉⚉	3002⚉⚉	3003⚉⚉	3004⚉⚉	3006⚉⚉	3009⚉⚉	3010⚉⚉	3018⚉⚉
	3019⚉⚉	3020⚉⚉	3021⚉⚉	3022⚉⚉	3053	3057	3080	3084
	3085	3087	3088	3094	3095	3110	3150	3153
	3155	3164	3165	3166	3167	3169	3170	3173
	3174	3175	3178	3179	3181	3191	3195	3196
	3197							
Metrobus	5022	5026	5028	5029	5040	5041	5042	5043
	5044	5045	5047	5048	5052	5053	5054	5055
	5067	5076	5077	5078	5079	5080	5081	5092
	5093	5100	5106	5107	5108	5110	5116	5118
	5119	5120	5121	5124	5153	5162	5163	5164
	5165	5170	5173	5179	5190			

In order to provide different levels of service Stagecoach competes with itself on certain routes. The Magic Bus services offers, as the lettering suggests, a cheaper service using older vehicles. The routes are also covered by more modern buses that charge the normal fare. The Magic Bus fleet uses the remaining Atlanteans at Princess Road depot along with some of the early Leyland Olympians. Pictured in Piccadilly is 4751, A751NNA. *Tony Wilson*

Manchester (Princess Road) - Stagecoach Manchester - Magic Bus ⛟ - Campus Link ⛟

Atlantean	4639⛟	4657⛟	4660⛟	4668⛟	4671⛟	4678⛟	4679⛟	4683⛟
	4690⛟	4693⛟	4705⛟	4725⛟	4726⛟	4743⛟	4747⛟	4749⛟
	4751⛟	4757⛟	4761⛟	4762⛟	4764⛟			
Olympian	701	702	703	704	705	706	707	708
	709	710	711	712	713	714	715	716
	717	718	719	720	721	722	723	724
	725	726	727	728	729	730	3026⛟	3027⛟
	3028⛟	3029⛟	3030⛟	3031⛟	3032⛟	3033⛟	3034⛟	3035⛟
	3036⛟	3137	3139	3212	3213	3214	3215	3216
	3221	3255	3260	3268	3269	3272	3277	
Dominator	2001	2002	2003	2004	2005	2006	2007	2008
	2009	2010	2011	2012	2013	2014	2015	2016
	2017	2018	2019	2020	2021	2022	2023	2024
	2025	2026	2027	2028	2029	2030	2031	2032
	2033	2034	2035	2036	2037	2038	2039	2040
National	255⛟	256⛟	257⛟	267⛟	271⛟			
Volvo B10M Bus	801	802	803	804	805	806	807	808
	809	810	825	826	827	828	829	830
	831	832	833	834	835	836	937	938
	939	940	941	942	943	944	945	946
	947	948	949	950	951	952	953	954
	955	956	957	958	959	960	961	962
	963	964	965	966	967	968	969	970
	971	972	973					
Volvo B6	301	302	303	304	305	306	307	308
	309	310	311	312	313	314	315	316
	317	318	319					
Mercedes-Benz	543	544	545	554	556	557	558	559
	561	562	563	564	565	566		
Dodge S75	1726	1727	1728					

Stockport (Daw Bank)

Olympian	3024	3025	3055	3056	3058	3060	3065	30
	3069	3070	3072	3074	3077	3082	3089	30
	3114	3117	3118	3119	3121	3122	3124	31
	3126	3132	3133	3135	3138	3143	3145	31
	3147	3149	3156	3158	3172	3176	3184	31
	3193	3198	3205	3208	3210	3234	3289	32
	3300							
Metrobus	5017	5020	5037	5072	5074	5091	5141	51
	5144	5145	5158	5159				
National	240	251	252	253	258	259	260	26
	264	265	269	272	273			
Volvo B10M Bus	811	812	813	814	815	816	817	81
	819	820	821	822	823	824	849	85
	851	852	853	854	855	856	857	85
	859	860	861	862	863	864	865	86
	867	868	869	870	871	872	873	87
	875	876	877	878	879	880	881	88
	883	884	885	886	887	889	890	89
	892	893	894					
Volvo B6	349	350	351	352	353	354	355	35
	357							
Dodge S75	1721	1724						
Coach	1w	2w	7	8				

Stockport (Charles Street)

Mercedes-Benz	401	402	403	405	406	407	408	40
	410	412	413	415	417	418	419	42
	421	422	423	424	425	426	427	42
	429	501	502	503	504	505	506	50
	508	509	510	511	512	513	514	51
	516	517	518	519	520	521	522	52
	524	525	526	527	528	530	531	53
	533	534	535	536	537	538	539	54
	541	542						

Hyde Road depot is the home for all of Stagecoach Manchester's fleet of Volvo B6s. These carry the later early ALX200 body style as illustrated by 323, P323JND which is seen entering the central Piccadilly area from Oldham Street.
Tony Wilson

MIDLAND RED

Midland Red (South) Ltd, Railway Terrace, Rugby, Warwickshire, CV21 3HS

1	A75NAC	Leyland Tiger TRCTL11/2R	Plaxton Paramount 3200 E	C47FT	1983	
2	A76NAC	Leyland Tiger TRCTL11/2R	Plaxton Paramount 3200 E	C49F	1983	
4	230HUE	Leyland Leopard PSU3E/4R	Plaxton Supreme IV Express	C49F	1980	Ex Midland Red North, 1981
5	331HWD	Leyland Leopard PSU3E/4R	Plaxton Supreme IV Express	C49F	1980	Ex Midland Red North, 1981
6	3273AC	Leyland Leopard PSU3E/4R	Plaxton Supreme IV Express	C49F	1980	Ex Midland Red North, 1981
7	RNV413V	Leyland Leopard PSU3E/4R	Plaxton Supreme IV Express	C49F	1979	Ex Premier Travel, 1991
11	FYX824W	Leyland Leopard PSU3E/4R	Duple Dominant II Express	C49F	1980	Ex Busways, 1996
12	HTY139W	Leyland Leopard PSU3E/4R	Duple Dominant II Express	C49F	1980	Ex Busways, 1996
16	YBO16T	Leyland Leopard PSU3E/2R	East Lancashire	B51F	1979	Ex G & G, Leamington, 1993
18	YBO18T	Leyland Leopard PSU3E/2R	East Lancashire	B51F	1979	Ex G & G, Leamington, 1993
29	NAK29X	Leyland Leopard PSU3F/4R	Duple Dominant IV	C47F	1981	Ex East Midland, 1994

34-39

		Volvo B10M-62		Plaxton Expressliner 2	C46FT	1997	
34	R34AKV	36	R36AKV	37	R37AKV	38	R38AKV	39	R39AKV
35	R35AKV						

43	J702CWT	Volvo B10M-60	Plaxton Premiére 350	C48FT	1992	Ex Cambus (Premier), 1997
69w	E315NWK	Volvo B10M-61	Ikarus Blue Danube	C49F	1987	Ex David R Grasby, 1995
70	BIW4977	Leyland Tiger TRCTL11/3R	Plaxton Paramount 3200 E	C49FT	1984	
73	491GAC	Leyland Tiger TRCTL11/3RH	Plaxton Paramount 3200 II	C51F	1984	
74	4828VC	Leyland Tiger TRCTL11/3R	Plaxton Paramount 3500 II	C51F	1985	Ex Sovereign, 1990
75	9737VC	Leyland Tiger TRCTL11/3R	Plaxton Paramount 3500 II	C51F	1985	Ex Sovereign, 1990
76	6253VC	Leyland Tiger TRCTL11/3RH	Plaxton Paramount 3200 II	C51F	1986	Ex Thames Transit, 1991
88	A8GGT	Leyland Tiger TRCTL11/3RH	Plaxton Paramount 3200	C51F	1984	Ex Cheltenham & Gloucester, 1993
90	5520HU	Leyland Tiger TRCTL11/3R	Plaxton Paramount 3200 E	C57F	1983	Ex Cheltenham & Gloucester, 1990
91	420GAC	Leyland Tiger TRCTL11/3R	Plaxton Paramount 3200 E	C46FT	1983	Ex Cheltenham & Gloucester, 1991

101-105

		Dennis Dart		Alexander Dash		B40F	1996		
101	P101HNH	102	P102HNH	103	P103HNH	104	P104HNH	105	P105HNH

106-112

		Dennis Dart SLF		Alexander ALX200		B37F	1998		
106	R106...	108	R108...	109	R109...	110	R110...	112	R112...
107	R107...								

The Midland Red operation based at Stratford-upon-Avon retains links with the past through the use of Stratford Blue names on minibuses; Stratford Blue being the local bus operation absorbed into its parent Midland Red by National Bus in 1971. Pictured in the town centre is Stagecoach Midland Red 363, N363AVV.

201-216

Volvo B10M-55   Alexander PS   DP48F*   1995   206-212 are B49F

201	M201LHP	205	M205LHP	208	N208TDU	211	N211TDU	214	N214TDU
202	M202LHP	206	N206TDU	209	M209LHP	212	N212TDU	215	N215TDU
203	M203LHP	207	N207TDU	210	M210LHP	213	N213TDU	216	N216TDU
204	M204LHP								

217-228

Volvo B10M-55   Alexander PS   DP48F   1996-98

217	P217HBD	220	P220HBD	223	R223CRW	225	R225CRW	227	R227CRW
218	P218HBD	221	R221CRW	224	R224CRW	226	R226CRW	228	R228CRW
219	P219HBD								

300	E433YHL	Mercedes-Benz 709D	Reeve Burgess Beaver	B25F	1988	Ex Loftys, Bridge Trafford, 1993
301	G301WHP	Mercedes-Benz 709D	PMT	B25F	1989	
302	G302WHP	Mercedes-Benz 709D	PMT	B25F	1989	
303	G303WHP	Mercedes-Benz 709D	PMT	B25F	1989	
304	J304THP	Mercedes-Benz 709D	Alexander AM	B25F	1992	
305	J305THP	Mercedes-Benz 709D	Alexander AM	B25F	1992	
306	K306ARW	Mercedes-Benz 709D	Wright Nimbus	B25F	1992	
307	L307SKV	Mercedes-Benz 709D	Wright Nimbus	B25F	1993	

308-330

Mercedes-Benz 709D   Alexander Sprint   B23F   1994

308	L308YDU	313	L313YDU	318	L318YDU	323	L323YDU	327	L327YKV
309	L309YDU	314	L314YDU	319	L319YDU	324	L324YDU	328	L328YKV
310	L310YDU	315	L315YDU	320	L320YDU	325	L325YDU	329	L329YKV
311	L311YDU	316	L316YDU	321	L321YDU	326	L326YKV	330	L330YKV
312	L312YDU	317	L317YDU	322	L322YDU				

331-346

Mercedes-Benz 709D   Alexander Sprint   B23F   1995

331	M331LHP	335	M335LHP	338	M338LHP	341	M341LHP	344	M344LHP
332	M332LHP	336	M336LHP	339	M339LHP	342	M342LHP	345	M345LHP
334	M334LHP	337	M337LHP	340	M340LHP	343	M343LHP	346	M346KWK

347-372

Mercedes-Benz 709D   Alexander Sprint   B25F   1996

347	N347AVV	353	N353AVV	358	N358AVV	363	N363AVV	368	N368AVV
348	N348AVV	354	N354AVV	359	N359AVV	364	N364AVV	369	N369AVV
349	N349AVV	355	N355AVV	360	N360AVV	365	N365AVV	370	N370AVV
350	N350AVV	356	N356AVV	361	N361AVV	366	N366AVV	371	N371AVV
351	N351AVV	357	N357AVV	362	N362AVV	367	N367AVV	372	N372AVV
352	N352AVV								

400	F71LAL	Mercedes-Benz 811D	Alexander AM	DP33F	1988	Ex Skills, Nottingham, 1991

401-418

Mercedes-Benz 811D   Wright   B33F*   1991   *402/4/7-12 are DP33F
*401/3/5/6/13/7/8 are B31F

401	H401MRW	405	H405MRW	409	J409PRW	413	J413PRW	416	J416PRW
402	H402MRW	406	H406MRW	410	J410PRW	414	J414PRW	417	J417PRW
403	H403MRW	407	J407PRW	411	J411PRW	415	J415PRW	418	J418PRW
404	H404MRW	408	J408PRW	412	J412PRW				

419	G115OGA	Mercedes-Benz 811D	Alexander AM	DP33F	1988	Ex Beaton, Blantyre, 1992

420-425

Mercedes-Benz 811D   Wright   B31F   1993

420	K420ARW	422	K422ARW	423	K423ARW	424	K424ARW	425	K425ARW
421	K421ARW								

426	CSV219	Mercedes-Benz 811D	Optare StarRider	C29F	1989	Ex Brents Coaches, Watford, 1993
427	H912XGA	Mercedes-Benz 814D	Reeve Burgess Beaver	DP31F	1990	Ex Loftys, Bridge Trafford, 1993

Opposite:- **Stagecoach Midland Red is the operating name of Midland Red (South) Limited, now a subsidiary of Stagecoach West Ltd., the erstwhile Western Travel company based in Cheltenham. Co-operation within the West grouping allow vehicles to be moved to suit operational needs. In 1991, 420GAC arrived from Cheltenham and is now numbered 91 and is shown here in Stratford-upon-Avon. Also acquired, but from outside the company, is a long version of the Reeve Burgess Beaver body built on a Mercedes-Benz 814 chassis-cowl. Numbered 427, H912XGA is fitted with thirty-one high-back seats.**

Service buses from the Stagecoach Midland Red fleet travel as far north as Leicester as illustrated by smartly-turned-out National 605, NOE605R. This vehicle, like many within the fleet, has been fitted with a DAF engine, though there is no outwardly visible indication, the engine tone has noteably changed. It is expected more of this batch will be withdrawn when the next delivery of Alexander PS-bodied Volvo buses arrive. *Tony Wilson*

451-456   Volvo B6-9.9M   Alexander Dash   DP40F   1994

451	L451YAC	**453**	L453YAC	**454**	L454YAC	**455**	L455YAC	**456**	L456YAC
452	L452YAC							

503	JOX503P	Leyland National 11351A/1R	B49F	1976	Ex Midland Red, 1981
504	JOX504P	Leyland National 11351A/1R	B49DL	1976	Ex Midland Red, 1981
507	XGR728R	Leyland National 11351A/1R (DAF)	B49F	1977	Ex United, 1993
553	NOE553R	Leyland National 11351A/1R	B49F	1977	Ex Midland Red, 1981
571	NOE571R	Leyland National 11351A/1R	B49F	1977	Ex Midland Red, 1981
578	NOE578R	Leyland National 11351A/1R	B49F	1977	Ex Midland Red, 1981
582	NOE582R	Leyland National 11351A/1R (DAF)	B49F	1977	Ex Midland Red, 1981
586	NOE586R	Leyland National 11351A/1R	B49F	1977	Ex Midland Red, 1981
587	NOE587R	Leyland National 11351A/1R	B49F	1977	Ex Cheltenham & Gloucester, 1994
590	NOE590R	Leyland National 11351A/1R	B49DL	1977	Ex Midland Red, 1981
591	YEU446V	Leyland National 10351B/1R	B44F	1981	Ex Cheltenham & Gloucester, 1994
595	GOL426N	Leyland National 11351/1R	B49F	1975	Ex Cheltenham & Gloucester, 1994
598	KHT124P	Leyland National 11351/1R	B52F	1976	Ex Cheltenham & Gloucester, 1994
600	SAE753S	Leyland National 11351A/1R	B52F	1978	Ex Cheltenham & Gloucester, 1994

602-772   Leyland National 11351A/1R(DAF)   B49F*   1977-80   Ex Midland Red, 1981

*624, 708 are B52F; 755/6 have LPG engines

602	NOE602R	**621**	PUK621R	**626**	PUK626R	**708**	TOF708S	**755**	XOV755T
603	NOE603R	**622**	PUK622R	**627**	PUK627R	**709**	TOF709S	**756**	XOV756T
604	NOE604R	**623**	PUK623R	**628**	PUK628R	**710**	TOF710S	**760**	XOV760T
605	NOE605R	**624**	PUK624R	**629**	PUK629R	**753**	XOV753T	**771**	BVP771V
606	NOE606R	**625**	PUK625R	**707**	TOF707S	**754**	XOV754T	**772**	BVP772V

802	SHH392X	Leyland National 2 NL116AL11/1R	B52F	1982	Ex Cheltenham & Gloucester, 1995
803	TAE639S	Leyland National 11351A/1R(DAF)	B52F	1978	Ex Cheltenham & Gloucester, 1995
808	BVP808V	Leyland National 2 NL116L11/1R	B49F	1980	Ex North Western, 1991
809	SVV589W	Leyland National 2 NL116L11/1R	B49F	1980	Ex Luton & District, 1991
816	BVP816V	Leyland National 2 NL116L11/1R (DAF)	B49F	1980	Ex Midland Red, 1981
817	BVP817V	Leyland National 2 NL116L11/1R (DAF)	B49F	1980	Ex Midland Red, 1981
818	BVP818V	Leyland National 2 NL116L11/1R (DAF)	B49F	1980	Ex Midland Red, 1981
819	F661PWK	Leyland Lynx LX112L10ZR1R Leyland	B51F	1988	
820	F660PWK	Leyland Lynx LX112L10ZR1R Leyland	B51F	1988	

821-830 Iveco Daily 49.10 Marshall C29 B23F 1993* Ex Stagecoach Selkent, 1995

821	K521EFL	823	K523EFL	825	K525EFL	827	K527EFL	829	K529EFL
822	K522EFL	824	K524EFL	826	K526EFL	828	K528EFL	830	K530EFL

833	N183CMJ	Iveco TurboDaily 59.12	Alexander	B29F	1996	Long term Iveco demonstrator

902-912 Leyland Olympian ONLXB/1R Eastern Coach Works H45/32F 1983-84

902	A542HAC	904	A544HAC	906	A546HAC	910	B910ODU	912	B912ODU
903	A543HAC	905	A545HAC	907	A547HAC	911	B911ODU		

927	NHU671R	Bristol VRT/SL3/6LXB	Eastern Coach Works	H43/27D	1979	Ex Cheltenham & Gloucester, 1994
928	LHT725P	Bristol VRT/SL3/501(6LXB)	Eastern Coach Works	H39/31F	1976	Ex Cheltenham & Gloucester, 1994
929	NHU672R	Bristol VRT/SL3/6LXB	Eastern Coach Works	H43/27D	1979	Ex Cheltenham & Gloucester, 1994
932	CBV16S	Bristol VRT/SL3/501(6LXB)	Eastern Coach Works	H43/31F	1977	Ex Ribble, 1994
936	ONH846P	Bristol VRT/SL3/6LXB	Eastern Coach Works	H43/31F	1976	Ex Bluebird, 1993
940	PEU511R	Bristol VRT/SL3/6LXB	Eastern Coach Works	DPH43/31F	1977	Ex Badgerline, 1993
943	GTX754W	Bristol VRT/SL3/501	Eastern Coach Works	H43/31F	1980	Ex Red & White, 1993
944	HUD475S	Bristol VRT/SL3/6LXB	Eastern Coach Works	H43/31F	1977	Ex Oxford Bus Company, 1993
945	HUD480S	Bristol VRT/SL3/6LXB	Eastern Coach Works	H43/31F	1977	Ex Oxford Bus Company, 1993
946	HUD479S	Bristol VRT/SL3/6LXB	Eastern Coach Works	H43/31F	1977	Ex Oxford Bus Company, 1993
947	AET181T	Bristol VRT/SL3/6LXB	Eastern Coach Works	H43/31F	1979	Ex East Midland, 1994
948	VTV170S	Bristol VRT/SL3/6LXB	Eastern Coach Works	H43/31F	1978	Ex East Midland, 1994
960	B960ODU	Leyland Olympian ONLXB/1R	Eastern Coach Works	DPH42/30F	1984	
961	B961ODU	Leyland Olympian ONLXB/1R	Eastern Coach Works	DPH42/30F	1984	
962	C962XVC	Leyland Olympian ONLXB/1RH	Eastern Coach Works	DPH42/29F	1985	
963	C963XVC	Leyland Olympian ONLXB/1RH	Eastern Coach Works	DPH42/29F	1985	
964	C964XVC	Leyland Olympian ONLXB/1RH	Eastern Coach Works	DPH42/29F	1985	

970-988 Leyland Atlantean AN68A/2R Alexander AL H49/37F 1978-80 Ex Busways, 1995-96

970	SCN252S	976	AVK172V	980	AVK181V	983	AVK168V	987	AVK140V
971	SCN253S	977	EJR106W	981	VCU304T	985	AVK167V	988	AVK145V
972	SCN265S	978	SCN276S	982	AVK174V	986	AVK169V	989	AVK143V
975	VCU310T	979	SCN281S						

990	MVK521R	Leyland Atlantean AN68A/2R	Alexander AL	H48/31F	1976	Ex Cheltenham & Gloucester (S&D), 1997
991	MVK558R	Leyland Atlantean AN68A/2R	Alexander AL	H48/31F	1977	Ex Cheltenham & Gloucester (S&D), 1997
992	UNA840S	Leyland Atlantean AN68A/1R	Park Royal	H43/32F	1977	Ex Western Buses, 1997
993	BNC936T	Leyland Atlantean AN68A/1R	Park Royal	H43/32F	1979	Ex Western Buses, 1997
1053	PIB8109	Leyland National 10351A/2R		B22DL	1978	Ex London Buses, 1991

Previous Registrations:

230HUE	BVP786V, 331HWD	A6GGT	E630KCX
3273AC	BVP788V	A75NAC	A190GVC, 420GAC
331HWD	BVP787V	A76NAC	A191GVC, 491GAC
420GAC	CDG213Y	A8GGT	A202RHT
4828VC	C211PPE	BIW4977	A70KDU
491GAC	B73OKV	CSV219	F846TLU
498FYB	CDG207Y	E315NWK	E422GAC, 6267AC, E315NWK, 4012VC
552OHU	A201RHT	HTY139W	FYX819W, KSU460
6253VC	YDK917, JPU817, C472CAP	PIB8109	THX119S
9737VC	C212PPE	RNV413V	KUB546V, 4012VC
9984PG	FYX815W	WSU293	From New

Allocations:-

Banbury (Canal Street) - Midland Red

Mercedes-Benz	300	301	302	303	304	305	402	419
Volvo B6	452	454	455	456				
National	571	591	595	598	624	707	708	709
Leopard	5	6	12	29				
Tiger	1	70	74	75	90	91		
Volvo B10M	69							
Bristol VRT	927	932	940	943	948			

Coventry (Rowley Road) - Midland Red - Park & Ride ♥

Iveco	821	822	823	824	825	826	827	828
	829	830						
Mercedes-Benz	326	327	328	329	330♥	331♥	332	343
	344	345	346	347	348	349	350	407
	417							
National	600							
Leopard	18							
Atlantean	970	971	972					

Leamington Spa (Station Approach)

Iveco	833							
Mercedes-Benz	308	309	334	335	336	337	338	339
	340	341	342	352	366	367	368	369
	370	371	372	415	416			
Leopard	4	7						
Tiger	76	88						
National	504							
National 2	802	808	809	816	817	818		
Lynx	819	820						
Atlantean	979	981	982	983	985	986	987	988
	989							
Olympian	905	906	907	910	911	960	961	962

Nuneaton (Newtown Road)

Mercedes-Benz	310	311	312	313	314	315	316	317
	318	319	320	321	322	323	324	325
	351	401	414	420	421	422	423	424
	425							
Dart	101	102	103	104	105			
National	503	507	553	587	605	625	626	754
	755	756	803					
Leopard	16							
Volvo PS	203	204	205	206	207	208	209	210
	211	212	213	214	215	216		
Bristol VR	928	929	944	945	947			
Atlantean	992	993						
Olympian	912							

Rugby (Railway Terrace) - Midland Red - National Express ⁝

Mercedes-Benz	306	307	353	354	355	356	357	358
	359	360	403	404	405	406	408	413
	418							
National	578	586	590	602	603	604	606	622
	623	629	710	753	771	772	1053	
Tiger	2	73						
Volvo B10M	34⁝	35⁝	36⁝	37⁝	38⁝	39⁝	43⁝	
Bristol VR	936	946						
Atlantean	990	991						
Olympian	902	903						

Stratford-on-Avon (Avenue Farm) - Midland Red - Stratford Blue

Mercedes-Benz	361	362	363	364	365	400	409	410
	411	412	426	427				
Volvo B6	451	453						
National	582	621	627	628	760			
Leopard	11							
Volvo PS	201	202	217	218	219	220		
Atlantean	975	976	977	978	980			
Olympian	963	964						

Unallocated:-
| Volvo B10M | 69 | | | | | | | |

OXFORD

Thames Transit Ltd, Horspath Road, Cowley, Oxfordshire, OX4 2RY

1	L723JUD	Volvo B10M-60	Jonckheere Deauville 45	C49FT	1994	
2	L724JUD	Volvo B10M-60	Jonckheere Deauville 45	C49FT	1994	
3	3063VC	Volvo B10M-60	Plaxton Paramount 3500 III	C49FT	1990	Ex Stagecoach Midland Red, 1997
5	L212GJO	Volvo B10M-60	Jonckheere Deauville 45	C49FT	1993	
6	9258VC	Volvo B10M-60	Plaxton Paramount 3500 III	C49FT	1990	Ex Stagecoach Midland Red, 1997
8	N41MJO	Volvo B10M-62	Berkhof Excellence 1000LD	C51FT	1996	
9	M103XBW	Volvo B10M-62	Berkhof Excellence 1000LD	C51FT	1995	
10	H639UWR	Volvo B10M-60	Plaxton Paramount 3500 III	C48FT	1991	Ex Wallace Arnold, 1994
11	H640UWR	Volvo B10M-60	Plaxton Paramount 3500 III	C48FT	1991	Ex Wallace Arnold, 1994
12	N42MJO	Volvo B10M-62	Berkhof Excellence 1000LD	C51FT	1996	
14	N43MJO	Volvo B10M-62	Berkhof Excellence 1000LD	C51FT	1996	
15	H641UWR	Volvo B10M-60	Plaxton Paramount 3500 III	C48FT	1991	Ex Wallace Arnold, 1994
16	M104XBW	Volvo B10M-62	Berkhof Excellence 1000LD	C51FT	1995	
17	H650UWR	Volvo B10M-60	Plaxton Paramount 3500 III	C48FT	1991	Ex Wallace Arnold, 1994
18	L155LBW	Volvo B10M-62	Jonckheere Deauville 45	C49FT	1994	
19	N45MJO	Volvo B10M-62	Berkhof Excellence 1000LD	C51FT	1996	
20	J420HDS	Volvo B10M-60	Plaxton Excalibur	C44FT	1992	Ex Busways, 1997
21	L159LBW	Volvo B10M-62	Jonckheere Deauville 45	C49FT	1994	
22	J456FSR	Volvo B10M-61	Plaxton Expressliner	C46FT	1992	Ex Stagecoach Midland Red, 1997
23	N46MJO	Volvo B10M-62	Berkhof Excellence 1000LD	C51FT	1996	
24	J424HDS	Volvo B10M-60	Plaxton Excalibur	C44FT	1992	Ex Busways, 1997
25	M105XBW	Volvo B10M-62	Berkhof Excellence 1000LD	C51FT	1995	
26	M106XBW	Volvo B10M-62	Berkhof Excellence 1000LD	C51FT	1995	
28	M107XBW	Volvo B10M-62	Berkhof Excellence 1000LD	C42FT	1995	
29	L156LBW	Volvo B10M-62	Jonckheere Deauville 45	C49FT	1994	
30	L157LBW	Volvo B10M-62	Jonckheere Deauville 45	C49FT	1994	
31	L158LBW	Volvo B10M-62	Jonckheere Deauville 45	C49FT	1994	
32	N47MJO	Volvo B10M-62	Berkhof Excellence 1000LD	C51FT	1996	
33	N48MJO	Volvo B10M-62	Berkhof Excellence 1000LD	C51FT	1996	
50	E829ATT	Mercedes-Benz 709D	Reeve Burgess Beaver	DP25F	1988	
64	F724FDV	Mercedes-Benz 709D	Reeve Burgess Beaver	B25F	1989	
74	F734FDV	Mercedes-Benz 709D	Reeve Burgess Beaver	B25F	1989	
122	D122PTT	Ford Transit VE6	Mellor	B16F	1987	
132	D132PTT	Ford Transit VE6	Mellor	B16F	1987	

201-206

Mercedes-Benz 711D   Marshall C19   DP28F   1995

201	N201CUD	203	N203CUD	204	N204CUD	205	N205CUD	206	N206CUD
202	N202CUD								

305-324

Mercedes-Benz 709D   Reeve Burgess Beaver   DP25F   1988

305	E305BWL	311	F311EJO	316	F316EJO	319	F319EJO	322	F322EJO
306	E306BWL	312	F312EJO	317	F317EJO	320	F320EJO	323	F323EJO
309	E309BWL	314	F314EJO	318	F318EJO	321	F321EJO	324	F324EJO

326-346

Mercedes-Benz 709D   Reeve Burgess Beaver   B25F   1989

326	F776FDV	329	F766FDV	332	F769FDV	339	F409KOD	345	F403KOD
327	F764FDV	330	F767FDV	333	F770FDV	344	F402KOD	346	F746FDV
328	F765FDV	331	F768FDV						

347-354

Mercedes-Benz 709D   Carlyle   B29F   1990

347	G947TDV	349	G949TDV	351	G951TDV	353	G843UDV	354	G954TDV
348	G948TDV	350	G950TDV	352	G952TDV				

355-366

Mercedes-Benz 811D   Carlyle   B33F   1990

355	G831UDV	358	G834UDV	361	G837UDV	363	G839UDV	365	G841UDV
356	G832UDV	359	G835UDV	362	G838UDV	364	G840UDV	366	G842UDV
357	G833UDV	360	G836UDV						

Many of Stagecoach Oxford's fleet are now gaining corporate livery following the delivery of large numbers of both Dennis Darts and Volvo Olympians. Repainting of existing vehicles is also underway as illustrated by Dart 3025, M74VJO. During 1998 forty-one of the original fleet of Darts will move to the East London and Selkent operations, the first six having moved as we go to press. In their place, Stagecoach Oxford will receive the current batch of new single-doored low-floor Darts from Alexander as well some single-doored examples from the London fleets. *Andrew Jarosz*

370	H988FTT	Mercedes-Benz 811D	Marshall C19	B29F	1991	Ex Dockland Transit, 1997
399	H790GTA	Mercedes-Benz 811D	Marshall C19	B29F	1991	Ex Dockland Transit, 1997
403	H104HDV	Mercedes-Benz 811D	Marshall C19	B29F	1991	Ex Dockland Transit, 1997
408	H109HDV	Mercedes-Benz 811D	Marshall C19	B29F	1991	Ex Dockland Transit, 1997

501-513   Volvo Olympian   Alexander RL   H45/27F   1997

501	R501UWL	504	R504UWL	507	R507UWL	510	R510UWL	512	R512UWL
502	R502UWL	505	R505UWL	508	R508UWL	511	R511UWL	513	R513UWL
503	R503UWL	506	R506UWL	509	R509UWL				

514-526   Volvo Olympian   Alexander RL   H45/23D   1998

514	R414XFC	517	R417XFC	520	R420XFC	523	R423XFC	525	R425XFC
515	R415XFC	518	R418XFC	521	R421XFC	524	R424XFC	526	R426XFC
516	R416XFC	519	R419XFC	522	R422XFC				

801-829   Dennis Dart SLF   Alexander ALX200   B37F   1998

801	R801YUD	807	R807YUD	813	R813YUD	819	R819YUD	825	R825YUD
802	R802YUD	808	R808YUD	814	R814YUD	820	R720YUD	826	R826YUD
803	R803YUD	809	R809YUD	815	R815YUD	821	R821YUD	827	R827YUD
804	R804YUD	810	R810YUD	816	R816YUD	822	R822YUD	828	R828YUD
805	R805YUD	811	R811YUD	817	R817YUD	823	R823YUD	829	R829YUD
806	R706YUD	812	R812YUD	818	R818YUD	824	R824YUD		

Opposite, top:- **The principal commuting service between Oxford and London is known as the** *Oxford Tube* **and directly competes with Go-Ahead's** *City Link* **and their associated rail operation,** *Thames Trains.* **For the present the gold and red** *Oxford Tube* **livery will continue and the scheme is illustrated by 5, L212GJO, seen at the London end of the service.** *Colin Lloyd.*
Opposite, bottom:- **The liveries applied to Dennis Darts acquired with Thames Transit varied dependent on the route within Oxford to which they were allocated. Shown here is that used for the** *City Cavalier* **routes between Barton and Sommertown.** *R Sharman*

901	N901PFC	Dennis Lance 11SDA3113	Plaxton Verde	B49F	1996			
902	N902PFC	Dennis Lance 11SDA3113	Plaxton Verde	B49F	1996			
903	N903PFC	Dennis Lance 11SDA3113	Plaxton Verde	B49F	1996			

904-912

Volvo B10B — Plaxton Paladin — B..F — 1998

904	R904XFC	906	R906XFC	908	R908XFC	910	R910XFC	912	R912XFC
905	R905XFC	907	R907XFC	909	R909XFC	911	R911XFC		

1801	L801HJO	Optare MetroRider MREL	Optare	B18F	1993	On loan from Southern Electric
1802	L802HJO	Optare MetroRider MREL	Optare	B18F	1993	On loan from Southern Electric
1803	L803HJO	Optare MetroRider MREL	Optare	B18F	1993	On loan from Southern Electric
1804	L804HJO	Optare MetroRider MREL	Optare	B18F	1993	On loan from Southern Electric
2110	L248FDV	Iveco Daily 49-12 - Hybrid	Mellor	B13D	1994	
2111	L247FDV	Iveco Daily 49-12 - Hybrid	Mellor	B13D	1994	

3000-3005

Dennis Dart 9.8SDL3035 — Plaxton Pointer — B39D — 1994

3000	L709JUD	3002	L711JUD	3003	L712JUD	3004	L713JUD	3005	L714JUD
3001	L710JUD							

3014-3050

Dennis Dart 9.8SDL3054 — Plaxton Pointer — B37D — 1995

3014	M59VJO	3022	M69VJO	3030	M81WBW	3037	M89WBW	3044	M97WBW
3015	M61VJO	3023	M71VJO	3031	M82WBW	3038	M91WBW	3045	M98WBW
3016	M62VJO	3024	M73VJO	3032	M83WBW	3039	M92WBW	3046	M101WBW
3017	M63VJO	3025	M74VJO	3033	M84WBW	3040	M93WBW	3047	M102WBW
3018	M64VJO	3026	M75VJO	3034	M85WBW	3041	M94WBW	3048	M103WBW
3019	M65VJO	3027	M76VJO	3035	M86WBW	3042	M95WBW	3049	N47EJO
3020	M67VJO	3028	M78VJO	3036	M87WBW	3043	M96WBW	3050	N48EJO
3021	M68VJO	3029	M79VJO						

3051	N51KBW	Dennis Dart 9.8SDL3054	Plaxton Pointer	B37D	1996
3052	N52KBW	Dennis Dart 9.8SDL3054	Plaxton Pointer	B37D	1996
3053	N53KBW	Dennis Dart 9.8SDL3054	Plaxton Pointer	B37D	1996
3054	N54KBW	Dennis Dart 9.8SDL3054	Plaxton Pointer	B37D	1996

3055-3062

Dennis Dart 9.8SDL3054 — Plaxton Pointer — B40F — 1996

3055	N56KBW	3057	N58KBW	3059	N61KBW	3061	N63KBW	3062	N64KBW
3056	N57KBW	3058	N59KBW	3060	N62KBW			

3063	R63UFC	Dennis Dart	Plaxton Pointer	B40F	1997
3064	R64UFC	Dennis Dart	Plaxton Pointer	B40F	1997
3065	R65UFC	Dennis Dart	Plaxton Pointer	B40F	1997

Ancilliary vehicles

98	LSV670	Leyland Tiger TRCTL11/3RZ	Plaxton Paramount 3500 II	C53F	1987	
103	D103PTT	Ford Transit VE6	Mellor	B16F	1987	
137	D137PTT	Ford Transit VE6	Mellor	B16F	1987	
789	D789NDV	Ford Transit 190D	Mellor	B16F	1987	
3318	AFJ738T	Bristol LH6L	Plaxton Supreme III Express	C43F	1979	Ex Devon General, 1996

Previous Registrations:

3063VC	G543LWU	J424HDS	J424HDS, KSU464
9258VC	G554LWU	LSV670	C129KJO
J420HDS	J420HDS, KSU462		

Allocations:-

Chipping Norton

Lance	901	902	903

Oxford (Horspath Road, Cowley) - Stagecoach Oxford - Oxford Tube

Transit	122							
MetroRider	1801	1802	1803	1804				
Mercedes-Benz	50	64	74	201	202	203	204	305
	306	308	309	310	312	313	314	316
	318	319	320	321	322	323	324	326
	327	328	329	330	331	333	339	347
	348	349	350	355	356	357	358	359
	360	363	364	365	366	399	403	408
Volvo Coach	1	2	3	5	6	8	9	10
	11	12	14	15	16	17	18	19
	20	21	22	23	24	25	26	28
	29	30	31	32	33			
Dart	3000	3001	3002	3003	3004	3005	3016	3017
	3018	3019	3020	3021	3022	3023	3024	3025
	3026	3027	3028	3029	3030	3031	3032	3033
	3034	3035	3036	3037	3038	3039	3040	3041
	3042	3043	3044	3045	3046	3047	3048	3049
	3050	3051	3052	3053	3054	3055	3056	3057
	3058	3059	3060	3061	3062	3063	3064	3065
Olympian	514	515	516	517	518	519	520	521
	522	523	524	525	526			

Witney (Corn Street) - Stagecoach Oxford

Transit	132							
Mercedes-Benz	205	206	311	332	344	345	346	351
	352	353	354	361	362			
Olympian	501	502	503	504	505	506	507	508
	509	510	511	512	513			

During 1997 Stagecoach Oxford commenced delivery of two batches of Volvo Olympians. The first comprised thirteen single-doored examples which are all based at Witney. The second batch are dual-doored examples and these are to be used on city services where increased patronage warrants extra capacity, such as the *Blackbird Flyer* route which now operates round the clock.
Andrew Jarosz

RED & WHITE

Red & White Services Ltd; The Valleys Bus Company Ltd; Aberdare Bus Company Ltd,
Rhondda Buses Ltd; Parfitts Motor Services Ltd
1 St David's Road, Cwmbran, Torfaen   NP44 1QX

16	E316HLO	Mercedes-Benz L307D	Pilcher Green	M12	1988	Ex Rhondda (Parfitts), 1997
105	F105YWO	MCW MetroRider MF150/104	MCW	DP25F	1988	Ex Rhondda, 1997
106	F106YWO	MCW MetroRider MF150/103	MCW	DP25F	1988	Ex Rhondda, 1997
112	F112YWO	MCW MetroRider MF150/103	MCW	DP25F	1988	Ex Rhondda, 1997
114	F114YWO	MCW MetroRider MF150/103	MCW	DP25F	1988	Ex Rhondda, 1997
149	F392DHL	Mercedes-Benz 709D	Reeve Burgess Beaver	B20F	198	Ex Rhondda, 1997
150	M866LNY	Mercedes-Benz 711D	Plaxton Beaver	B27F	1995	Ex Rhondda, 1997
151	N151MTG	Mercedes-Benz 811D	UVG Citi Star	B31F	1995	Ex Rhondda, 1997

152-160

		Mercedes-Benz 711D		UVG Citi Star		B27F		1995	Ex Rhondda, 1997		
152	N152MTG	154	N154MTG	156	N156MTG	158	N158MTG	160	N160MTG
153	N153MTG	155	N155MTG	157	N157MTG	159	N159MTG		

161	P161TDW	Mercedes-Benz 709D	Plaxton Beaver	B27F	1996	Ex Rhondda, 1997
162	P162TDW	Mercedes-Benz 709D	Plaxton Beaver	B27F	1996	Ex Rhondda, 1997

163-171

		Mercedes-Benz 711D		Plaxton Beaver		B27F		1996	Ex Rhondda, 1997		
163	P163TNY	165	P165TNY	167	P167TNY	169	P169TNY	171	P171TNY
164	P164TNY	166	P166TNY	168	P168TNY	170	P170TNY		

203-208

		Volvo Olympian		Alexander RL		H--/--F		1998			
203	R203DHB	205	R205DHB	206	R206DHB	207	R207DHB	208	R208DHB
204	R204DHB								

220	D183VRP	Mercedes-Benz L608D	Alexander AM	B20F	1986	Ex Rhondda, 1997
230	D164VRP	Mercedes-Benz L608D	Alexander AM	B20F	1986	Ex Rhondda, 1997
252	F125YVP	MCW MetroRider MF158/16	MCW	B28F	1988	Ex Rhondda (Parfitts), 1997
254	G689KNW	Optare MetroRider	Optare	B29F	1990	Ex Rhondda, 1997
255	K320FYG	Optare MetroRider	Optare	B29F	1993	Ex Rhondda (Parfitts), 1997
256	J797MHF	Optare MetroRider	Optare	B29F	1991	Ex Rhondda (Parfitts), 1997
257	L839MWT	Optare MetroRider	Optare	B31F	1993	Ex Rhondda (Parfitts), 1997
258	L840MWT	Optare MetroRider	Optare	B31F	1993	Ex Rhondda (Parfitts), 1997
301	H301PAX	Mercedes-Benz 709D	PMT Ami	C25F	1991	
302	J302TUH	Mercedes-Benz 709D	PMT Bursley	B25F	1991	
303	J303TUH	Mercedes-Benz 709D	PMT Bursley	B25F	1991	

304-317

		Mercedes-Benz 811D		Wright NimBus		B33F		1992			
304	J304UKG	307	J307UKG	311	K311YKG	314	K314YKG	316	K316YKG
305	J305UKG	309	K309YKG	312	K312YKG	315	K315YKG	317	K317YKG
306	J306UKG	310	K310YKG	313	K313YKG				

318	K318YKG	Mercedes-Benz 709D	Wright NimBus	B25F	1992	
319	K319YKG	Mercedes-Benz 709D	Alexander Sprint	B25F	1992	
320	K320YKG	Mercedes-Benz 709D	Alexander Sprint	B25F	1992	
321	K321YKG	Mercedes-Benz 709D	Alexander Sprint	B25F	1992	
322	K322YKG	Mercedes-Benz 811D	Wright NimBus	B33F	1992	
323	K323YKG	Mercedes-Benz 811D	Wright NimBus	B33F	1992	
324	K324YKG	Mercedes-Benz 811D	Wright NimBus	B33F	1992	
325	K325YKG	Mercedes-Benz 811D	Wright NimBus	B33F	1992	
326	L326CHB	Mercedes-Benz 811D	Marshall C16	B33F	1993	
327	L327CHB	Mercedes-Benz 811D	Marshall C16	B33F	1993	
328	L328CHB	Mercedes-Benz 811D	Marshall C16	B33F	1993	
329	L329CHB	Mercedes-Benz 811D	Marshall C16	B33F	1993	
330	L685CDD	Mercedes-Benz 709D	Alexander Sprint	B25F	1994	Ex Cheltenham & Gloucester, 1994
331	L331CHB	Mercedes-Benz 811D	Marshall C16	B33F	1993	
332	H556TUG	Mercedes-Benz 709D	Dormobile Routemaker	DP25F	1990	Ex Graham's, Tredegar, 1994

In December 1997 the operations of Rhondda Buses and Parfitts were acquired by Stagecoach and placed under the operational control of Stagecoach Red & White, part of Stagecoach West Ltd. The first repaint was of Optare-bodied Mercedes-Benz O405, 550 N550 MTG, seen in January 1998 in Wood Street, Cardiff. *John Jones*

334-360

Mercedes-Benz 709D   Alexander Sprint   B25F   1994

334	L334FWO	340	L340FWO	346	M346JBO	351	M351JBO	356	M356JBO
335	L335FWO	341	L341FWO	347	M347JBO	352	M352JBO	357	M357JBO
336	L336FWO	342	L342FWO	348	M348JBO	353	M353JBO	358	M358JBO
337	L337FWO	343	L343FWO	349	M349JBO	354	M354JBO	359	M359JBO
338	L338FWO	344	M344JBO	350	M350JBO	355	M355JBO	360	M360JBO
339	L339FWO	345	M345JBO						

361-371

Mercedes-Benz 709D   Alexander Sprint   B25F   1995

361	M361LAX	364	M364LAX	366	M366LAX	368	M368LAX	370	M370LAX
362	M362LAX	365	M365LAX	367	M367LAX	369	M369LAX	371	M371LAX
363	M363LAX							

372-384

Mercedes-Benz 709D   Alexander Sprint   B25F   1996

372	N372PNY	375	N375PNY	378	N378PNY	381	N381PNY	383	N383PNY
373	N373PNY	376	N376PNY	379	N379PNY	382	N382PNY	384	N384PNY
374	N374PNY	377	N377PNY	380	N380PNY				

391	GHB146N	Bristol RESL6L	Eastern Coach Works	B44F	1974	Ex Cynon Valley, 1992
392	HTG354N	Bristol RESL6L	Eastern Coach Works	B44F	1975	Ex Cynon Valley, 1992
393	GHB148N	Bristol RESL6L	Eastern Coach Works	B44F	1974	Ex Cynon Valley, 1992
400	G505XLO	Leyland Swift LBM6T/2RA	Reeve Burgess Harrier	B41F	1989	Ex Rhondda (Parfitts), 1997
401	E308HPU	Leyland Swift LBM6T/2RA	Wadham Stringer Vanguard	B37F	1988	Ex Rhondda, 1997
402	E309HPU	Leyland Swift LBM6T/2RA	Wadham Stringer Vanguard	B37F	1988	Ex Rhondda (Parfitts), 1997
423	NWO457R	Leyland National 11351A/1R/SC (Volvo)		DP48F	1977	Ex National Welsh, 1991
427	NWO461R	Leyland National 11351A/1R/SC (DAF)		DP48F	1977	Ex National Welsh, 1991
434	NWO468R	Leyland National 11351A/1R/SC (Volvo)		DP48F	1977	Ex National Welsh, 1991
440	G40TGW	Dennis Dart 8.5SDL3003	Carlyle Dartline	B28F	1990	Ex Stagecoach Selkent, 1998
442	UTX726S	Leyland National 10351A/1R		B44F	1978	Ex Cynon Valley, 1992

Pictured in Pontypridd is Red & White 758, M758LAX, one of twenty-one Volvo B10M with Alexander bodywork delivered in 1995. Fitted with high-back seating they are often found on the longer distance services such as the X78 on which the vehicle was working when seen. *John Jones*

449	DDW434V	Leyland National 10351A/1R		B44F	1980	Ex Cynon Valley, 1992
475	YBO150T	Leyland National 10351A/1R		B44F	1979	Ex TGM Buses, Cardiff, 1992
497	BYW397V	Leyland National 10351A/2R		B44F	1979	Ex Rhondda (Parfitts), 1997
499	BHY999V	Leyland National 2 NL116L11/1R		DP48F	1980	Ex Rhondda, 1997
500	YSX934W	Leyland National 2 NL106L11/1R		B44F	1981	Ex Fife Scottish, 1994
501	RSG814V	Leyland National 2 NL116L11/1R		B52F	1980	Ex Fife Scottish, 1994
502	YSX932W	Leyland National 2 NL106L11/1R		B44F	1981	Ex Fife Scottish, 1994
503	YSX933W	Leyland National 2 NL106L11/1R		B44F	1981	Ex Fife Scottish, 1994
504	MSO13W	Leyland National 2 NL116L11/1R		B52F	1980	Ex Fife Scottish, 1994
505	RSG815V	Leyland National 2 NL116L11/1R		B52F	1980	Ex Fife Scottish, 1994
506	WAS765V	Leyland National 2 NL116L11/1R		B52F	1980	Ex Fife Scottish, 1994
507	WAS767V	Leyland National 2 NL116L11/1R		B52F	1980	Ex Fife Scottish, 1994
508	MSO14W	Leyland National 2 NL116L11/1R		B52F	1980	Ex Fife Scottish, 1994
510	YSX935W	Leyland National 2 NL106L11/1R		B44F	1981	Ex Fife Scottish, 1994
512	RSG824V	Leyland National 2 NL116L11/1R		B52F	1980	Ex Fife Scottish, 1994
513	RSG825V	Leyland National 2 NL116L11/1R		B52F	1980	Ex Fife Scottish, 1994
514	RSG823V	Leyland National 2 NL116L11/1R		B52F	1980	Ex Fife Scottish, 1995
515	DMS22V	Leyland National 2 NL116L11/1R		B52F	1980	Ex Fife Scottish, 1995
516	NLS987W	Leyland National 2 NL116L11/1R		B52F	1980	Ex Fife Scottish, 1995
517	DMS20V	Leyland National 2 NL116L11/1R		B52F	1980	Ex Fife Scottish, 1995
550	N550MTG	Mercedes-Benz 0405	Optare Prisma	B49F	1995	Ex Rhondda, 1997
551	N551MTG	Mercedes-Benz 0405	Optare Prisma	B49F	1995	Ex Rhondda, 1997
554	P54XBO	Dennis Dart SLF	Wright	B43F	1997	Ex Rhondda, 1997
556	P56XBO	Dennis Dart SLF	Marshall Capital C39	B43F	1997	Ex Rhondda (Parfitts), 1997
557	P57XBO	Dennis Dart SLF	Marshall Capital C39	B43F	1997	Ex Rhondda (Parfitts), 1997
558	P58XBO	Dennis Dart SLF	Marshall Capital C39	B43F	1997	Ex Rhondda (Parfitts), 1997

559	P59VTG	Dennis Dart SLF	Marshall C37	B40F	1997	Ex Rhondda, 1997
560	L414SFL	Dennis Dart 9.8SDL3054	Marshall C37	DP37F	1994	Ex Rhondda, 1997
561	P61VTG	Dennis Dart SLF	Marshall C37	B40F	1997	Ex Rhondda, 1997
562	N62MTG	Dennis Dart 9.8SDL3054	Plaxton Pointer	B40F	1995	Ex Rhondda (Parfitts), 1997
563	N63MTG	Dennis Dart 9.8SDL3054	Plaxton Pointer	B40F	1995	Ex Rhondda (Parfitts), 1997
564	M64HHB	Dennis Dart 9.8SDL3054	Wright Handy-bus	B39F	1995	Ex Rhondda, 1997
565	M65HHB	Dennis Dart 9.8SDL3054	Wright Handy-bus	B39F	1995	Ex Rhondda, 1997
566	M562JTG	Dennis Dart 9.8SDL3040	Plaxton Pointer	B43F	1994	Ex Rhondda (Parfitts), 1997
567	M67HHB	Dennis Dart 9.8SDL3054	Wright Handy-bus	B39F	1995	Ex Rhondda, 1997
568	M68HHB	Dennis Dart 9SDL3031	Marshall C36	B34F	1994	Ex Rhondda, 1997
569	M69HHB	Dennis Dart 9SDL3031	Marshall C36	B34F	1994	Ex Rhondda, 1997
570	M625KKG	Dennis Dart 9.8SDL3040	Plaxton Pointer	B44F	1994	Ex Rhondda (Parfitts), 1997
583	L83CWO	Dennis Dart 9SDL3034	Plaxton Pointer	B35F	1993	Ex Rhondda, 1997
584	L84CWO	Dennis Dart 9SDL3034	Plaxton Pointer	B35F	1993	Ex Rhondda, 1997
585	L85CWO	Dennis Dart 9SDL3034	Plaxton Pointer	B35F	1993	Ex Rhondda, 1997
586	L86CWO	Dennis Dart 9SDL3024	Wright Handy-bus	B35F	1993	Ex Rhondda, 1997
587	L87CWO	Dennis Dart 9SDL3024	Wright Handy-bus	B35F	1993	Ex Rhondda, 1997
588	L270EHB	Dennis Dart 9.8SDL3035	Plaxton Pointer	B43F	1994	Ex Rhondda, 1997
589	L89CWO	Dennis Dart 9SDL3024	Wright Handy-bus	B35F	1993	Ex Rhondda, 1997
590	K402EDT	Dennis Dart 9SDL3016	Northern Counties Paladin	B35F	1992	Ex Rhondda, 1997
591	K91BNY	Dennis Dart 9SDL3011	Plaxton Pointer	B35F	1993	Ex Rhondda, 1997
592	K92BNY	Dennis Dart 9SDL3011	Plaxton Pointer	B35F	1993	Ex Rhondda, 1997
593	K93BNY	Dennis Dart 9SDL3011	Plaxton Pointer	B35F	1993	Ex Rhondda, 1997
594	K94AAX	Dennis Dart 9SDL3011	Wright Handy-bus	B35F	1993	Ex Rhondda, 1997
595	K95AAX	Dennis Dart 9SDL3011	Wright Handy-bus	B35F	1993	Ex Rhondda, 1997
596	K96AAX	Dennis Dart 9SDL3016	Plaxton Pointer	B35F	1992	Ex Rhondda, 1997
597	K97XNY	Dennis Dart 9SDL3011	Plaxton Pointer(1995)	B35F	1992	Ex Rhondda, 1997
598	K98XNY	Dennis Dart 9.8SDL3017	Wright Handy-bus	B39F	1992	Ex Rhondda, 1997
599	J454JRH	Dennis Dart 9.8SDL3017	Plaxton Pointer	B40F	1991	Ex Rhondda, 1997

608	SKG908S	Leyland National 11351A/1R		B49F	1977	Ex National Welsh, 1991
609	PKG741R	Leyland National 11351A/1R(Volvo)		B49F	1977	Ex National Welsh, 1991
619	SKG923S	Leyland National 11351A/1R(DAF)		B49F	1978	Ex National Welsh, 1991
652	NOE573R	Leyland National 11351A/1R(Volvo)		B49F	1976	Ex Midland Red South, 1992
653	NOE572R	Leyland National 11351A/1R(DAF)		B49F	1977	Ex Midland Red South, 1992
654	NOE576R	Leyland National 11351A/1R		B49F	1976	Ex Midland Red South, 1992
658w	BPT903S	Leyland National 11351A/1R		B49F	1978	Ex Go-Ahead Northern, 1992
663	PHW985S	Leyland National 11351A/1R(DAF)		B52F	1978	Ex Cheltenham & Gloucester, 1995

681	J41GGB	Leyland Lynx LX2R11C15Z4S	Leyland Lynx 2	B51F	1991	Ex Rhondda, 1997
682	J42GGB	Leyland Lynx LX2R11C15Z4S	Leyland Lynx 2	B51F	1991	Ex Rhondda, 1997
686	F262WSD	Leyland Lynx LX112L10ZR1R	Leyland Lynx	B52F	1988	Ex Western Buses (AA), 1998
691	E87KGV	Leyland Lynx LX112L10ZR1R	Leyland Lynx	B52F	1988	Ex Rhondda, 1997
692	E62WDT	Leyland Lynx LX112TL11ZR1R	Leyland Lynx	B49F	1987	Ex Rhondda, 1997
693	E63WDT	Leyland Lynx LX112TL11ZR1R	Leyland Lynx	B49F	1987	Ex Rhondda, 1997
694	D109NDW	Leyland Lynx LX112TL11ZR1	Leyland Lynx	B48F	1987	Ex Cynon Valley, 1992
695	E113RBO	Leyland Lynx LX112TL11ZR1	Leyland Lynx	B48F	1987	Ex Cynon Valley, 1992
696	E114SDW	Leyland Lynx LX112TL11ZR1	Leyland Lynx	B48F	1987	Ex Cynon Valley, 1992
697	E115SDW	Leyland Lynx LX112TL11ZR1	Leyland Lynx	B48F	1988	Ex Cynon Valley, 1992
698	F74DCW	Leyland Lynx LX2R11C15Z4R	Leyland Lynx 2	DP45F	1989	Ex Cynon Valley, 1992

701-708

		Volvo B6-9.9M		Alexander Dash		B40F	1994		
701	L701FWO	**703**	L703FWO	**705**	L705FWO	**707**	L707FWO	**708**	L708FWO
702	L702FWO	**704**	L704FWO	**706**	L706FWO				

711-718

		Volvo B6-9m		Plaxton Pointer		B35F	1994	Ex Rhondda, 1997	
711	M71HHB	**714**	M74HHB	**715**	M75HHB	**716**	M76HHB	**718**	M78HHB
713	M73HHB								

719	L79CWO	Volvo B6-9.9M	Plaxton Pointer	B40F	1994	Ex Rhondda, 1997
721	L81CWO	Volvo B6-9.9M	Plaxton Pointer	B40F	1994	Ex Rhondda, 1997
722	L82CWO	Volvo B6-9.9M	Plaxton Pointer	B40F	1994	Ex Rhondda, 1997
744	A14RBL	Volvo Citybus B10M-50	East Lancashire (1995)	DP53F	1984	Ex Rhondda, 1997
745	A15RBL	Volvo B10M-56	Van Hool Alizée L	B51F	1994	Ex Rhondda, 1997
748	YLP528	Volvo B10M-61	Van Hool Alizée	C51FT	1983	Ex Rhondda (Parfitts), 1997

750-770

Volvo B10M-55 — Alexander PS — DP48F — 1995

750	M750LAX	755	M755LAX	759	M759LAX	763	M763LAX	767	M767RAX
751	M751LAX	756	M756LAX	760	M760LAX	764	M764LAX	768	M768RAX
752	M752LAX	757	M757LAX	761	M761LAX	765	M765RAX	769	M769RAX
753	M753LAX	758	M758LAX	762	M762LAX	766	M766RAX	770	M770RAX
754	M754LAX								

771-784

Volvo B10M-62 — Plaxton Premiére Interurban DP51F — 1996-97

771	P771TTG	774	P774TTG	778	R778CDW	781	R781CDW	783	R783CDW
772	P772TTG	775	R775CDW	779	R779CDW	782	R782CDW	784	R784CDW
773	P773TTG	776	R776CDW	780	R780CDW				

785-792

Volvo B10M-55 — Alexander PS — DP48F — 1998

785	R785DHB	788	R788DHB	790	R790DHB	791	R791DHB	792	R792DHB
787	R787DHB	789	R789DHB						

803	OHV719Y	Leyland Titan TNLXB2RR	Leyland	H44/27F	1983	Ex East London, 1997
804	NUW619Y	Leyland Titan TNLXB2RR	Leyland	H44/27F	1982	Ex East London, 1997
805	NUW651Y	Leyland Titan TNLXB2RR	Leyland	H44/27F	1982	Ex East London, 1997
806	KYV542X	Leyland Titan TNLXB2RR	Leyland	H44/27F	1982	Ex East London, 1997
807	NUW606Y	Leyland Titan TNLXB2RR	Leyland	H44/27F	1982	Ex East London, 1997
808	NUW646Y	Leyland Titan TNLXB2RR	Leyland	H44/27F	1982	Ex East London, 1997
809	A905SYE	Leyland Titan TNLXB2RR	Leyland	H44/29F	1983	Ex East London, 1998
825	TWS909T	Bristol VRT/SL3/6LXB	Eastern Coach Works	H43/31F	1979	Ex Cheltenham & Gloucester, 1992
827	A541HAC	Leyland Olympian ONLXB/1R	Eastern Coach Works	H43/31F	1983	Ex Midland Red South, 1993
828	A548HAC	Leyland Olympian ONLXB/1R	Eastern Coach Works	H43/31F	1983	Ex Midland Red South, 1993
829	A549HAC	Leyland Olympian ONLXB/1R	Eastern Coach Works	H43/31F	1983	Ex Midland Red South, 1993
830	AET185T	Bristol VRT/SL3/6LXB	Eastern Coach Works	H43/31F	1979	Ex East Midland, 1993
831w	DAK201V	Bristol VRT/SL3/501	Eastern Coach Works	H43/31F	1979	Ex East Midland, 1994
832	CBV6S	Bristol VRT/SL3/501(6LXB)	Eastern Coach Works	H43/31F	1977	Ex Ribble, 1994
833	DBV26W	Bristol VRT/SL3/6LXB	Eastern Coach Works	H43/31F	1980	Ex Ribble, 1994

834-844

Bristol VRT/SL3/501* — Eastern Coach Works — H43/31F — 1980 Ex National Welsh, 1991

*836 is fitted with a 6LXB engine

834	BUH232V	838w	GTX743W	841w	GTX748W	843	GTX750W	844	GTX753W
836	GTX738W						

845w	WAX194S	Bristol VRT/SL3/501(6LXB)	Eastern Coach Works	H43/31F	1977	Ex Ribble, 1994
846	KVF247V	Bristol VRT/SL3/6LXB	Eastern Coach Works	H43/31F	1980	Ex Cambus (Viscount), 1997
847	LWU466V	Bristol VRT/SL3/6LXB	Eastern Coach Works	H43/31F	1980	Ex Cambus (Viscount), 1997
860	KVF248V	Bristol VRT/SL3/6LXB	Eastern Coach Works	H43/31F	1980	Ex Cambus (Viscount), 1997
865	WDA1T	Leyland Titan TNLXB1RF	Park Royal	H43/29F	1978	Ex Stagecoach Selkent, 1994
866	WDA2T	Leyland Titan TNLXB1RF	Park Royal	H43/29F	1979	Ex Stagecoach Selkent, 1994
867	WDA5T	Leyland Titan TNLXB1RF	Park Royal	H43/29F	1979	Ex Stagecoach Selkent, 1994
868	AVK163V	Leyland Atlantean AN68A/2R	Alexander AL	H49/37F	1980	Ex Busways, 1995
869	AVK166V	Leyland Atlantean AN68A/2R	Alexander AL	H49/37F	1980	Ex Busways, 1995
870	AVK173V	Leyland Atlantean AN68A/2R	Alexander AL	H49/37F	1980	Ex Busways, 1995
871	VBA166S	Leyland Atlantean AN68A/1R	Northern Counties	H43/32F	1978	Ex Stagecoach Manchester, 1996
872w	VBA178S	Leyland Atlantean AN68A/1R	Northern Counties	H43/32F	1978	Ex Stagecoach Manchester, 1996
873	VBA188S	Leyland Atlantean AN68A/1R	Northern Counties	H43/32F	1978	Ex Stagecoach Manchester, 1996
874	VBA190S	Leyland Atlantean AN68A/1R	Northern Counties	H43/32F	1978	Ex Stagecoach Manchester, 1996
900	AAX465A	Leyland Tiger TRCTL11/3R	Plaxton Paramount 3200	C51F	1983	Ex National Welsh, 1991
906w	AAX544A	Leyland Tiger TRCTL11/3R	Plaxton Paramount 3200	C46F	1983	Ex National Welsh, 1991
907	AAX575A	Leyland Tiger TRCTL11/3R	Plaxton Paramount 3200	C46F	1983	Ex National Welsh, 1991
909	AAX538A	Leyland Tiger TRCTL11/3R	Plaxton Paramount 3200	C46F	1983	Ex National Welsh, 1991
912	AAX489A	Leyland Tiger TRCTL11/3R	Plaxton Paramount 3200	C46F	1983	Ex National Welsh, 1991

Opposite:- **The Stagecoach corporate livery is well able to carry a prominent and attractive style of route-branding lettering or the large Stagecoach name in addition to normal fleet name. This adaptability is shown by Red & White 909, AAL538A, as it loads passengers for the X74 service to Chepstow. The lower picture shows Red & White 705, L705FWO one of the 1994 intake of the model. Further examples of the Volvo B6 have been acquired with the Rhondda operation bringing into the fleet Plaxton Pointer examples.** *T S Powell*

913	A13RBL	Leyland Tiger TRBL10/2RZA	East Lancashire (1995)	DP53F	1990	Ex Rhondda, 1997	
914	AAX516A	Leyland Tiger TRCTL11/3R	Plaxton Paramount 3200	C46F	1983	Ex National Welsh, 1991	
916	CYJ492Y	Leyland Tiger TRCTL11/3R	Plaxton Paramount 3200	C50F	1983	Ex Stagecoach South, 1994	
917	CYJ493Y	Leyland Tiger TRCTL11/3R	Plaxton Paramount 3200	C50F	1983	Ex Stagecoach South, 1994	
918	A17RBL	Leyland Tiger TRBTL11/2RP	Duple Dominant	B55F	1988	Ex Rhondda, 1997	
920	A20RBL	Leyland Tiger TRBTL11/2RP	Plaxton Derwent II	B54F	1988	Ex Rhondda, 1997	
926	EWR656Y	Leyland Tiger TRBTL11/2R	Duple Dominant	DP47F	1983	Ex Rhondda, 1997	
935	A227MDD	Leyland Tiger TRCTL11/3R	Plaxton Paramount 3200	C51F	1984	Ex Cheltenham & Gloucester, 1994	

940-951

		Dennis Javelin 11SDA2133	Plaxton Premiére Interurban DP47F	1994

940	M940JBO	943	M943JBO	946	M946JBO	948	M948JBO	950	M950JBO
941	M941JBO	944	M944JBO	947	M947JBO	949	M949JBO	951	M951JBO
942	M942JBO	945	M945JBO						

952	H159EJU	Dennis Javelin 12SDA1907	Duple 320	C53F	1991	Ex Whites of Calver, 1995
953	F243OFP	Dennis Javelin 12SDA1907	Duple 320	C53F	1991	Ex Whites of Calver, 1995
954	HIL8410	Dennis Javelin 12SDA1907	Duple 320	C53F	1991	Ex Whites of Calver, 1995
955	M101CCD	Dennis Javelin 11SDL2133	Plaxton Premiere Interurban	DP47F	1994	Ex Stagecoach South, 1996
956	M107CCD	Dennis Javelin 11SDL2133	Plaxton Premiere Interurban	DP47F	1994	Ex Stagecoach South, 1996
973	GGM71W	Leyland Leopard PSU3F/4R	Plaxton Supreme IV Express	C49F	1981	Ex Rhondda, 1997
999	B973OSB	Dennis DorchesterSDA810	Plaxton Paramount 3500 II	C46FT	1985	Ex Rhondda, 1997

Ancilliary Vehicles:-

RW02	BTX332J	Leyland Leopard PSU4A/2R	Willowbrook BET	B F	1971	Ex National Welsh, 1991
RW03	TKG518J	Leyland Leopard PSU4A/2R	Willowbrook BET	B F	1971	Ex National Welsh, 1991
RW13	HJT45N	Bristol LH6L	Eastern Coach Works	B43F	1975	Ex Stagecoach South (EK), 1996
RW16	MUR214L	AEC Reliance 6U3ZR	Plaxton Elite III	C53F	1973	Ex Edmunds, Rassau, 1991

Previous Registrations:

A13RBL	G399PNN	AAX575A	SDW923Y
A14RBL	B176FFS, WLT444, B660EGG	AAX465A	SDW916Y
A15RBL	B947ASU	AAX489A	SDW928Y
A17RBL	F311RMH	B973OSB	B405OSB, 705DYE, B983EGG, WLT364
A20RBL	F604CET	CYJ492Y	XUF531Y, 401DCD
A227MDD	A71KDU, 552OHU, A873MRW, YJV806	CYJ493Y	XUF532Y, 2880CD, 402DCD
AAX516A	SDW927Y	HIL8410	E759JAY
AAX538A	SDW925Y	WAX194S	CBV8S
AAX544A	SDW922Y	YLP528	MSU571Y

The arrival of a further batch of Plaxton Interurbans in January 1998 is witnessed by Red & White 775, R775CDW pictured in Cardiff shortly after its entry into service. The model has been widely used by Stagecoach for express services, though the only such vehicle in the 1998 programme are articulated vehicles to be supplied with the quality Jonckheere Mistral product.
John Jones

Allocations:-

Aberdare (Cwmbach New Road, Cwmbach) - Red & White

Mercedes-Benz	303	307	310	319	320	322	326	328
	331	332	360	384				
Bristol RESL	391	392	393					
National 2	501	502	503	504	507	512	513	514
	515	516						

Brynmawr (Warwick Road) - Red & White

Mercedes-Benz	312	361	362	363	364	365	366	367
	368	369	370	371	376			
Volvo PS	775	776	778	779	780	781	782	783
	784							
Javelin Interurban	949	950	951					
Tiger	935							
Bristol VR	830	844	848					

Caerphilly (Bedwas House Ind Est, Bedwas) - Red & White

Mercedes-Benz	149	156	157	158	159	160	161	162
	169	170	171					
MetroRider	105							
National	475							
Volvo B6	711	712	713	714	715	716	717	718
	719	721	722					

Chepstow (Bulwark Road) - Red & White

Outstation - Cinderford

Mercedes-Benz	375						
National	427	442	449	619			
National 2	500						
Javelin Interurban	940	943	944	945	946	947	948
Tiger	900	907	909	912	916	917	926
Bristol VR	860						
Titan	804	806	806	807	808	809	
Olympian	203	204	205	827	828	829	

Crosskeys (Risca Road) - Red & White

Mercedes-Benz	334	335	336	359	383			
Volvo B10M PS	751	752	763	764	765	766	767	768
	769	770	771	772	773	774		
Atlantean	873							
Bristol VR	834	836	843	846				

Cwmbran (St David's Road) - Red & White

Outstations - Abergavenny and Brecon

Mercedes-Benz	305	306	309	313	315	316	317	321
	323	324	325	330	344	345	346	347
	348	349	350	351	352	353	354	355
	356	357	358	377	378	379	380	381
	382							
National	423	434	608	609				
National 2	505	508	517					
Javelin Interurban	955	956						
Volvo B10M PS	785	786	787	788	789	790	791	792
Lynx	694	695	696	697	698			
Bristol VR	832	833						
Atlantean	868	869	870	871	874			

Merthyr Tydfil (Merthyr Industrial Estate, Pant) - Red & White

Mercedes-Benz	301	302	311	314	338	339	340	341
	342	343	372	373	374			
Volvo B6	701	702	703	704	705			
Volvo B10M PS	750	753	754	755	756	757	758	
	759	760	761	762				
National 2	506	510						
Volvo Citibus	744							
Javelin Interurban	941	942						
Tiger	914							

New Tredegar (Jones Street, Phillipstown) - Red & White - Rail Link ♠ - Trawscambria ♦

Mercedes-Benz	16♠							
MetroRider	252	255	256	257♠	258			
' Volvo B10M	748♦							
Dart	440	556	557	558	562	563	566	570
Swift	400	402						

Pengam (Commercial Street) - Red & White

Volvo B6	706	707	708
Volvo B10M	745		
Javalin Coach	952	953	954
Bristol VR	825		

Porth (Aberrhondda Road) - Rhondda Trawscambria ♦

Mercedes-Benz	150	151	152	153	154	155	163	164
	165	166	167	168	220	230		
MetroRider	106	112	114	254				
Swift	401							
Dart	554	559	560	561	564	565	567	568
	569	583	584	585	586	587	588	589
	590	591	592	593	594	595	596	597
	598	599						
Leopard	973							
National	497	499						
Lynx	681	682	686	691	692	693		
Prisma	550	551						
Tiger	913	918	920					
Dorchester	999♦							

Ross on Wye - Red & White

Mercedes-Benz	304	318	327	329	337
National	653	654	663		
Titan	865	866	867		
Olympian	206	207	208		

Unallocated

National	478	658		
Tiger	902	906		
National	652			
Bristol VR	831	838	841	845
Atlantean	872			
Titan	803	805		

RIBBLE

Stagecoach Ribble, Frenchwood Avenue, Preston, Lancashire, PR1 4LU.
Burnley & Pendle Transport Co Ltd, Frenchwood Avenue, Preston, Lancashire, PR1 4LU.

105	P977UBV				Volvo B10M-62			Plaxton Premiére Interurban DP51F	1996		
106	P978UBV				Volvo B10M-62			Plaxton Premiére Interurban DP51F	1996		
107	P979UBV				Volvo B10M-62			Plaxton Premiére Interurban DP51F	1996		

108-114
Volvo B10M-62 — Plaxton Premiére Interurban DP51F — 1997

| 108 | P108DCW | 110 | P110DCW | 112 | P112DCW | 113 | P113DCW | 114 | P114DCW |
| 109 | P109DCW | | | | | | | | |

138-144
Dennis Javelin 11SDL2129 — Plaxton Premiére Interurban DP47F — 1993

| 138 | L138BFV | 140 | L140BFV | 142 | L142BFV | 143 | L143BFV | 144 | L144BFV |
| 139 | L139BFV | 141 | L141BFV | | | | | | |

145-161
Dennis Javelin 11SDL2133 — Plaxton Premiére Interurban DP47F — 1993

145	L145BFV	149	L149BFV	153	L153BFV	157	L157BFV	159	L159CCW
146	L146BFV	150	L150BFV	155	L155BFV	158	L158BFV	161	L161CCW
148	L148BFV	151	L151BFV	156	L156BFV				

162-168
Dennis Javelin 11SDL2133 — Plaxton Premiére Interurban DP47F — 1994 — Ex Stagecoach South, 1994

| 162 | L101SDY | 164 | L104SDY | 166 | L102SDY | 167 | L105SDY | 168 | L107SDY |
| 163 | L103SDY | 165 | L106SDY | | | | | | |

176-180
Dennis Lance SLF 11SDA3201 — Berkhof 2000 — B35F — 1996

| 176 | N176LCK | 177 | N177LCK | 178 | N178LCK | 179 | N179LCK | 180 | N180LCK |

181-196
Dennis Lance 11SDA3101 — Alexander PS — B45F — 1992 — Ex East London, 1997

181	J101WSC	185	J105WSC	188	J108WSC	191	J411WSC	194	J114WSC
182	J102WSC	186	J106WSC	189	J109WSC	192	J112WSC	195	J115WSC
183	J103WSC	187	J107WSC	190	J110WSC	193	J113WSC	196	J116WSC
184	J104WSC								

237-256
Volvo B6-9.9M — Alexander Dash — DP40F — 1993

| 237 | L237CCW | 240 | L240CCW | 251 | L251CCK | 253 | L253CCK | 256 | L256CCK |
| 239 | L239CCW | 241 | L241CCK | 252 | L252CCK | 255 | L255CCK | | |

Stagecoach Express lettering is used by Ribble for the commuter services into Manchester from Lancashire and the north as well as on inter-town services. Service 152 links Preston with Burnley, and Ribble 161, L161CCW is seen at the Burnley end of the route.
Richard Godfrey

257-265		Volvo B6-9.9M		Alexander Dash		DP40F	1993 Ex Fife Scottish, 1994		
257	L667MSF	259	L669MSF	261	L661MSF	263	L663MSF	265	L665MSF
258	L668MSF	260	L660HKS	262	L662MSF	264	L664MSF		

277-287		Volvo B6-9.9M		Alexander Dash		B40F	1993 Ex Cumberland 1994-96		
277	L277JAO	279	L279JAO	283	L283JAO	285	L272LHH	287	L274LHH
278	L278JAO	281	L281JAO	284	L271LHH	286	L273LHH		

293	J263KRN	Leyland Swift ST2R44C97A4	Reeve Burgess Harrier	B39F	1991	Ex Hyndburn 1996
294	J264KRN	Leyland Swift ST2R44C97A4	Reeve Burgess Harrier	B39F	1991	Ex Hyndburn 1996
295	G767CDU	Leyland Swift LBM6T/2RA	Reeve Burgess Harrier	B39F	1990	Ex Hyndburn 1996
296	H36YCW	Leyland Swift ST2R44C97A4	Reeve Burgess Harrier	B39F	1990	Ex Hyndburn 1996
297	H37YCW	Leyland Swift ST2R44C97A4	Reeve Burgess Harrier	B39F	1990	Ex Hyndburn 1996
298	H38YCW	Leyland Swift ST2R44C97A4	Reeve Burgess Harrier	B39F	1990	Ex Hyndburn 1996
299	H39YCW	Leyland Swift ST2R44C97A4	Reeve Burgess Harrier	B39F	1990	Ex Hyndburn 1996

333	FUH33V	Leyland National 2 NL116L11/1R		B49F	1980	Ex Burnley & Pendle, 1997
339	BUH239V	Leyland National 2 NL106L11/1R		B44F	1980	Ex Burnley & Pendle, 1997
340	BUH240V	Leyland National 2 NL106L11/1R		B44F	1980	Ex Burnley & Pendle, 1997

344-349		Leyland National 2 NL116L11/1R		B52F		1980	Ex Burnley & Pendle, 1997		
344	XRN44V	346	XRN46V	347	XRN47V	348	XRN48V	349	XRN49V
345	XRN45V								

357	KHH377W	Leyland National 2 NL116L11/1R	B52F	1980	Ex Cumberland, 1993
370	HHH370V	Leyland National 2 NL116L11/1R	B52F	1980	Ex Cumberland, 1993
385	RRM384X	Leyland National 2 NL116AL11/1R	DP52F	1982	Ex Cumberland, 1993
386	RRM386X	Leyland National 2 NL116AL11/1R	B52F	1982	Ex Cumberland, 1993
387	SHH387X	Leyland National 2 NL116AL11/1R	B52F	1982	Ex Cumberland, 1993
390	SHH390X	Leyland National 2 NL116AL11/1R	B52F	1982	Ex Cumberland, 1993
396	WAO396Y	Leyland National 2 NL116HLXB/1R	B52F	1982	Ex Cumberland, 1993
397	SNS831W	Leyland National 2 NL116AL11/1R	B52F	1981	Ex Cumberland, 1993
399	SHH388X	Leyland National 2 NL116AL11/1R	B52F	1982	Ex Cumberland, 1993

401-406		Volvo B10M-55		Alexander P		DP53F*	1988 Ex Burnley & Pendle, 1997		
							*401 is B53F		
401	E61JFV	403	E63JFV	404	E64JFV	405	E65JFV	406	E66JFV
402	E62JFV								

407	G67PFR	Volvo B10M-55	East Lancashire EL2000	B51F	1990	Ex Burnley & Pendle, 1997
408	G68PFR	Volvo B10M-55	East Lancashire EL2000	B51F	1990	Ex Burnley & Pendle, 1997

417-423		Volvo B10M-55		Alexander PS		B51F	1991 Ex Burnley & Pendle, 1997		
417	H617ACK	419	H619ACK	421	H621ACK	422	H622ACK	423	H623ACK
418	H618ACK	420	H620ACK						

424	J24MCW	Volvo B10M-50	East Lancashire EL2000	B45F	1992	Ex Burnley & Pendle, 1997
425	J25MCW	Volvo B10M-50	East Lancashire EL2000	B45F	1992	Ex Burnley & Pendle, 1997
426	K26WBV	Volvo B10M-50	East Lancashire EL2000	B45F	1993	Ex Burnley & Pendle, 1997
427	K27WBV	Volvo B10M-50	East Lancashire EL2000	B45F	1993	Ex Burnley & Pendle, 1997

428-442		Volvo B10M-55		Alexander PS		DP48F	1994-95		
428	M782PRS	431	M231TBV	434	M234TBV	437	M794PRS	440	M797PRS
429	M783PRS	432	M232TBV	435	M235TBV	438	M795PRS	441	M798PRS
430	M230TBV	433	M233TBV	436	M236TBV	439	M796PRS	442	M799PRS

Opposite:- **In 1996 Ribble Buses won a tender to operate low floor buses on Route M10 which links Salford, Eccles and Brookhouse with Manchester. Berkhof bodywork, to the style already delivered to Stagecoach South, was chosen for the five buses. Shown here is 177, N177LCK. The type was augmented by Alexander-bodied Dennis Lances that had previously worked with East London.** *Tony Wilson*
Opposite, bottom:- **The integration of Burnley & Pendle fleet into the Ribble took place as planned during 1997, and several of the former Burnley vehicles gained corporate livery during the year. Pictured in Burnley is 1307, F107XCW, one of the fifteen Volvo B10M double-deck buses supplied to Burnley. In recent months several of the buses from that fleet have been moved into Ribble, and are expected to be based at a variety of depots in due course.** *Malc McDonald*

451	M451VCW	Volvo B10M-55	Alexander PS	B48F	1995	
452	M452VCW	Volvo B10M-55	Alexander PS	B48F	1995	
453	M453VCW	Volvo B10M-55	Alexander PS	B48F	1995	
454	M454VCW	Volvo B10M-55	Alexander PS	B48F	1995	
464	K740DAO	Volvo B10M-55	Alexander PS	B48F	1994	Ex Cumberland, 1996

465-472 — Volvo B10M-55 — Alexander PS — B49F — 1996

465	P127XCN	467	P129XCN	469	P131XCN	471	P133XCN	472	P134XCN
466	P128XCN	468	P130XCN	470	P132XCN				

473-482 — Volvo B10M-55 — Alexander PS — B49F — 1997

473	R473MCW	475	R475MCW	477	R477MCW	479	R479MCW	481	R481MCW
474	R474MCW	476	R476MCW	478	R478MCW	480	R480MCW	482	R482MCW

568-591 — Mercedes-Benz 709D — Alexander Sprint — B23F* — 1990   579/80 ex Magicbus, 1990   *568-572 are DP25F

568	G568PRM	573	G573PRM	578	G578PRM	583	G183PAO	588	G188PAO
569	G569PRM	574	G574PRM	579	G179PAO	584	G184PAO	589	G189PAO
570	G570PRM	575	G575PRM	580	G180PAO	585	G185PAO	590	G190PAO
571	G571PRM	576	G576PRM	581	G181PAO	586	G186PAO	591	G191PAO
572	G572PRM	577	G577PRM	582	G182PAO	587	G187PAO		

595-608 — Mercedes-Benz 709D — Alexander Sprint — B25F — 1993

595	K115XHG	598	K118XHG	600	K120XHG	605	L125DRN	608	L128DRN
596	K116XHG	599	L119DRN						

610-628 — Mercedes-Benz 709D — Alexander Sprint — B23F — 1992-93

610	K610UFR	613	K613UFR	617	K617UFR	620	K620UFR	627	K627UFR
611	K611UFR	614	K614UFR	618	K618UFR	621	K621UFR	628	K628UFR
612	K612UFR	616	K616UFR	619	K619UFR	624	K624UFR		

629-637 — Mercedes-Benz 709D — Alexander Sprint — B25F — 1993

629	L629BFV	631	L631BFV	633	L633BFV	635	L635BFV	637	K112XHG
630	L630BFV	632	L632BFV	634	L634BFV	636	L636BFV		

638-644 — Mercedes-Benz 709D — Alexander Sprint — B25F — 1996

638	N519BJA	640	N451VOD	642	N453VOD	643	N454VOD	644	N455VOD
639	N520BJA	641	N452VOD						

647-659 — Mercedes-Benz 709D — Alexander Sprint — B25F — 1996

647	N456VOD	650	N459VOD	653	N462VOD	656	N465VOD	658	N467VOD
648	N457VOD	651	N460VOD	654	N463VOD	657	N466VOD	659	N468VOD
649	N458VOD	652	N461VOD	655	N464VOD				

660-667 — Mercedes-Benz 709D — Alexander Sprint — B25F — 1996

660	N201LFV	662	N194LFV	664	N196LFV	666	N198LFV	667	N199LFV
661	N202LFV	663	N195LFV	665	N197LFV				

668-672 — Mercedes-Benz Vario O814 — Plaxton Beaver 2 — B27F — 1997

668	R668LFV	669	R669LFV	670	R670LFV	671	R671LFV	672	R672LFV

Opposite, top:- **Ribble took just five of the new Mercedes-Benz Vario model and these have been placed in service at Blackburn where they are expected to shortly replace the former Hyndburn Iveco minibuses which will move to Stagecoach Devon. Pictured at Accrington bus station is 669, R669LFV.**
Paul Wigan
Opposite, bottom:- **Burnley & Pendle took delivery of East Lancashire-bodied Volvo B10M buses as well as Alexander products. Now in corporate livery is 424, J24MCW which is seen in the town.**

675	K75XCW	Optare MetroRider MR03	Optare	B29F	1993	Ex Burnley & Pendle, 1997
676	J176MCW	Optare MetroRider MR09	Optare	B23F	1992	Ex Burnley & Pendle, 1997
677	J177MCW	Optare MetroRider MR09	Optare	B23F	1992	Ex Burnley & Pendle, 1997
678	L178KHG	Optare MetroRider MR17	Optare	B29F	1994	Ex Burnley & Pendle, 1997
679	L179KHG	Optare MetroRider MR17	Optare	B29F	1994	Ex Burnley & Pendle, 1997
702w	WSK219	AEC Routemaster R2RH	Park Royal	H36/28R	1960	Ex United Counties, 1992

714-722

		Iveco TurboDaily 59.12	Mellor	B27F	1996	Ex Hyndburn, 1996

714w	N188GFR	716w	N190GFR	718w	N464HRN	720w	L447FFR	722w	L446FFR
715w	N189GFR	717w	N463HRN	719w	L448FFR	721w	L445FFR		

776w	XSU906	Mercedes-Benz 709D	Reeve Burgess Beaver	C19F	1987	Ex Burnley & Pendle, 1997
778	H78CFV	Mercedes-Benz 811D	Alexander AM	B31F	1991	Ex Burnley & Pendle, 1997
779	H79CFV	Mercedes-Benz 811D	Alexander AM	B31F	1991	Ex Burnley & Pendle, 1997
784w	E84HRN	Mercedes-Benz 709D	Robin Hood	B29F	1987	Ex Burnley & Pendle, 1997

785-790

		Mercedes-Benz 811D	Robin Hood	B29F	1987-88	Ex Burnley & Pendle, 1997

785	E85HRN	787	E87HRN	788	E88HRN	789	E89HRN	790	E90JHG
786	E86HRN								

791	E91LBV	Mercedes-Benz 709D	Alexander AM	B25F	1988	Ex Burnley & Pendle, 1997
792	E92LHG	Mercedes-Benz 709D	Alexander AM	B25F	1988	Ex Burnley & Pendle, 1997
793	E93LHG	Mercedes-Benz 709D	Alexander AM	B25F	1988	Ex Burnley & Pendle, 1997
794	E94LHG	Mercedes-Benz 709D	Alexander AM	B25F	1988	Ex Burnley & Pendle, 1997
796	G96MRN	Mercedes-Benz 811D	Reeve Burgess Beaver	B31F	1990	Ex Burnley & Pendle, 1997
797	G97MRN	Mercedes-Benz 811D	Reeve Burgess Beaver	B31F	1990	Ex Burnley & Pendle, 1997
798	G98PCK	Mercedes-Benz 811D	Reeve Burgess Beaver	B31F	1990	Ex Burnley & Pendle, 1997

815-841

		Leyland National 2 NL106L11/1R		B44F	1980	813/4/42 ex Cumberland, 1993

815	YRN815V	820	YRN820V	831w	DBV831W	835	DBV835W	841	DBV841W
817	YRN817V	829	DBV829W	832	DBV832W	839	DBV839W		

848w	JCK848W	Leyland National 2 NL106AL11/1R		B44F	1981	
866	LFR866X	Leyland National 2 NL106AL11/1R		B44F	1981	
871	LFR871X	Leyland National 2 NL106AL11/1R		B44F	1981	
877	LFR877X	Leyland National 2 NL106AL11/1R		B44F	1981	
889	ARN889Y	Leyland National 2 NL116HLXB/1R		DP49F	1983	
890	ARN890Y	Leyland National 2 NL116HLXB/1R		B52F	1983	
895	CEO720W	Leyland National 2 NL116L11/1R		B49F	1980	Ex Cumberland, 1993
901	AFM1W	Leyland National 2 NL116AL11/2R	East Lancs Greenway(1992)	B48F	1981	Ex Hyndburn, 1996
902	WPC316X	Leyland National 2 NL116AL11/2R	East Lancs Greenway(1992)	B48F	1981	Ex Hyndburn, 1996
903	NOE595R	Leyland National 11351/1R	East Lancs Greenway(1992)	B48F	1976	Ex Hyndburn, 1996
904	CWX669T	Leyland National 11351A/1R	East Lancs Greenway(1992)	B48F	1981	Ex Hyndburn, 1996
905	MDS866V	Leyland National 2 NL116L11/1R		B52F	1980	Ex Western Buses, 1996
906	MDS859V	Leyland National 2 NL116L11/1R		B48F	1980	Ex Western Buses, 1996
907	MDS858V	Leyland National 2 NL116L11/1R		B48F	1980	Ex Western Buses, 1996
908	RFS582V	Leyland National 2 NL116L11/1R		B52F	1980	Ex Western Buses, 1996
909	RFS584V	Leyland National 2 NL116L11/1R		B52F	1980	Ex Western Buses, 1996
910	MSO17W	Leyland National 2 NL116L11/1R		B48F	1981	Ex Western Buses, 1996

1030-1043

		Leyland Leopard PSU4E/4R	East Lancashire	B47F	1978-80	Ex Burnley & Pendle, 1997

1030w	MFV30T	1036	MFV36T	1039w	DBV39W	1041w	DBV41W	1043w	DBV43W
1035w	MFV35T	1038w	DBV38W	1040w	DBV40W	1042w	DBV42W		

1057w	VFV7V	Leyland Leopard PSU3E/4R	Duple Dominant II	C53F	1979	Ex Burnley & Pendle, 1997
1122	J122AHH	Volvo B10M-60	Plaxton Expressliner	C46FT	1992	Ex Cumberland, 1995
1123	J123AHH	Volvo B10M-60	Plaxton Expressliner	C46FT	1992	Ex Cumberland, 1995
1124	J124AHH	Volvo B10M-60	Plaxton Expressliner	C46FT	1992	Ex Cumberland, 1995
1164	M164SCK	Volvo B10M-62	Plaxton Expressliner 2	C46FT	1994	
1165	M165SCK	Volvo B10M-62	Plaxton Expressliner 2	C46FT	1994	
1201	SND432X	Leyland Atlantean AN68A/1R	Northern Counties	H43/32F	1981	Ex Stagecoach Manchester, 1996
1202w	FVR294V	Leyland Atlantean AN68A/1R	Northern Counties	H43/32F	1981	Ex Stagecoach Manchester, 1996
1205	LFV205X	Leyland Atlantean AN68C/2R	East Lancashire	H50/36F	1981	Ex Lancaster, 1993
1210	GBV110N	Leyland Atlantean AN68/2R	Alexander AL	H49/35F	1975	Ex Hyndburn, 1996
1211	GBV101N	Leyland Atlantean AN68/2R	Alexander AL	H49/35F	1974	Ex Hyndburn, 1996

The Leyland Olympian has firmly established itself as the main double-deck bus to meet Stagecoach's requirement. As low-floor double-deck buses are needed, the choice has turned to Dennis while the future model from Volvo remains unknown. Pictured in Manchester Square, Blackpool is 2196, H196WFR. *Paul Wigan*

1235-1239

| | | | | | | | | | | Leyland Atlantean AN68C/1R | East Lancashire | H46/30F | 1980-81 Ex Hyndburn, 1996 |

1235	RGV40W	**1236**	RBJ36W	**1237**	RGV37W	**1238**	RGV38W	**1239**	RGV39W

1296w	VCW196V	Leyland Atlantean AN68A/1R	East Lancashire	H45/33F	1979	Ex Hyndburn, 1996
1301	E101JFV	Volvo Citybus B10M-50	Alexander RV	DPH47/35F	1988	Ex Burnley & Pendle, 1997
1302	E102JFV	Volvo Citybus B10M-50	Alexander RV	DPH47/35F	1988	Ex Burnley & Pendle, 1997

1303-1312

| | | | | | | | | | | Volvo Citybus B10M-50 | Alexander RV | H47/37F | 1989 | Ex Burnley & Pendle, 1997 |

1303	F103XCW	**1305**	F105XCW	**1307**	F107XCW	**1309**	F109XCW	**1311**	F111XCW
1304	F104XCW	**1306**	F106XCW	**1308**	F108XCW	**1310**	F110XCW	**1312**	F112XCW

1313	H113ABV	Volvo Citybus B10M-50	Alexander RV	H47/37F	1991	Ex Burnley & Pendle, 1997
1314	H114ABV	Volvo Citybus B10M-50	Alexander RV	DPH47/35F	1991	Ex Burnley & Pendle, 1997
1315	H115ABV	Volvo Citybus B10M-50	Alexander RV	DPH47/35F	1991	Ex Burnley & Pendle, 1997

1481	TRN481V	Leyland Atlantean AN68A/1R	Eastern Coach Works	H43/31F	1980	Ex Cumberland, 1993
2021w	CBV21S	Bristol VRT/SL3/501(6LXB)	Eastern Coach Works	H43/31F	1977	
2030	DBV30W	Bristol VRT/SL3/6LXB	Eastern Coach Works	H43/31F	1980	
2040w	FDV813V	Bristol VRT/SL3/6LXB	Eastern Coach Works	H43/31F	1980	Ex Magicbus, 1990
2042	RRP858R	Bristol VRT/SL3/501	Eastern Coach Works	H43/31F	1977	Ex United Counties, 1990
2043w	FDV817V	Bristol VRT/SL3/6LXB	Eastern Coach Works	H43/31F	1980	Ex Magicbus, 1990
2044	FDV833V	Bristol VRT/SL3/6LXB	Eastern Coach Works	H43/31F	1980	Ex Magicbus, 1990
2045	FDV784V	Bristol VRT/SL3/6LXB	Eastern Coach Works	H43/31F	1980	Ex Magicbus, 1990
2051	LFJ882W	Bristol VRT/SL3/6LXC	Eastern Coach Works	H43/31F	1980	Ex United Counties, 1993
2052	LFJ883W	Bristol VRT/SL3/6LXC	Eastern Coach Works	H43/31F	1980	Ex United Counties, 1993
2053	LFJ858W	Bristol VRT/SL3/6LXB	Eastern Coach Works	H43/31F	1980	Ex United Counties, 1993
2054w	LFJ859W	Bristol VRT/SL3/6LXB	Eastern Coach Works	H43/31F	1980	Ex United Counties, 1993
2055	LFJ885W	Bristol VRT/SL3/6LXC	Eastern Coach Works	H43/31F	1980	Ex United Counties, 1993
2056	LFJ866W	Bristol VRT/SL3/6LXB	Eastern Coach Works	H43/31F	1980	Ex United Counties, 1993
2057	LFJ861W	Bristol VRT/SL3/6LXB	Eastern Coach Works	H43/31F	1980	Ex United Counties, 1993
2058	LFJ884W	Bristol VRT/SL3/6LXC	Eastern Coach Works	H43/31F	1980	Ex United Counties, 1993
2095	OSR195R	Bristol VRT/LL3/6LXB	Alexander AL	H49/35F	1977	Ex Burnley & Pendle, 1997
2097	OSR197R	Bristol VRT/LL3/6LXB	Alexander AL	H49/35F	1977	Ex Burnley & Pendle, 1997

2101-2132

| | | | | | | | | Leyland Olympian ONLXB/1R* | Eastern Coach Works | H45/32F | 1981-83 *2124-30 are ONLXBT/1R |

2101 GFR101W	**2108** JFR8W	**2114** OFV14X	**2122** OFV22X	**2127** VRN827Y
2103 JFR3W	**2109** JFR9W	**2115** OFV15X	**2123** OFV23X	**2128** VRN828Y
2104 JFR4W	**2110** JFR10W	**2118** OFV18X	**2124** SCK224X	**2130** VRN830Y
2105 JFR5W	**2111** JFR11W	**2119** OFV19X	**2125** SCK225X	**2131** DBV131Y
2106 JFR6W	**2112** JFR12W	**2120** OFV20X	**2126** SCK226X	**2132** DBV132Y
2107 JFR7W	**2113** JFR13W	**2121** OFV21X		

2135 CWR525Y	Leyland Olympian ONLXB/1R	Eastern Coach Works	H45/32F	1983 Ex Hyndburn, 1996
2136 CWR526Y	Leyland Olympian ONLXB/1R	Eastern Coach Works	H45/32F	1983 Ex Hyndburn, 1996

2137-2152

Leyland Olympian ONLXB/1R   Eastern Coach Works   H45/32F   1983-84

2137 DBV137Y	**2142** A142MRN	**2143** A143MRN	**2145** A145OFR	**2152** B152TRN

2156-2178

Leyland Olympian ONLXB/1R   Eastern Coach Works   DPH41/26F   1984-85

2156 A156OFR	**2158** A158OFR	**2171** C171ECK	**2173** C173ECK	**2178** C178ECK
2157 A157OFR	**2159** A159OFR	**2172** C172ECK		

2187 G187JHG	Leyland Olympian ONLXB/2RZ	Alexander RL	DPH51/31F	1989
2188 G188JHG	Leyland Olympian ONLXB/2RZ	Alexander RL	DPH51/31F	1989
2193 H193WFR	Leyland Olympian ON2R50G16Z4	Alexander RL	H51/36F	1990
2195 H195WFR	Leyland Olympian ON2R50G16Z4	Alexander RL	H51/36F	1990
2196 H196WFR	Leyland Olympian ON2R50G16Z4	Alexander RL	H51/36F	1990
2197 H197WFR	Leyland Olympian ON2R50G16Z4	Alexander RL	H51/36F	1990
2198 J198HFR	Leyland Olympian ON2R56G13Z4	Alexander RL	DPH43/27F	1991

2213-2222

Leyland Olympian ONLXB/1R   Alexander RL   H45/32F   1984-85 Ex Highland Scottish, 1991

2213 A978OST	**2215** B891UAS	**2220** B896UAS	**2221** B897UAS	**2222** B898UAS
2214 A979OST	**2218** B894UAS			

2224-2235

Volvo Olympian YN2RV18Z4   Northern Counties Palatine   H49/33F   1996

2224 P224VCK	**2227** P227VCK	**2230** P230VCK	**2232** P232VCK	**2234** P234VCK
2225 P225VCK	**2228** P228VCK	**2231** P231VCK	**2233** P233VCK	**2235** P235VCK
2226 P226VCK	**2229** P229VCK			

2236-2245

Volvo Olympian YN2RV18Z4   Alexander RL   H45/27F   1996

2236 P260VPN	**2238** P262VPN	**2240** P270VPN	**2242** P272VPN	**2244** P274VPN
2237 P261VPN	**2239** P263VPN	**2241** P271VPN	**2243** P273VPN	**2245** P275VPN

2246-2268

Volvo Olympian   Alexander RL   H45/27F   1997

2246 R246NBV	**2251** R251NBV	**2256** R256NBV	**2261** R261NBV	**2265** R265NBV
2247 R247NBV	**2252** R252NBV	**2257** R257NBV	**2262** R262NBV	**2266** R266NBV
2248 R248NBV	**2253** R253NBV	**2258** R258NBV	**2263** R263NBV	**2267** R267NBV
2249 R249NBV	**2254** R254NBV	**2259** R259NBV	**2264** R264NBV	**2268** R268NBV
2250 R250NBV	**2255** R255NBV	**2260** R260NBV		

Previous Registrations:

XSU906	E206FRN	WSK219	WLT528

Allocations:-

Blackburn (George Street)

Iveco	714	715	716	717	718	719	720	721
	722							
Mercedes-Benz	570	577	578	583	598	599	605	
	620	621	624	628	630	631	668	669
	670	671	672					
National	831	833	848	907	910			
Greenway	901	902	903	904				
Volvo PS	430	431	432	435				
Volvo B6	237	239	240	241	257	260	261	263
	264	284	285	286	287			

Atlantean	1210	1211					
Bristol VR	2030	2045					
Olympian	2103	2104	2106	2110	2111	2114	2118	2127
	2130	2142	2143	2171			

Bolton (Goodwin Street)

MetroRider	676	677					
Mercedes-Benz	571	575	576	579	581	582	584	585
	586	587	588	589	590	591	660	661
	662	663	664	665	666	667		
National	370	386	387	390	817	832	839	841
	857	858	866	905	906	909		
Lance	176	177	178	179	180	181	182	183
	184	185	186	187	188	189	190	191
	192	193	194	195	196			
Volvo PS	436	437	438	439	440	441	442	451
	452	465	466	467	468	469	470	471
	472							
Atlantean	1235	1237	1238	1239				
Olympian	2112	2121	2125	2135	2136			

Burnley(Colne Road) - Stagecoach Ribble - Stagecoach Burnley & Pendle §

MetroRider	675§	678§	679§					
Mercedes-Benz	778§	779§	785§	786§	787§	788§	789§	790§
	791§	792§	793§	794§	796§	797§	798§	
National	333§	339§	340§	344	345	346§	347	348
	349§							
Javelin	144	145	146	148	149	150	151	153
	155	156	157	158	159	162	163	164
	165	166	167	168				
Leopard	1036							
Volvo Bus	401§	402§	403§	404§	405§	406§	407§	408§
	417§	418§	419§	420§	421§	422§	423§	424§
	425§	426§	427§	473§	474§	475§	476§	477§
	478§	479§	480§	481§	482§			
Volvo B10M DD	1301§	1302§	1303	1304	1305	1306§	1307§	1308§
	1309§	1310§	1311§	1312§	1313§	1314	1315	
Olympian	2101	2108	2122	2156	2172	2173	2198	2246§
	2247§	2248§	2249§	2250§	2251§	2252§	2253§	2254§
	2255§							

Fleetwood-based services have expanded from the Zippy services of a few years ago requiring full-sized buses now, and took several Olympians for a period early in 1997. Photographed in Poulton on service F7 is Volvo B10M 435, M235TBV. Since the picture was taken the vehicle has been re-allocated to Blackburn.
Paul Wigan

Chorley (Eaves Lane)

Mercedes-Benz	573	580	608	618	619	629	633	634
	635	636						
National	357	385	396	829	871	895		
Atlantean	1481							
Olympian	2105	2109	2120	2123	2124	2126	2128	2157
	2193	2195	2196	2197	2213	2214	2215	2218
	2236	2237	2238	2239	2256	2257	2258	2259
	2260	2261	2262	2263	2264	2265	2266	2267
	2268							

Clitheroe (Pimlico Road)

Mercedes-Benz	568	595	596					
National	815	908						
Volvo PS	433	434	453					
Bristol VR	2042	2043	2044	2051	2052	2053	2055	2056
	2057	2058						
Olympian	2113	2158	2159	2178				

Fleetwood (Sidings Road)

Mercedes-Benz 709	574	610	611	612	613	614	632
	637	638	639	640			
Volvo B6	262	277	278	281	283		
Volvo PS	428	429	454	464			

Preston (Selbourne Street)

Outstations - Garstang and Poulton-le-Fylde

Mercedes-Benz	569	572	600	616	617	627	641	642
	643	644	647	648	649	650	651	652
	653	654	655	656	657	658	659	
Volvo B6	251	252	253	255	256	258	259	265
	279							
National	397	399	820	835	877	889	890	
Javelin	138	139	140	141	142	143	161	
Volvo Interurban	105	106	107	108	109	110	112	113
	114							
Expressliner	1122	1123	1124	1164	1165			
Atlantean	1201	1205	1236					
Olympian	2107	2115	2119	2131	2132	2137	2145	2152
	2187	2188	2220	2221	2222	2224	2225	2226
	2227	2228	2229	2230	2231	2232	2233	2234
	2235	2240	2241	2242	2243	2244	2245	

Unlicenced

Swift	293	294	295	296	297	298	299	
Mercedes-Benz	776	784						
Leopard	1030	1035	1038	1039	1040	1041	1042	1043
	1057							
National	814	831	833	848				
Atlantean	1202	1296						
Routemaster	702							
Bristol VR	2021	2040	2043	2054	2095	2097		

SELKENT

South East London and Kent Bus Company, 180 Bromley Road,
Catford, London SE6 2XA

601-640

Dennis Dart 9.8SDL3054   Alexander Dash   B40F   1995-96

601	N601KGF	609	N609KGF	617	P617PGP	625	P625PGP	633	P633PGP
602	N602KGF	610	N610KGF	618	P618PGP	626	P626PGP	634	P634PGP
603	N603KGF	611	N611LGC	619	P619PGP	627	P627PGP	636	P636PGP
604	N604KGF	612	N612LGC	620	P620PGP	628	P628PGP	637	P637PGP
605	N605KGF	613	N613LGC	621	P621PGP	629	P629PGP	638	P638PGP
606	N606KGF	614	N614LGC	622	P622PGP	630	P630PGP	639	P639PGP
607	N607KGF	615	P615PGP	623	P623PGP	631	P631PGP	640	P640PGP
608	N608KGF	616	P616PGP	624	P624PGP	632	P632PGP		

DRL110-127

Dennis Dart 9SDL3024   Plaxton Pointer   B34F   1993   Ex East London, 1997

110	K110SRH	117	K117SRH	120	K120SRH	123	K123SRH	127	K127SRH
112	K112SRH	118	K118SRH						

DT31-55

Dennis Dart 8.5SDL3003   Carlyle Dartline   B28F*   1990   *31/55 are DP28F

31	G31TGW	32	G32TGW	38	G38TGW	39	G39TGW	55	WLT575

DW59-71

Dennis Dart 8.5SDL3003   Wright Handy-bus   B28F   1991

59	JDZ2359	61	JDZ2361	63	JDZ2363	65	JDZ2365	71	JDZ2371
60	JDZ2360	62	JDZ2362	64	JDZ2364				

Selkent and East London now share a common numbering system as well as many of the administrative duties. The Volvo Olympians also share a common numbering system between Alexander and Northern Counties bodies. Seen in Bromley is VN87, R87XNO.
Gerry Mead

L7-145

Leyland Olympian ONLXB/1RH Eastern Coach Works H42/26D 1986

7	C807BYY	53	C53CHM	76	C76CHM	107	C107CHM	125	D125FYM
9	C809BYY	54	C54CHM	77	C77CHM	108	C108CHM	126	D126FYM
10	C810BYY	55	C55CHM	80	C80CHM	109	C109CHM	127	D127FYM
11	C811BYY	57	C57CHM	81	C81CHM	110	C110CHM	128	D128FYM
12	C812BYY	60	C60CHM	82	C82CHM	111	C111CHM	129	D129FYM
15	C815BYY	61	C61CHM	83	C83CHM	112	C112CHM	130	D130FYM
18	C818BYY	62	C62CHM	86	C86CHM	114	C114CHM	131	D131FYM
19	C819BYY	64	C64CHM	87	C87CHM	115	C115CHM	132	D132FYM
23	C23CHM	67	C67CHM	91	WLT491	116	C116CHM	133	D133FYM
28	C28CHM	68	C68CHM	92	C92CHM	117	C117CHM	134	D134FYM
29	C29CHM	69	C69CHM	94	C94CHM	118	C118CHM	136	D136FYM
30	C30CHM	70	C70CHM	97	C97CHM	119	C119CHM	137	D137FYM
42	C42CHM	71	C71CHM	98	C98CHM	120	C120CHM	141	D141FYM
43	C43CHM	72	C72CHM	103	C103CHM	121	C121CHM	142	D142FYM
44	C44CHM	73	C73CHM	104	C104CHM	122	C122CHM	144	D144FYM
48	C45CHM	74	C74CHM	105	C105CHM	123	D123FYM	145	D145FYM
51	C51CHM	75	C75CHM	106	C106CHM	124	D124FYM		

L260	VLT20	Leyland Olympian ONLXB/1RH	Eastern Coach Works	DPH42/26D	1986
L262	VLT14	Leyland Olympian ONLXB/1RH	Eastern Coach Works	DPH42/26D	1986
L263	D367JJD	Leyland Olympian ONLXB/1RH	Eastern Coach Works	DPH42/26D	1986

301-352

Volvo Olympian YN2RV18Z4 Northern Counties Palatine I H45/23D 1995

301	M301DGP	312	M312DGP	323	N323HGK	333	N353HGK	343	N343HGK
302	M302DGP	313	M313DGP	324	N324HGK	334	N334HGK	344	N344HGK
303	M303DGP	314	M314DGP	325	N325HGK	335	N335HGK	345	N345HGK
304	M304DGP	315	M315DGP	326	N326HGK	336	N336HGK	346	N346HGK
305	M305DGP	316	M316DGP	327	N327HGK	337	N337HGK	347	N347HGK
306	M306DGP	317	M317DGP	328	N328HGK	338	N338HGK	348	N348HGK
307	M307DGP	318	M318DGP	329	N329HGK	339	N339HGK	349	N349HGK
308	M308DGP	319	M319DGP	330	N330HGK	340	N340HGK	350	N350HGK
309	M309DGP	320	M320DGP	331	N331HGK	341	N341HGK	351	N351HGK
310	M310DGP	321	N321HGK	332	N332HGK	342	N342HGK	352	N352HGK
311	M311DGP	322	N322HGK						

LV1-12

Dennis Lance 11SDA3112 Plaxton Verde B42D 1994

1	L201YAG	4	L204YAG	7	L207YAG	9	L209YAG	11	L211YAG
2	L202YAG	5	L205YAG	8	L208YAG	10	L210YAG	12	WLT461
3	L203YAG	6	L206YAG						

MB1-18

Mercedes-Benz Vario O810 Plaxton Beaver 2 B29F 1997

1	R501YWC	5	R505YWC	9	R509YWC	13	R513YWC	16	R516YWC
2	R502YWC	6	R506YWC	10	R510YWC	14	R514YWC	17	R517YWC
3	R503YWC	7	R507YWC	11	R511YWC	15	R515YWC	18	R518YWC
4	R504YWC	8	R508YWC	12	R512YWC					

SLD20-29

Dennis Dart SLF Alexander ALX200 B33F 1997

20	R120VPU	22	R122VPU	24	R124VPU	26	R126VPU	28	R128VPU
21	R121VPU	23	R123VPU	25	R125VPU	27	R127VPU	29	R129VPU

Opposite, top:- **Super Low-floor Dart 21, R121VPU is pictured on LRT service 314 shortly after delivery. The Alexander ALX200 bodywork to Stagecoach standard, is enhanced with black window surrounds.** *Richard Godfrey*

Opposite, bottom:- **The Alexander-bodied Dennis Lance buses were transferred north to Ribble in 1996 while the Plaxton-bodied batch remain in the capital. Representing the type is LV10, L210YAG seen working LRT route 208.** *Gerry Mead*

Shortly after Stagecoach took over the operations of Selkent and East London a batch of fifty-two Northern Counties-bodied Volvo Olympians were suppied with index marks ranging from 301 to 353, the last mark being applied to fleet number 333. That vehicle, 333, N353HGK, is pictured in Blackheath while heading for Oxford Circus. *Gerry Mead*

T9-230

						Leyland Titan TNLXB2RRSp		Park Royal		H44/26D*		1978-80 * Several are H44/22D
												Ex East London, 1996

9	WYV9T	20	WYV20T	38	WYV38T	140	CUL140V	214	CUL214V
10	WYV10T	26	WYV26T	40	WYV40T	175	CUL175V	222	CUL222V
17	WYV17T	37	WYV37T	66	WYV66T	193	CUL193V	223	CUL223V
19	WYV19T								

T230	EYE230V	Leyland Titan TNLXB2RR	Park Royal	H44/26D	1981	Ex East London, 1996
T260	GYE260W	Leyland Titan TNLXB2RR	Park Royal/Leyland	H44/26D	1981	Ex East London, 1997
T262	GYE262W	Leyland Titan TNLXB2RR	Park Royal/Leyland	H44/26D	1981	Ex East London, 1997
T263	GYE263W	Leyland Titan TNLXB2RR	Park Royal/Leyland	H44/26D	1981	Ex East London, 1997
T267	GYE267W	Leyland Titan TNLXB2RR	Park Royal/Leyland	H44/26D	1981	

T368-822

						Leyland Titan TNLXB2RR		Leyland		H44/24D		1981-82
												*T439/71/98,504/58/60 Ex East London, 1997

368	KYV368X	504	KYV504X	740	OHV740Y	797	OHV797Y	814	OHV814Y
439	KYV439X	558	NUW558Y	748	OHV748Y	804	OHV804Y	815	RYK815Y
447	KYV447X	560	NUW560Y	770	OHV770Y	805	OHV805Y	816	RYK816Y
471	KYV471X	616	NUW616Y	771	OHV771Y	810	OHV810Y	818	RYK818Y
498	KYV498X	680	OHV680Y	772	OHV772Y	812	OHV812Y	821	RYK821Y
501	KYV501X	721	OHV721Y	785	OHV785Y	813	OHV813Y	822	RYK822Y

T828-999

						Leyland Titan TNLXB2RR*		Leyland		H44/24D		1983-84 *999 is H44/24F
												*T881/2/3/5 are TNL112RR; T877/80 are TNTL112RR;

828	A828SUL	841	A841SUL	854	A854SUL	880	A880SUL	950	A950SYE
829	A829SUL	842	A842SUL	856	A856SUL	881	A881SUL	951	A951SYE
830	A830SUL	843	A843SUL	857	A857SUL	882	A882SUL	961	A961SYE
834	A834SUL	845	A845SUL	859	A859SUL	883	A883SUL	976	A976SYE
836	A836SUL	847	A847SUL	866	A866SUL	885	A885SUL	978	A978SYE
837	A837SUL	848	A848SUL	868	A868SUL	925	A925SYE	988	A988SYE
838	A838SUL	850	A850SUL	877	A877SUL	926	A926SYE	999	A999SYE

T1003-1076

		Leyland Titan TNLXB2RR		Leyland H44/24D		1984	*1032 is H44/26F	

1003	A603THV	1029	A629THV	1034	A634THV	1045	A645THV	1065	A65THX
1025	A625THV	1030	A630THV	1035	A635THV	1048	A648THV	1067	A67THX
1027	A627THV	1031	A631THV	1036	A636THV	1052	A652THV	1076	A76THX
1028	A628THV	1032	A632THV						

T1079-1122

		Leyland Titan TNLXB2RR		Leyland		H44/24D	1984	*1108/12 are H44/29F
								*1113/5-8 are H44/26F; 1122 is O44/22F

1079	B79WUV	1091	B91WUV	1101	B101WUV	1112	B112WUV	1117	B117WUV
1081	B81WUV	1092	B92WUV	1103	B103WUV	1113	B113WUV	1118	B118WUV
1083	B83WUV	1096	B96WUV	1106	B106WUV	1115	B115WUV	1122	B122WUV
1089	B89WUV	1099	B99WUV	1108	B108WUV	1116	B116WUV		

VN82-100

		Volvo Olympian		Northern Counties Palatine	H45/23D	1997	

82	R82XNO	86	R86XNO	90	R190XNO	94	R94XNO	98	R99XNO
83	R83XNO	87	R87XNO	91	R91XNO	95	R95XNO	99	R207XNO
84	R84XNO	88	R188XNO	92	R92XNO	96	R96XNO	100	R210XNO
85	R85XNO	89	R89XNO	93	R93XNO	97	R97XNO		

VN101-110

		Volvo Olympian		Northern Counties Palatine	H--/--D	On order	

101		103		105		107		109	
102		104		106		108		110	

Ancilliary Vehicles

		Leyland Titan TNLXB2RRSp		Park Royal		H44/26D	1979-80	

T86	CUL86V	T114	CUL114V	T130	CUL130V	T142	CUL142V	T224	CUL224V
T98	CUL98V	T120	CUL120V	T137	CUL137V				

MT4t	F394DHL	Mercedes-Benz 709D	Reeve Burgess Beaver	B23F	1988

Previous Registrations:

D367JJD	D263FYL, VLT9	VLT20	D260FYM	WLT491	C91CHM
G32TGW	VLT240, G32TGW	WLT461	L212YAG	WLT575	G41TGW
VLT14	D262FYL				

Note: All vehicles were formerly London Buses, 1994 unless indicated otherwise or new later. All buses in red livery except training buses which are in corporate livery.

The first Leyland Olympians were supplied to London Buses in 1986 and carry Eastern Coach Works bodies. These which were delivered to the Selkent district have have remained there since. Showing fleet number 121, C121CHM was pictured in Blackheath in Stagecoach's all red livery used for the two London units.
Richard Godfrey

Allocations:-

Bromley (Hastings Road)

Dart	DT32	SLD20	SLD21	SLD22	SLD23	SLD24	SLD25	SLD26
	SLD27	SLD28	SLD29	622	623			
Lance	LV1	LV2	LV3	LV4	LV5	LV6	LV7	LV8
	LV9	LV10	LV11	LV12				
Titan	T137	T142	T267	T368	T439	T447	T471	T498
	T504	T558	T560	T616	T680	T721	T740	T748
	T770	T772	T785	T810	T837	T841	T842	T877
	T880	T881	T885	T925	T951	T961	T978	T988
	T1003	T1025	T1028	T1029	T1030	T1035	T1052	T1065
	T1089	T1096	T1103	T1108	T1112	T1113	T1115	T1116
	T1117	T1118	T1122					

Catford (Bromley Road)

Dart	DRL110	DRL112	DRL117	DRL118	DRL120	DRL123	DRL127	DT31
	DT38	DT39	DW59	DW60	DW61	DW62	DW63	DW64
	DW65	DW71	615	616	617	618	619	620
	621	624						
Mercedes-Benz	MB8	MB16	MB17	MT4				
Olympian	L9	L11	L18	L48	L62	L64	L69	L70
	L72	L73	L80	L81	L82	L91	L94	L97
	L103	L105	L110	L115	L119	L125	L130	L134
	L136	L142	L144	L260	L262	L263	VN82	VN83
	VN84	VN85	VN86	VN87	VN89	VN91	VN92	VN94
	VN96							
Titan	T9	T10	T17	T19	T20	T26	T37	T38
	T40	T66	T114	T120	T140	T175	T193	T214
	T222	T223	T224	T230	T260	T262	T263	T771
	T797	T804	T805	T812	T813	T814	T815	T816
	T818	T821	T822	T828	T829	T830	T834	T936
	T838	T843	T845	T847	T848	T850	T854	T856
	T857	T859	T866	T868	T882	T883	T926	T950
	T976	T999	T1027	T1031	T1032	T1034	T1036	T1045
	T1091	T1092	T1099	T1101	T1106			

Plumstead (Pettman Crescent)

Mercedes-Benz	MB1	MB2	MB3	MB4	MB5	MB6	MB7	MB9
	MB13	MB14	MB18					
Dart	601	602	603	604	605	606	607	608
	609	610	611	612	613	614	625	626
	627	628	629	630	631	632	633	634
	635	636	637	638	639	640	DT55	
Olympian	L7	L10	L12	L15	L19	L22	L23	L28
	L19	L22	L23	L28	L29	L30	L42	L43
	L44	L51	L53	L54	L55	L57	L60	L61
	L67	L68	L71	L74	L75	L76	L77	L83
	L86	L87	L92	L98	L104	L106	L107	L108
	L109	L111	L112	L114	L116	L117	L118	L120
	L121	L122	L123	L124	L126	L127	L128	L129
	L131	L132	L133	L137	L141	L145	301	302
	303	304	305	306	307	308	309	310
	311	312	313	314	315	316	317	318
	319	320	321	322	323	324	325	326
	327	328	329	330	331	332	333	334
	335	336	337	338	339	340	341	342
	343	344	345	346	347	348	349	350
	351	352	VN88	VN90	VN93	VN95	VN97	VN98
	VN99	VN100						
Titan	T86	T98	T130					

SOUTH YORKSHIRE SUPERTRAM

South Yorkshire Supertram Ltd, 11 Arundel Gate, Sheffield, S1 2PN.

Depot: Nunnery, Sheffield

01-25		Siemens		Duewag		ST88T	1993-94			
01	04	07	10	13	16	18	20	22	24
02	05	08	11	14	17	19	21	23	25
03	06	09	12	15					

Livery: Silver

Stagecoach Holdings became the preferred bidder for South Yorkshire Supertram Ltd. The company holds the concession to operate and maintain the Supertram system in Sheffield until March 2024. The network consists of twenty-nine kilometres of track and the twenty-five silver-grey trams. The main link runs from the city through the Lower Don valley to the Meadowhall shopping complex. Pictured in the city centre is tram 17. With tram operations in Portugal also, Stagecoach is establishing itself as a surface transport specialist. *David Longbottom*

STAGECOACH SOUTH

Stagecoach (South) Ltd, Lewes Enterprise Centre, 112 Malling Street, Lewes, East Sussex, BN7 2RB

1-11			Dennis Dart SLF		Alexander ALX200		B37F	1997		
1	R701DNJ	**4**	R704DNJ	**6**	R706DNJ	**8**	R708DNJ		**10**	R710DNJ
2	R702DNJ	**5**	R705DNJ	**7**	R707DNJ	**9**	R709DNJ		**11**	R711DNJ
3	R703DNJ									

100-118			Leyland National 11351A/1R				B52F	1979		
100	AYJ100T	**109**	ENJ909V	**112**	ENJ912V	**115**	ENJ915V		**117**	ENJ917V
102	AYJ102T	**110**	ENJ910V	**114**	ENJ914V	**116**	ENJ916V		**118**	ENJ918V
107	AYJ107T	**111**	ENJ911V							

119-126			Leyland National 2 NL116L11/1R				B52F	1980	124 fitted with TL11 engine	
119	GYJ919V	**121**	GYJ921V	**123**	HFG923V	**125**	OUF262W		**126**	SYC852
120	GYJ920V	**122**	GYJ922V	**124**	JNJ194V					

127	FDV830V	Leyland National 2 NL116L11/1R	B52F	1980
128	FDV831V	Leyland National 2 NL116L11/1R	B52F	1980

129-138			Leyland National 2 NL116AL11/1R				B49F*	1982	*129 is B45F	
									130 is fitted with TL11 engine	
129	HUF603X	**131**	HUF625X	**133**	HUF639X	**135**	HUF604X		**137**	HUF592X
130	HUF579X	**132**	PMT199X	**134**	HUF451X	**136**	HUF593X		**138**	HUF626X

139	FDV829V	Leyland National 2 NL116L11/1R	B48F	1980	
140	CPO98W	Leyland National 2 NL106L11/1R	B41F	1980	Ex Portsmouth, 1990
142	CPO100W	Leyland National 2 NL106L11/1R	DP40F	1980	Ex Portsmouth, 1990
143	ERV115W	Leyland National 2 NL106AL11/1R	B41F	1981	Ex Portsmouth, 1990
144	ERV116W	Leyland National 2 NL106AL11/1R	B41F	1981	Ex Portsmouth, 1990
145	ERV117W	Leyland National 2 NL106AL11/1R	B41F	1981	Ex Portsmouth, 1990
146	ERV118W	Leyland National 2 NL106AL11/1R	B41F	1981	Ex Portsmouth, 1990
147	BCW827V	Leyland National 2 NL106L11/1R	B44F	1980	Ex Ribble, 1994
148	UFG48S	Leyland National 11351A/2R	B52F	1977	
149	JCK849W	Leyland National 2 NL106AL11/1R	B44F	1981	Ex Ribble, 1994
150	PEX620W	Leyland National 2 NL116L11/1R	B49F	1981	Ex Cambus, 1997
151	PEX621W	Leyland National 2 NL116L11/1R	B49F	1981	Ex Cambus, 1997
154	VOD604S	Leyland National 11351A/1R	B52F	1978	Ex Devon General, 1987
155	VOD605S	Leyland National 11351A/1R	B52F	1978	Ex Devon General, 1987
157	UHG757R	Leyland National 11351A/1R	B49F	1977	Ex Ribble, 1986
159	YRN816V	Leyland National 2 NL106L11/1R	B44F	1980	Ex Ribble, 1994
160	YRN821V	Leyland National 2 NL106L11/1R	B44F	1980	Ex Ribble, 1994
162	FPR62V	Leyland National 11351A/1R	B49F	1980	
163	PCD73R	Leyland National 11351A/1R	B49F	1976	
164	VFX984S	Leyland National 11351A/1R	B49F	1978	
169	WYJ169S	Leyland National 11351A/2R(DAF)	B48F	1978	
173	YCD73T	Leyland National 11351A/2R	B52F	1978	
174	YCD74T	Leyland National 11351A/2R	B48F	1978	
176	YCD76T	Leyland National 11351A/2R	B48F	1978	
177	YCD77T	Leyland National 11351A/2R	B48F	1978	
179	PCD79R	Leyland National 11351A/1R	B49F	1977	
180	PCD80R	Leyland National 11351A/1R	B49F	1977	

Worthing is now one of the main centres of operation of Leyland National 2s with fifteen currently allocated. Photographed in the town is 123, HFG923V. The vehicle displays an interesting promotion for todays' increasing pressure to move away from cars back into public transport. *Gerry Mead*

182	YCD82T	Leyland National 11351A/2R				B48F	1978			
189	AYJ89T	Leyland National 11351A/1R				B52F	1979			
190	TEL490R	Leyland National 11351A/1R				DP48F	1977			
191	AYJ91T	Leyland National 11351A/1R				B52F	1979			
192	AYJ92T	Leyland National 11351A/1R				B52F	1979			
195	AYJ95T	Leyland National 11351A/1R				B52F	1979			
196	RJT146R	Leyland National 11351A/1R				B49F	1977			
197	AYJ97T	Leyland National 11351A/1R				B52F	1979			

201-206   Leyland Olympian ON2R56G13Z4 Alexander RL   H51/36F   1988

| 201 | F601MSL | 203 | F603MSL | 204 | F604MSL | 205 | F605MSL | 206 | F606MSL |
| 202 | F602MSL | | | | | | | | |

207-214   Leyland Olympian ON2R56G13Z4 Alexander RL   DPH51/31F   1989

| 207 | G807RTS | 209 | G809RTS | 211 | G211SSL | 213 | G213SSL | 214 | G214SSL |
| 208 | G808RTS | 210 | G210SSL | 212 | G212SSL | | | | |

215-219   Leyland Olympian ON2R56G13Z4 Alexander RL   H51/34F   1990

| 215 | H815CBP | 216 | H816CBP | 217 | H817CBP | 218 | H818CBP | 219 | H819CBP |

220	J720GAP	Leyland Olympian ON2R56G13Z4 Alexander RL	DPH47/27F	1992
221	J721GAP	Leyland Olympian ON2R56G13Z4 Alexander RL	DPH47/27F	1992
222	J722GAP	Leyland Olympian ON2R56G13Z4 Alexander RL	DPH47/27F	1992
223	J623GCR	Leyland Olympian ON2R56G13Z4 Alexander RL	H47/30F	1991
224	J624GCR	Leyland Olympian ON2R56G13Z4 Alexander RL	H47/30F	1991

225-234

Leyland Olympian ON2R56G13Z4 Alexander RL   H51/34F   1990

| 225 | G705TCD | 227 | G707TCD | 229 | G709TCD | 231 | G701TCD | 233 | G703TCD |
| 226 | G706TCD | 228 | G708TCD | 230 | G710TCD | 232 | G702TCD | 234 | G704TCD |

235-240

Leyland Olympian ON2R50G13Z4 Alexander RL   DPH43/27F 1992

| 235 | K235NHC | 237 | K237NHC | 238 | K238NHC | 239 | K239NHC | 240 | K240NHC |
| 236 | K236NHC | | | | | | | | |

241-250

Volvo Olympian YN2RV18Z4   Northern Counties Palatine II DPH43/25F 1993

| 241 | L241SDY | 243 | L243SDY | 245 | L245SDY | 247 | L247SDY | 249 | L249SDY |
| 242 | L242SDY | 244 | L244SDY | 246 | L246SDY | 248 | L248SDY | 250 | L250SDY |

254	K714ASC	Leyland Olympian ON2R50G13Z4 Alexander RL	H47/32F	1992	Ex Fife Scottish, 1994
255	K715ASC	Leyland Olympian ON2R50G13Z4 Alexander RL	H47/32F	1992	Ex Fife Scottish, 1994
256	K716ASC	Leyland Olympian ON2R50G13Z4 Alexander RL	H47/32F	1992	Ex Fife Scottish, 1994
257	K717ASC	Leyland Olympian ON2R50G13Z4 Alexander RL	H47/32F	1992	Ex Fife Scottish, 1994

260-290

Volvo Olympian   Alexander RL   H51/36F*   1996-97   *260-3 are H51/32F
                                                                 *288-90 are DPH47/32F

260	P260WPN	265	P265VPN	276	P276VPN	282	P282VPN	287	P287VPN
261	P261WPN	266	P266VPN	277	P277VPN	283	P283VPN	288	P288VPN
262	P262WPN	267	P267VPN	278	P278VPN	284	P284VPN	289	P289VPN
263	P263WPN	268	P268VPN	279	P279VPN	285	P285VPN	290	P290VPN
264	P264VPN	269	P269VPN	281	P281VPN	286	P286VPN		

341-359

Volvo Olympian YN2RC16V3   Alexander RL   DPH47/28F 1996

341	N341MPN	345	N345MPN	349	N349MPN	353	N353MPN	357	N357MPN
342	N342MPN	346	N346MPN	350	N350MPN	354	N354MPN	358	N358MPN
343	N343MPN	347	N347MPN	351	N351MPN	355	N355MPN	359	N359MPN
344	N344MPN	348	N348MPN	352	N352MPN	356	N356MPN		

360-380

Volvo Olympian YN2RC16V3   Alexander RL   H47/32F   1995

360	N360LPN	365	N365LPN	369	N369LPN	373	N373LPN	377	N377LPN
361	N361LPN	366	N366LPN	370	N370LPN	374	N374LPN	378	N378LPN
362	N362LPN	367	N367LPN	371	N371LPN	375	N375LPN	379	N379LPN
363	N363LPN	368	N368LPN	372	N372LPN	376	N376LPN	380	N380LPN
364	N364LPN								

381-399

Volvo Olympian YN2RC16V3   Alexander RL   DPH47/28F 1995-96

381	N381LPN	385	N385LPN	389	N389LPN	393	N393LPN	397	N397LPN
382	N382LPN	386	N386LPN	390	N390LPN	394	N394LPN	398	N398LPN
383	N383LPN	387	N387LPN	391	N391LPN	395	N395LPN	399	N399LPN
384	N384LPN	388	N388LPN	392	N392LPN	396	N396LPN		

400	400DCD	Volvo B6-9.9M	Alexander Dash	DP35F	1994
401	401DCD	Volvo B6-9.9M	Alexander Dash	DP35F	1994
402	402DCD	Volvo B6-9.9M	Alexander Dash	DP35F	1994
403	403DCD	Volvo B6-9.9M	Alexander Dash	DP31F	1994

451-455

Dennis Dart   Alexander Dash   DP40F   1996

| 451 | N451PAP | 452 | N452PAP | 453 | N453PAP | 454 | N454PAP | 455 | N455PAP |

Opposite, top:- **The Stagecoach South pool of vehicles supplies five of its operations, while the sixth, United Counties, maintains a separate fleet. The upper picture shows 150, PEX620W, a Leyland National 2 transferred from Cambus during 1997. The year saw the displacement of earlier mark 1 Nationals following the delivery of eleven low-floor Dennis Darts.**
Gerry Mead
Opposite, bottom:- **Canterbury Park & Ride vehicles are liveried in two-tone blue and include the five Berkhof-bodied Dennis Lance and three Optare-bodied DAF SB220s. One of the latter, 1403, J403LKO, is seen operating the service in Canterbury.** *Paul Wigan*

456-467 — Dennis Dart — Alexander Dash — B40F — 1996

456	N456PAP	459	N459PAP	462	N462PAP	464	N464PAP	466	N466PAP
457	N457PAP	460	N460PAP	463	N463PAP	465	N465PAP	467	N467PAP
458	N458PAP	461	N461PAP						

501-580 — Dennis Dart 9.8SDL3017 — Alexander Dash — B41F* — 1991-92 *535-80 are B40F

501	J501GCD	517	J517GCD	533	J533GCD	549	J549GCD	565	K565NHC
502	J502GCD	518	J518GCD	534	J534GCD	550	J550GCD	566	K566NHC
503	J503GCD	519	J519GCD	535	J535GCD	551	J551GCD	567	K567NHC
504	J504GCD	520	J520GCD	536	J536GCD	552	J552GCD	568	K568NHC
505	J505GCD	521	J521GCD	537	J537GCD	553	K553NHC	569	K569NHC
506	J506GCD	522	J522GCD	538	J538GCD	554	K554NHC	570	K570NHC
507	J507GCD	523	J523GCD	539	J539GCD	555	K655NHC	571	K571NHC
508	J508GCD	524	J524GCD	540	J540GCD	556	K556NHC	572	K572NHC
509	J509GCD	525	J525GCD	541	J541GCD	557	K557NHC	573	K573NHC
510	J510GCD	526	J526GCD	542	J542GCD	558	K558NHC	574	K574NHC
511	J511GCD	527	J527GCD	543	J543GCD	559	K559NHC	575	K575NHC
512	J512GCD	528	J528GCD	544	J544GCD	560	K660NHC	576	K576NHC
513	J513GCD	529	J529GCD	545	J545GCD	561	K561NHC	577	K577NHC
514	J514GCD	530	J530GCD	546	J546GCD	562	K562NHC	578	K578NHC
515	J515GCD	531	J531GCD	547	J547GCD	563	K563NHC	579	K579NHC
516	J516GCD	532	J532GCD	548	J548GCD	564	K564NHC	580	K580NHC

581	J701YRM	Dennis Dart 9.8DL3017	Alexander Dash	B41F	1991	Ex Cumberland, 1992
582	J702YRM	Dennis Dart 9.8DL3017	Alexander Dash	B41F	1991	Ex Cumberland, 1992
583	J703YRM	Dennis Dart 9.8DL3017	Alexander Dash	B41F	1992	Ex Cumberland, 1992

584-588 — Dennis Dart 9.8DL3017 — Alexander Dash — B40F — 1992

584	K584ODY	585	K585ODY	586	K586ODY	587	K587ODY	588	K588ODY

601-605 — Volvo B10M-55 — Northern Counties Paladin — DP49F — 1994

601	L601VCD	602	L602VCD	603	L603VCD	604	404DCD	605	405DCD

606-635 — Volvo B10M-55 — Alexander PS — DP48F — 1994

606	406DCD	612	412DCD	618	L618TDY	624	L624TDY	630	L630TDY
607	407DCD	613	413DCD	619	419DCD	625	L625TDY	631	L631TDY
608	408DCD	614	414DCD	620	420DCD	626	L626TDY	632	L632TDY
609	L609TDY	615	M615APN	621	421DCD	627	L627TDY	633	L633TDY
610	410DCD	616	L616TDY	622	422DCD	628	L628TDY	634	L634TDY
611	411DCD	617	L617TDY	623	423DCD	629	L629TDY	635	L635TDY

636-652 — Volvo B10M-55 — Alexander PS — DP48F — 1995

636	M636BCD	639	M639BCD	642	N642LPN	645	N645LPN	651	M651BCD
637	M637BCD	640	N640LPN	643	N643LPN	650	M650BCD	652	M652BCD
638	M638BCD	641	N641LPN	644	N644LPN				

655	415DCD	Volvo B10M-55	Alexander PS	DP48F	1994	Ex Ribble, 1994
656	416DCD	Volvo B10M-55	Alexander PS	DP48F	1994	Ex Ribble, 1994
657	417DCD	Volvo B10M-55	Alexander PS	DP48F	1994	Ex Ribble, 1994
658	418DCD	Volvo B10M-55	Alexander PS	DP48F	1994	Ex Ribble, 1994
659	K789DAO	Volvo B10M-55	Alexander PS	DP48F	1993	Ex Cumberland, 1994
660	K790DAO	Volvo B10M-55	Alexander PS	DP48F	1993	Ex Cumberland, 1994
661	K791DAO	Volvo B10M-55	Alexander PS	DP48F	1993	Ex Cumberland, 1994

662-670 — Volvo B10M-55 — Northern Counties Paladin — DP47F — 1995

662	M662ECD	664	M664ECD	667	M667ECD	669	M669ECD	670	M670ECD
663	M663ECD	665	M665ECD	668	M668ECD				

Opposite, top:- **Double-deck buses at Stagecoach South had been dominated by the Bristol VR inherited from National Bus Company days. These are being replaced by new Volvo Olympians of which a further delivery is due - and former London Titans which are being displaced in the Capital. However, in addition to these types there are twenty-two Metrobuses, all based at Thanet, and 7748, E748SKR, is illustrated here.** *Terry Blackman*

Opposite, bottom:-**Volvo Olympians with South consist of several batches and have varying seating layouts. Shown with East Kent operating names is 283, P283VPN.** *Gerry Mead*

671	M311YSC	Volvo B10M-55	Alexander PS	DP48F	1995	Ex Fife Scottish, 1995
672	M312YSC	Volvo B10M-55	Alexander PS	DP48F	1995	Ex Fife Scottish, 1995
673	M313YSC	Volvo B10M-55	Alexander PS	DP48F	1995	Ex Fife Scottish, 1995

684-692

Bristol VRT/SL3/6LXB — Eastern Coach Works — H43/31F — 1979-80

684	EAP984V	686	EAP986V	688	EAP988V	690	EAP990V	691	EAP991V
685	EAP985V	687	EAP987V						

749	BKE849T	Bristol VRT/SL3/6LXB	Eastern Coach Works	H43/31F	1979	Ex Hastings & District, 1989
759	BKE859T	Bristol VRT/SL3/6LXB	Eastern Coach Works	H43/31F	1979	Ex Hastings & District, 1989
787	AET187T	Bristol VRT/SL3/6LXB	Eastern Coach Works	H43/31F	1979	Ex East Midland, 1993

841-850

Mercedes-Benz 709D — Alexander Sprint — B23F* — 1990 — *841-3 are DP25F

841	G71APO	844	G974ARV	847	G977ARV	849	H679BTP	850	H680BTP
843	G73APO	845	G975ARV	848	G978ARV				

853-888

Mercedes-Benz 709D — Alexander Sprint — B25F — 1993

853	K853ODY	861	K861ODY	868	K868ODY	875	K875ODY	882	L882SDY
854	K854ODY	862	K862ODY	869	K869ODY	876	K876ODY	883	L883SDY
855	K855ODY	863	K863ODY	870	K870ODY	877	K877ODY	884	L884SDY
856	K856ODY	864	K864ODY	871	K871ODY	878	K878ODY	885	L885SDY
857	K857ODY	865	K865ODY	872	K872ODY	879	K879ODY	886	L886SDY
858	K858ODY	866	K866ODY	873	K873ODY	880	K880ODY	887	L887SDY
859	K859ODY	867	K867ODY	874	K874ODY	881	L881SDY	888	L188SDY
860	K860ODY								

889-904

Mercedes-Benz 709D — Alexander Sprint — B25F* — 1995 — *894-904 are B23F

889	M889ECD	892	N192LPN	895	N195LPN	898	N198LPN	902	N202LPN
890	M890ECD	893	N193LPN	896	N196LPN	899	N199LPN	903	N203LPN
891	N191LPN	894	N194LPN	897	N197LPN	901	N201LPN	904	N204LPN

905-977

Mercedes-Benz 709D — Alexander Sprint — B25F* — 1996 — *924-77 are B23F

905	N905NAP	920	N920NAP	935	N935NAP	950	N950NAP	964	N964NAP
906	N906NAP	921	N921NAP	936	N936NAP	951	N951NAP	965	N965NAP
907	N907NAP	922	N922NAP	937	N937NAP	952	N952NAP	966	N966NAP
908	N908NAP	923	N923NAP	938	N938NAP	953	N953NAP	967	N967NAP
909	N909NAP	924	N924NAP	939	N939NAP	954	N954NAP	968	N968NAP
910	N910NAP	925	N925NAP	940	N940NAP	955	N955NAP	969	N969NAP
911	N911NAP	926	N926NAP	941	N941NAP	956	N956NAP	970	N970NAP
912	N912NAP	927	N927NAP	942	N942NAP	957	N957NAP	971	N971NAP
913	N913NAP	928	N928NAP	943	N943NAP	958	N958NAP	972	N972NAP
914	N914NAP	929	N929NAP	944	N944NAP	959	N959NAP	973	N973NAP
915	N915NAP	930	N930NAP	945	N945NAP	960	N960NAP	974	N974NAP
916	N916NAP	931	N931NAP	946	N946NAP	961	N961NAP	975	N975NAP
917	N917NAP	932	N932NAP	947	N947NAP	962	N962NAP	976	N976NAP
918	N918NAP	933	N933NAP	948	N948NAP	963	N963NAP	977	N977NAP
919	N919NAP	934	N934NAP	949	N949NAP				

1094	GPJ894N	Leyland National 11351/1R		B49F	1975	Ex Alder Valley, 1992
1105	M105CCD	Dennis Javelin 11SDL2133	Plaxton Premiere Interurban	DP47F	1995	
1106	M106CCD	Dennis Javelin 11SDL2133	Plaxton Premiere Interurban	DP47F	1995	
1108	M108CCD	Dennis Javelin 11SDL2133	Plaxton Premiere Interurban	DP47F	1995	
1115	MFN115R	Leyland National 11351A/1R		B49F	1976	Ex East Kent, 1993
1176	NPJ476R	Leyland National 11351A/1R		B49F	1976	Ex Alder Valley, 1992
1180	UMO180N	Leyland National 11351/1R		B49F	1974	Ex Alder Valley, 1992
1181	NFN81R	Leyland National 11351A/1R		DP48F	1977	Ex East Kent, 1993
1188	NFN88R	Leyland National 11351A/1R		DP48F	1977	Ex East Kent, 1993
1201	HPK503N	Leyland National 11351/1R		B49F	1975	Ex Alder Valley, 1992
1203	HPK505N	Leyland National 11351/1R		B49F	1975	Ex Alder Valley, 1992
1215	KPA366P	Leyland National 11351/1R		B49F	1975	Ex Alder Valley, 1992
1218	KPA369P	Leyland National 11351/1R		B49F	1975	Ex Alder Valley, 1992
1223	KPA374P	Leyland National 11351/1R		B49F	1975	Ex Alder Valley, 1992
1228	KPA379P	Leyland National 11351/1R		B49F	1975	Ex Alder Valley, 1992
1237	KPA388P	Leyland National 11351A/1R		B49F	1976	Ex Alder Valley, 1992

7960-7985   Bristol VRT/SL3/6LXB   Eastern Coach Works   H43/31F   1978-81 Ex Alder Valley, 1992

7960w	GGM80W	7966	WJM826T	7972	WJM832T	7979	CJH119V	7982	CJH142V
7961	GGM81W	7968	WJM828T	7977	CJH117V	7980	CJH120V	7985	CJH145V
7965	WJM825T	7969	WJM829T						

8211	D211VEV	Scania K112CRB	Berkhof Esprite 350	C40DT	1987	Ex East Kent, 1993
8243	SIB8243	Volvo B10M-60	Plaxton Paramount 3500 III	C49FT	1991	Ex East Kent, 1993

8404-8410   Volvo B10M-62   Plaxton Premiére 350   C53F*   1995   *8410 convertable to C49FT

8404	M404BFG	8406	M406BFG	8408	M408BFG	8409	M409BFG	8410	M410BFG
8405	M405BFG	8407	M407BFG						

8503	IIL3503	Volvo B10M-61	Van Hool Alizée	C49FT	1988	Ex Bluebird Buses, 1995
8505	IIL3505	Volvo B10M-61	Van Hool Alizée	C49FT	1988	Ex Bluebird Buses, 1995
8618	WVT618	Volvo B10M-61	Plaxton Paramount 3500 III	C50F	1987	Ex Bluebird Buses, 1995
8856	J856NKK	Scania K93CRB	Plaxton Paramount 3500 III	C49FT	1992	Ex East Kent, 1993
8909	J909NKP	Volvo B10M-60	Plaxton Expressliner	C49FT	1992	Ex East Kent, 1993
8910	K910TKP	Volvo B10M-60	Plaxton Expressliner 2	C49FT	1993	Ex East Kent, 1993

8911-8918   Volvo B10M-62   Plaxton Expressliner 2   C49FT   1994-95

8911	M911WJK	8913	M913WJK	8915	M915WJK	8917	M917WJK	8918	M918WJK
8912	M912WJK	8914	M914WJK	8916	M916WJK				

8996	PFN873	Bova FHD12.280	Bova Futura	C49FT	1986	Ex East Kent, 1993

Special event vehicles: (traditional liveries)

0135	CD7045	Leyland G7	Short	O27/24R	1922	
0409	409DCD	Leyland Titan PD3/4	Northern Counties	FCO39/30F	1964	
0424	424DCD	Leyland Titan PD3/4	Northern Counties	FCO39/30F	1964	
0770	HKE690L	Bristol VRT/SL2/6LXB	Eastern Coach Works	O43/34F	1973	Ex Hastings & District, 1989
0813	UF4813	Leyland Titan TD1	Brush	O27/24R	1929	
0946	MFN946F	AEC Regent V 3D3RA	Park Royal	H40/32F	1967	Ex Hastings & District, 1989

Names Vehicles:-

8910 Spirit of Hythe; 8911 Spirit of Sandwich; 8912 Spirit of Dover; 8913 Spirit of Canterbury; 8914 Spirit of Folkestone; 8915 Spirit of Walmer; 8916 Spirit of Deal; 8917 Spirit of Whitfield; 8918 Spirit of Ashford.

Previous Registrations:-

400DCD	M490BFG	CSU978	HWY718N, CSU934
401DCD	M401BFG	CSU992	OMA506V, TCS157
402DCD	M402BFG	HUF451X	RUF434X, XLD244
403DCD	M403BFG	HUF579X	RUF430X, 400DCD
404DCD	L604VCD	HUF592X	RUF437X, 407DCD
405DCD	L605VCD	HUF593X	RUF436X, 406DCD
406DCD	L606TDY	HUF603X	RUF429X, 415DCD
407DCD	L607TDY	HUF604X	RUF435X, 405DCD
408DCD	L608TDY	HUF625X	RUF431X, 411DCD
409DCD	from new	HUF626X	RUF438X, 410DCD
410DCD	M610APN	HUF639X	RUF433X, 420DCD
411DCD	M611APN	IIL3503	E625UNE, TXI2426, E936XSB
412DCD	M612APN	IIL3505	E623UNE, XIA257, E942XSB
413DCD	M613APN	JNJ194V	HFG924V, DSV943
414DCD	M614APN	NFX667	K716PCN
415DCD	L345KCK	OUF262W	JWV125W, LYJ145
416DCD	L346KCK	PFN873	C996FKM
417DCD	L347KCK	SIB8243	H826AHS
418DCD	L348KCK	SYC852	JWV126W
419DCD	L619TDY	WVT618	D202LWX
420DCD	L620TDY	XIA586	RYG773R
421DCD	L621TDY	XIA857	PKP548R, XIA256
422DCD	L622TDY	XSU612	PWT278W
423DCD	L623TDY	XSU682	OKG158M
424DCD	424DCD, AOR158B	XYK976	K719PCN
472YMF	J713CYG	YLJ332	J715CYG

As 1998 arrives, the numbers of Volvo B10M buses known to be on order are all detailed in the book, the final examples due from a Northern Counties order which has yet to be met, and may well be converted to Volvo B10B chassis. *Richard Godfrey*

Allocations:-

Aldershot (Halimote Road) - Hants & Surrey - South West Trains ♦

Outstations - Alton; Haslemere and Petersfield

Mercedes-Benz	865	866	867	868	869	870	871	872
	873	874	875	876	877	878	879	880
	905	906	907	908	909	910	911	912
	913	914						
Dart	522	523	570	571	572	575	576	577
	584	585	586	587	588	5004♦		
Natiohal	102	109	162	189	1094	1188	1201	1215
	1218	1223	1228	1237	1238	1256	1259	
Volvo PS	618	624	635	656	657			
Bristol VR	685	686	688	759	7650	7654	7667	7968
	7969	7972	7979	7980	7982	7985		
Olympian	223	236	239	351	352	353	391	392

Andover (Livingstone Road) - Hampshire Bus

Mercedes-Benz	854	855	856	857	858	859	860	
Dart	542	544	545	547	548	549	581	
National	107	115	116	117	174	190	191	192
Volvo NC	601	602	603	604	605			
Volvo PS	606	607	608	615	616	617		
Bristol VR	7397							
Olympian	203	205	213	214	257			

The 1998 Stagecoach Bus Handbook

Ashford (Brunswick Road) - East Kent

Mercedes-Benz	844	845	849	850	894	895	896	897
	898	922	923	945	946	947	948	949
	950	951	952					
National	1115	1181	1344					
Volvo PS	644	645						
Bristol VR	7652	7660	7674	7675				
Olympian	377	378	7806					

Basingstoke (Bus Station) - Hampshire Bus

Mercedes-Benz	853							
Dart	459	460	461	462	463	546	550	573
	574	578	582					
National	180	196						
Volvo PS/NC	625	627	631	643	651	652	655	658
	662	663	664	665	667	668	669	670
Bristol VR	749	787	7369	7371	7373	7422	7438	7446
	7448	7449	7450	7680	7965			
Olympian	201	202	204	207	208	224	268	269
	276	277	279	288	289	290	366	379
	380	393	394					

Chichester (Southgate) - Sussex Coastline - Sussex Bus ♥

Iveco	2651♥							
Omni	2136♥							
Mercedes-Benz	891♥	892♥	893	917	918	919	920	921
	2220♥							
Dart	541	553	554	555	580			
Leopard	2612♥	2682♥	2978♥	2992♥				
National 1	118	1203	2586♥	2857♥				
National 2	120	121	123	125	128♥	134	137	
Volvo PS	626	628	629					
Bristol VR	684	687						
Olympian	209	217	220	221	222	225	228	232
	278	281	282	341	342	395	396	397
	398	399						

Dover (Russell Street) - East Kent - East Kent Coaches ♠ - National Express ✈

Mercedes-Benz	953	954	955	956	957	958	959	960
	961	962	963	964	965			
Volvo Coach	8505✈							
Volvo Expressliner	8910✈	8911✈	8912✈	8913✈	8914✈	8915✈	8916✈	8917✈
	8918✈							
Scania Coach	8856✈							
Bova	8996♠							
National 1	197	1546	1898					
Volvo PS	633	639	640	641	642			
Bristol VR	690	7355	7655	7659	7663	7664		
Olympian	285	389	390	7826	7827	7828		

Eastbourne (Cavendish Place) - South Coast Buses

Outstations - Lewes; Uckfield and Seaford

Mercedes-Benz	881	882	883	884	885	886	887	888
	889	890						
Dart	451	452	453	454	455	456		
National 1	110	111	112	114	148	155	163	169
	173	176	177	179				
Volvo PS	609	612	613	614	619	620	636	637
	638	650	671	672	673			
Bristol VR	7621							

Volvo B10M DD	7301	7302	7303	7304	7305	7306	7307	7308
	7309							
Olympian	241	242	356	357	358	359	373	374
	388							

Folkestone (Kent Road, Cheriton) - East Kent

Outstation - New Romney

Mercedes-Benz	966	967	968	969	970	971	972	973
	974	975	976					
Dart	457	458						
Javelin Interurban	1106							
National	195							
Bristol VR	7653	7657	7665					
Titan	7209	7271	7272					
Olympian	286	287	354	355	375	376	7811	7812
	7813	7814	7821	7822	7823			

Hastings (Beaufort Road, Silverhill, St Leonards) - South Coast Buses

Dart	464	465	466	467	501	502	503	504
	505	506	507	508	509	510	511	512
	513	514	515	516	517	518	519	520
	521	579	583					
National 2	136	140	142	143	144	145	146	147
	149	159	160					
Titan	7203	7205	7215	7223	7233	7237	7240	7244
	7250	7268	7274	7279	7280	7287	7288	7290
Olympian	382	383	384	385	386	387		

Herne Bay (High Street) - East Kent - Canterbury Park & Ride ♣

Outstation - Canterbury

Mercedes-Benz	847	863	935	936	937	938	939	940
	941	942	943	944				
DAF Delta	1401♣	1402♣	1403♣					
Javelin Interurban	1105	1108						
Lance	1404♣	1405♣	1406♣	1407♣	1408♣			
Scania coach	8211							
Titan	7208	7224	7235	7247	7270	7281	7284	7285
Scania	7781	7782						
Olympian	226	227	230	254	255	256	283	284
	360	361	362	363	364	365	368	369
	370	371	372	381	7801	7802	7803	7804
	7805	7807	7808	7809	7810	7829		

Three Dennis Javelins remain with Stagecoach South, the remainder of the batch now being dispersed. Photographed in Chatham, 1108, M108CCD carries *The Dickensian* **names for its Medway service.**
Gerry Mead

Portsmouth (Langstone Point) - Sussex Coastline

Dart	551	552						
Volvo PS	621	622	623					
Titan	7201	7204	7207	7211	7214	7220	7221	7225
	7229	7231	7242	7243	7245	7248	7251	7259
	7261	7263	7269	7294	7296	7297	7298	
Olympian	215	216	218	219	229	231	233	234
	235	240	7824	7825	7830			

Thanet (Margate Road, Westwood) - East Kent - East Kent Coaches ♠National Express✈

Outstation - Deal

Mercedes-Benz	899	901	902	903	904	925	926	927
	928	929	930	931	932	933	934	977
National 1	182							
Volvo PS	632	634	659	660	661			
Coach	8243♠	8404♠	8405♠	8406♠	8407♠	8408♠	8409♠	8410♠
	8503✈	8618♠						
Volvo Expressliner	8909✈							
Bristol VR	7658	7661	7662	7669	7671	7679	7681	7682
	7683	7977						
Metrobus	7746	7747	7748	7749	7750	7751	7752	7753
	7754	7755	7761	7762	7763	7764	7765	7766
	7767	7771	7772	7773	7774	7775		
Olympian	264	265	266	267				

Winchester (The Broadway) - Hampshire Bus - South West Trains ♦ Park & Ride ♣

Outstations - Alton; Bishops Waltham; Stockbridge and Petersfield

Mercedes-Benz	861	915	916	924				
Dart	524	526	527	528	529	530	531	532
	533	534	535	536	537	538	539	540
	543	568	569	5003♦				
Volvo B6	400♣	401	402♣	403♣				
National	100	154	164	1176	1247			
DAF-Delta	5001♦	5002♦						
Bristol VR	7347	7353	7358	7435	7651	7668	7677	7961
	7966							
Olympian	206	210	211	212	246	247	248	249
	250	260	261	262	263			

Worthing (Library Place) - Sussex Coastline

Outstations - Henfield and Littlehampton

Mercedes-Benz	862	864						
Dart SLF	1	2	3	4	5	6	7	8
	9	10	11					
Dart	556	557	558	559	560	561	562	563
	564	565	566	567				
National 2	119	122	124	126	127	129	130	
	131	132	133	135	138	139	150	151
Volvo PS	610	611	630					
Olympian	237	238	243	244	245	343	344	345
	346	347	348	349	350			

Unallocated

Mercedes-Benz	841	848			
Omni	2402	2646			
National	113				
Bristol VR	684	691	7365	7368	7960

TRANSIT

Cleveland Transit Ltd, Church Road, Stockton-on-Tees, Cleveland, TS18 2HW

33	FSL61W	Leyland Leopard PSU3G/4R	Plaxton Supreme IV Express	C49F	1980	Ex Tayside, 1987
34	FSL62W	Leyland Leopard PSU3G/4R	Plaxton Supreme IV Express	C49F	1980	Ex Tayside, 1987
35	HDZ8683	Volvo B10M-61	Plaxton Paramount 3500	C53F	1984	Ex Allander, Milngavie, 1989
36	837XHW	Volvo B10M-61	Van Hool Alizée	C53F	1987	Ex Streamline, Bath, 1994
42	BUT24Y	Dennis Dorchester SDA801	Plaxton Paramount 3200	C49F	1983	Ex Leicester, 1987
43w	BPY403T	Leyland Leopard PSU3E/4R	Plaxton Supreme IV Express	C53F	1979	
44w	HPY423V	Leyland Leopard PSU3F/4R	Plaxton Supreme IV Express	C53F	1980	
51	IIL1321	Volvo B10M-61	Plaxton Paramount 3200 III	C50FT	1987	
60	B60WKH	Leyland National 2 NL116HLXCT/1R		B24DL	1985	
61	YAY21Y	Dennis Lancet SD506	Duple Dominant	B25DL	1982	Ex Leicester, 1987
71	K571DFS	Volvo B10M-60	Plaxton Premiére Interurban	DP53F	1993	Ex East Midland, 1995
72	K572DFS	Volvo B10M-60	Plaxton Premiére Interurban	DP53F	1993	Ex East Midland, 1995
73	K573DFS	Volvo B10M-60	Plaxton Premiére Interurban	DP53F	1993	Ex East Midland, 1995
76	K576DFS	Volvo B10M-60	Plaxton Premiére Interurban	DP53F	1993	Ex East Midland, 1995
77	K577DFS	Volvo B10M-60	Plaxton Premiére Interurban	DP51F	1993	Ex East Midland, 1995

78-85		Volvo B10M-62		Plaxton Premiére Interurban	DP51F	1996-97

78	P178PRH	80	P180PRH	82	R82SEF	84	R84SEF	85	R85SEF
79	P179PRH	81	P181PRH	83	R83SEF				

104-118		MCW Metrobus DR102/17*	MCW		H43/30F	1981	*104-6 are DR102/7

104	LAT514V	106	LAT506V	115	SAG525W	117	SAG527W	118	SAG528W
105	LAT505V	114	SAG524W	116	SAG526W				

Transit allocate fleet numbers to buses dependent on size and allocation with single-decks intended for Hartlepool numbered 5xx; Stockton 6xx and Hull 7xx. Pictured with its former fleet number 406, M406SPY is now numbered 506 and operates at Hartlepool. The Volvo B10M carries a Northern Counties Paladin body. *Tony Wilson*

121	YVN521T	Leyland Fleetline FE30AGR	Northern Counties	H43/31F	1979		
122	AVK142V	Leyland Atlantean AN68A/2R	Alexander AL	H49/37F	1980	Ex Busways, 1997	
124	SCN249S	Leyland Atlantean AN68A/2R	Alexander AL	H49/37F	1978	Ex Busways, 1997	
127	AVK147V	Leyland Atlantean AN68A/2R	Alexander AL	H49/37F	1980	Ex Busways, 1997	
128	AVK148V	Leyland Atlantean AN68A/2R	Alexander AL	H49/37F	1980	Ex Busways, 1997	

129-157

Leyland Fleetline FE30AGR   Northern Counties   H43/31F   1980-83

129	GAJ129V	135	GAJ135V	141	JAJ141W	147	PEF147X	153	VEF153Y
130	GAJ130V	136	GAJ136V	142	JAJ142W	148	PEF148X	154	YAJ154Y
131	GAJ131V	137	JAJ137W	143	JAJ143W	149	PEF149X	155	YAJ155Y
132	GAJ132V	138	JAJ138W	144	JAJ144W	150	VEF150Y	156	YAJ156Y
133	GAJ133V	139	JAJ139W	145	JAJ145W	151	VEF151Y	157	YAJ157Y
134	GAJ134V	140	JAJ140W	146	JAJ146W	152	VEF152Y		

189	PRX189B	Leyland Titan PD3/4	Northern Counties	O39/30F	1964	Ex Southdown, 1988

206-210

Dennis Dominator DDA904   Alexander RL   H43/32F   1984

206	B106UAT	207	B107UAT	208	B108UAT	209	B109UAT	210	B110UAT

211	C111CAT	Dennis Dominator DDA1007	East Lancashire	H43/28F	1986
212	C112CAT	Dennis Dominator DDA1007	East Lancashire	H43/28F	1986
213	C113CAT	Dennis Dominator DDA1007	East Lancashire	DPH43/28F	1986

214-222

Dennis Dominator DD906*   Northern Counties   H43/31F   1985-86 *219-22 are DDA1009

214	B214OAJ	216	B216OAJ	218	B218OAJ	220	C220WAJ	222	C222WAJ
215	B215OAJ	217	B217OAJ	219	C219WAJ	221	C221WAJ		

223-231

Dennis Dominator DDA1006   East Lancashire   H45/30F   1985-86

223	C123CAT	225	C125CAT	228	C128CAT	229	C129CAT	231	C131CAT
224	C124CAT	226	C122CAT						

232	E132SAT	Dennis Dominator DDA1014	East Lancashire (1992)	H45/21D	1987

233-241

Dennis Dominator DDA1014   East Lancashire   H45/32F   1987

233	E133SAT	235	E135SAT	237	E137SAT	239	E139SAT	241	E141SAT
234	E134SAT	236	E136SAT	238	E138SAT	240	E140SAT		

242-251

Dennis Dominator DDA1016   East Lancashire   H45/31F   1988

242	E142BKH	244	E144BKH	246	E146BKH	248	E148BKH	250	E150BKH
243	E143BKH	245	E145BKH	247	E147BKH	249	E149BKH	251	E151BKH

252-257

Dennis Dominator DDA1027   East Lancashire   H47/33F   1989

252	F152HAT	254	F154HAT	255	F155HAT	256	F156HAT	257	F157HAT
253	F153HAT								

270-282

Leyland Titan TNLXB2RR   Leyland   H44/29F   1982-83 Ex East London, 1997
273/7/81/3 are on loan to Red & White

270	NUW604Y	273	NUW642Y	276	NUW649Y	279	NUW666Y	281	NUW673Y
271	NUW606Y	274	NUW643Y	277	NUW659Y	280	NUW668Y	282	NUW675Y
272	NUW634Y	275	NUW648Y	278	NUW664Y					

283-290

Leyland Titan TNLXB2RR   Leyland   H44/29F   1984 Ex East London, 1997

283	A826SUL	285	A840SUL	287	A849SUL	289	A622THV	290	A626THV
284	A827SUL	286	A846SUL	288	A905SYE					

301-316 — Mercedes-Benz 811D — Wright NimBus — B26F — 1989 Ex Stagecoach Selkent, 1995

301	HDZ2601	305	HDZ2605	309	HDZ2609	312	HDZ2612	315	HDZ2615
303	HDZ2603	306	HDZ2606	310	HDZ2610	313	HDZ2613	316	HDZ2616
304	HDZ2604	307	HDZ2607	311	HDZ2611				

321	F621XMS	Mercedes-Benz 811D	Alexander Sprint	B28F	1988	Ex Stagecoach Selkent, 1996
324	F624XMS	Mercedes-Benz 811D	Alexander Sprint	B28F	1988	Ex Stagecoach Selkent, 1996
325	F625XMS	Mercedes-Benz 811D	Alexander Sprint	B28F	1988	Ex Stagecoach Selkent, 1996
329	F629XMS	Mercedes-Benz 811D	Alexander Sprint	B28F	1988	Ex Stagecoach Selkent, 1996

341-354 — Mercedes-Benz 709D — Alexander Sprint — B23F — 1996

341	N341KKH	344	N344KKH	347	N347KKH	350	P350NKH	353	P353NKH
342	N342KKH	345	N345KKH	348	N348KKH	351	P351NKH	354	P354NKH
343	N343KKH	346	N346KKH	349	P349NKH	352	P352NKH		

363	H401DMJ	Renault S75	Reeve Burgess Beaver	B29F	1990	Ex Busways, 1995

368-378 — Renault S75 — Plaxton Beaver — B28F — 1991 Ex Busways, 1995

368	J228JJR	375	K342PJR	376	K343PJR	377	K344PJR	378	K345PJR
371	J231JJR								

401-408 — Volvo B6-9.9M — Plaxton Pointer — B41F — 1993-94

401	L101GHN	403	L103GHN	405	M105PVN	407	M107PVN	408	M108PVN
402	L102GHN	404	M104PVN	406	M106PVN				

438-454 — Volvo B6-9.9M — Alexander Dash — DP40F — 1993 Ex Ribble, 1995

438	L238CCW	443	L243CCK	445	L245CCK	447	L247CCK	450	L250CCK
442	L242CCK	444	L244CCK	446	L246CCK	449	L249CCK	454	L254CCK

455-461 — Dennis Dart — Alexander Dash — B40F — 1996

455	P455EEF	457	P457EEF	459	P459EEF	460	P460EEF	461	P461EEF
456	P456EEF	458	P458EEF						

462-472 — Dennis Dart SLF — Alexander ALX200 — B37F — 1997

462	R462SEF	465	R465SEF	467	R467SEF	469	R469MVN	471	R471MVN
463	R463SEF	466	R466SEF	468	R468SEF	470	R470MVN	472	R472MVN
464	R464SEF								

501-510 — Volvo B10M-55 — Northern Counties Paladin — B48F — 1995

501	M401SPY	503	M403SPY	505	M405SPY	507	M407SPY	509	M409SPY
502	M402SPY	504	M404SPY	506	M406SPY	508	M408SPY	510	M410SPY

514-519 — Leyland National 2 NL116L11/2R — B50F* — 1980 *515/6 are DP48F, 517/8 are B45D

514	KAJ214W	516	KAJ216W	517	KAJ217W	518	KAJ218W	519	KAJ219W
515	KAJ215W								

521	YDC21Y	Dennis Falcon HC SDA409	Wadham Stringer Vanguard	B46D	1983	
523	YDC23Y	Dennis Falcon HC SDA409	Wadham Stringer Vanguard	B46D	1983	
525	YDC25Y	Dennis Falcon HC SDA409	Wadham Stringer Vanguard	B46D	1983	

527-532 — Dennis Falcon HC SDA417* — Northern Counties — B47D — 1985 *530-2 are SDA415

527	B27PAJ	529	B29PAJ	530	B30PAJ	531	B31PAJ	532	B32PAJ
528	B28PAJ								

Opposite, top:- **Transit 78, P178PRH, is seen on Stagecoach Express service 909 at Sheffield's Meadowhall shopping centre. Service 909 gained popularity with passengers in late 1996 when the frequency of the route was increased to meet demand.** *Richard Godfrey*
Opposite, bottom:- **Now renumbered 213, C113CAT is one of three East Lancashire-bodied Dennis Dominators remaining in service with Hull from the 1986 delivery. The body style, as can be seen, included large front windscreens, and this example is fitted with high-back seating.** *Tony Wilson*

533	SHN401R	Leyland National 11351A/2R		B50F	1977	
536	UFG52S	Leyland National 11351A/2R		B50F	1977	Ex Brighton & Hove, 1990
537	SHN407R	Leyland National 11351A/2R		B50F	1977	
539	UFG49S	Leyland National 11351A/2R		B50F	1977	Ex Brighton & Hove, 1990
540	RUF40R	Leyland National 11351A/2R		B44D	1977	Ex Brighton & Hove, 1990
541	F251JRM	Leyland Lynx LX112L10ZR1	Leyland Lynx	B51F	1989	Ex Cumberland, 1996
542	F252JRM	Leyland Lynx LX112L10ZR1	Leyland Lynx	B51F	1989	Ex Cumberland, 1996
543	F253KAO	Leyland Lynx LX112L10ZR1	Leyland Lynx	B51F	1989	Ex Cumberland, 1996
544	C544RAO	Leyland Lynx LX1126LXCTFR1 (Cummins) Leyland		B51F	1986	Ex Cumberland, 1996
545	E709MFV	Leyland Lynx LX112L10ZR1	Leyland	B51F	1988	Ex Cumberland, 1996
551	N551VDC	Volvo B10M-55	Alexander PS	DP48F	1995	
552	N552VDC	Volvo B10M-55	Alexander PS	DP48F	1995	
553	N553VDC	Volvo B10M-55	Alexander PS	DP48F	1995	

601-610

Leyland Lynx LX112L10ZR1S	Leyland Lynx	B49F	1989

601	F601UVN	603	F603UVN	605	F605UVN	607	F607UVN	609	F609UVN
602	F602UVN	604	F604UVN	606	F606UVN	608	F608UVN	610	F610UVN

611-620

Leyland Lynx LX2R11C15Z4R	Leyland Lynx	B49F	1989

611	G611CEF	613	G613CEF	615	G615CEF	617	G617CEF	619	G619CEF
612	G612CEF	614	G614CEF	616	G616CEF	618	G618CEF	620	G620CEF

621	J901UKV	Leyland Lynx LX2R11V18Z4S	Leyland Lynx 2	B49F	1991	Ex Volvo demonstrator, 1992

622-630

Leyland Lynx LX2R11V18Z4R	Leyland Lynx 2	B49F	1992

622	K622YVN	624	K624YVN	626	K626YVN	628	K628YVN	630	K630YVN
623	K623YVN	625	K625YVN	627	K627YVN	629	K629YVN		

631-642

Volvo B10B	Plaxton Verde	B52F	1994

631	L31HHN	634	L34HHN	637	L37HHN	639	M39PVN	641	M41PVN
632	L32HHN	635	L35HHN	638	M38PVN	640	M40PVN	642	M42PVN
633	L33HHN	636	L36HHN						

643-652

Volvo B10M-55	Northern Counties Paladin	B48F	1995-97

643	M543SPY	645	M545SPY	647	M547SPY	649	M549SPY	651	M551SPY
644	M544SPY	646	M546SPY	648	M548SPY	650	M550SPY	652	M552SPY

701-706

Scania N112CRB	East Lancashire	B50F	1988

701	F701BAT	703	F703BAT	704	F704BAT	705	F705BAT	706	F706CAG
702	F702BAT								

707-718

Volvo B10M-55	Northern Counties Paladin	B48F	1995

707	M707KRH	710	M710KRH	713	M713KRH	715	M715KRH	717	M717KRH
708	M708KRH	711	M711KRH	714	M714KRH	716	M716KRH	718	M718KRH
709	M709KRH	712	M712KRH						

800	C100HSJ	Scania N112DRB	East Lancashire	H47/33F	1986	Ex A1 Service, 1995

801-816

Scania N113DRB	East Lancashire	H51/37F	1989-90 *809-16 are H47/37F

801	G801JRH	805	G805JRH	808	G808LAG	811	H811WKH	814	H814WKH
802	G802JRH	806	G806JRH	809	H809WKH	812	H812WKH	815	H815WKH
803	G803JRH	807	G807LAG	810	H810WKH	813	H813WKH	816	H816WKH
804	G804JRH								

817	M817KRH	Volvo Olympian YN2RC16V3	Northern Counties Palatine	H47/29F	1995
818	M818KRH	Volvo Olympian YN2RC16V3	Northern Counties Palatine	H47/29F	1995
819	M819KRH	Volvo Olympian YN2RC16V3	Northern Counties Palatine	H47/29F	1995

823-827

Volvo Olympian YN2RC16V3	Northern Counties Palatine	H47/29F	1995

823	M223SVN	824	M224SVN	825	M225SVN	826	M226SVN	827	M227SVN

Eleven Dart SLF buses were placed in service at Stockton during 1997 and these are lettered to indicate the additional facility. Representing the batch is 463, R463SEF. *Andrew Jarosz*

828	P828FEF	Volvo Olympian	Northern Counties Palatine	H47/30F	1997
829	P829FEF	Volvo Olympian	Northern Counties Palatine	H47/30F	1997
830	P830FEF	Volvo Olympian	Northern Counties Palatine	H47/30F	1997

831-840

		Volvo Olympian		Alexander RL		H45/27F	1998
831	R831OVN	833	R833OVN	835	R835OVN	837	R837OVN	839	R839OVN
832	R832OVN	834	R834OVN	836	R836OVN	838	R838OVN	840	R840OVN

908	A208EHN	Dennis Dominator DDA167	Northern Counties	H43/31F	1983
909	A209EHN	Dennis Dominator DDA167	Northern Counties	H43/31F	1983
911	A211EHN	Dennis Dominator DDA167	Northern Counties	H43/31F	1983
913	A213FVN	Dennis Dominator DDA172	Northern Counties	H43/31F	1984
918	SAG518W	MCW Metrobus DR102/17	MCW	H43/30F	1981
922	SAG522W	MCW Metrobus DR102/17	MCW	H43/30F	1981

Ancilliary Vehicles

20	E460AFT	Mercedes-Benz 709D	Reeve Burgess Beaver	B20F	1987	Ex Busways, 1996
21	D403TFT	Mercedes-Benz 709D	Reeve Burgess Beaver	B20F	1987	Ex Busways, 1996
22	D411TFT	Mercedes-Benz 709D	Reeve Burgess Beaver	B20F	1987	Ex Busways, 1996
25	H71XKH	Leyland Swift ST2R44C97A4	Reeve Burgess Harrier	C34FT	1990	
26	XMS253R	Leyland Leopard PSU3C/3R	Alexander AY	B53F	1977	Ex Thamesdown, 1997

Previous Registrations:

837XHW	D556MVR	HDZ8683	A845UGB, 2367AT, A491WYS
E709MFV	E709MFV, BMN88G	IIL1321	D51ORH
FSL61W	GSL307W, 666TPJ	PRX189B	417DCD
FSL62W	GSL306W, 6689DP		

Photographed while new and undertaking private hire duties, Darlington-based 82, R82SEF, is a Volvo B10M with Plaxton Interurban bodywork. The Interurban is a special model for Stagecoach based on the Premiere 320 but designed for express service operation rather than full coach specification and is designated 'dual purpose' by the company. *David Longbottom*

Allocations:-

Darlington (Faverdale Industrial Estate) - Stagecoach Darlington

Mercedes-Benz	301	303	304	305	306	307	309	310
	311	312	341	342				
Renault S75	375	376	377	378				
Dart	455	456						
Volvo B6	401	402	404	405	438	442	443	
	444	445	446	447	449	450	454	
Volvo Interurban	82	83	84	85				
Volvo B10M PS	551	552	553					
Atlantean	122	124	127	128				
Fleetline	129	130	132	135	136	137	138	139
MetroBus	104	105	106					

Hartlepool (Brenda Road) - Stagecoach Hartlepool

Renault S75	363	368	371					
Dart	457	458	459	460	461			
Falcon	521	523	525	527	528	529	530	531
	532							
National	514	515	516	517	518	519	533	536
	537	539	540					
Lynx	541	542	543	544	545	601	602	603
	604	605	606					
Volvo B10M NC	501	502	503	504	505	506	507	508
	509	510						
Coach	33	34	35	36	42	51		
Fleetline	131	133	134					
Titan	270	271	272	273				

Kingston-upon-Hull (Foster Street, Stoneferry) - Stagecoach Kingston-upon-Hull

Mercedes-Benz	343	344	345	346	347	348	349	350
	351	352	353	354				
Lancet	61							
National	60							
Scania N113 SD	701	702	703	704	705	706		
Volvo B10M NC	707	708	709	710	711	712	713	714
	715	716	717	718				
Volvo Interurban	71	72	73	76	77	78	79	80
	81							
Metrobus	114	115	116	117	118	918	922	
Dominator	206	207	208	209	210	211	212	213
	223	224	225	226	228	229	231	232
	233	234	235	236	237	238	239	240
	241	242	243	244	245	246	247	248
	249	250	251	252	253	254	255	256
	257							
Scania N113 DD	800	801	802	803	804	805	806	807
	808	809	810	811	812	813	814	815
	816							
Olympian	817	818	819					

Stockton-on-Tees (Church Road) - Stagecoach Transit

Mercedes-Benz	313	315	316	321	324	325	329	
Volvo B6	403	406	407	408				
Dart SLF	462	463	464	465	466	467	468	469
	470	471	472					
Lynx	607	608	609	610	611	612	613	614
	615	616	617	618	619	620	621	622
	623	624	625	626	627	628	629	630
Volvo B10B	631	632	633	634	635	636	637	638
	639	640	641	642				
Volvo B10M NC	643	644	645	646	647	648	649	650
	651	652						
Fleetline	121	140	141	142	143	144	145	146
	147	148	149	150	151	152	153	154
	155	156	157					
Dominator	214	215	216	217	218	219	220	221
	222	909	911	913				
Titan	189 (PD3)	278	284	285	286			
Olympian	823	824	825	826	827	828	829	830

Withdrawn

Leopard	43	44

During 1997 the conversion and refurbishment of the six East Lancashire-bodied Scania N112s was completed. Photographed in Hull is one of the type, 704, F704BAT. Originally fitted with high-back seats the conversion included their replacement with bus seats.
B G Ridgway

UNITED COUNTIES

United Counties Omnibus Co Ltd, Rothersthorpe Avenue,
Northampton, NN4 9UT

81	WLT682	Leyland Tiger TRCTL11/3RZ	Plaxton Paramount 3500 II	C46FT	1986	
82	WLT908	Leyland Tiger TRCTL11/3RZ	Plaxton Paramount 3500 II	C46FT	1986	
85	647DYE	Leyland Tiger TRCTL11/3RZ	Plaxton Paramount 3500 II	C46FT	1986	

| *92-96* | | Volvo B10M-60 | | Plaxton Première 350 | C49FT | 1992 | Ex Park's, 1993 |
| | | | | | | | 94/5 ex Rainworth Travel, 1993 |

92	J430HDS	93	J439HDS	94	J445HDS	95	J446HDS	96	J450HDS

107	F107NRT	Volvo B10M-61	Plaxton Paramount 3500 III	C49FT	1988	Ex Cambus (Premier), 1996
116w	VLT255	Leyland Tiger TRCTL11/3RZ	Duple Laser 2	C44FT	1985	Ex Stagecoach Malawi, 1993
120	C120PNV	Leyland Tiger TRCTL11/3RZ	Plaxton Paramount 3200 IIE	C53F	1986	
121	C121PNV	Leyland Tiger TRCTL11/3RZ	Plaxton Paramount 3200 IIE	C53F	1986	
122	C122PNV	Leyland Tiger TRCTL11/3RZ	Plaxton Paramount 3200 IIE	C53F	1986	
125w	A729ANH	Volvo B10M-61	Plaxton Paramount 3200 E	C48FT	1983	Ex Stagecoach, 1988
126w	A728ANH	Volvo B10M-61	Plaxton Paramount 3200 E	C48FT	1983	Ex Stagecoach, 1988

United Counties took delivery of twenty-two Volvo B6s in 1993 with the majority still based in Bedford where 409, L409JBD is seen. *Malc McDonald*

130-135

Volvo B10M-61 · Plaxton Paramount 3200 III · C53F · 1988

130	E130ORP	132	E132ORP	133	E133ORP	134	E134ORP	135	F135URP
131	E131ORP								

144-149

Volvo B10M-60 · Plaxton Premiére 350 · C50F · 1992 · Ex Wallace Arnold, 1995

144	J752CWT	146	K758FYG	147	K759FYG	148	K760FYG	149	K761FYG
145	J753CWT								

150-162

Volvo B10M-60 · Plaxton Premiére Interurban · DP53F* · 1993 · *155-162 are DP51F

150	K150DNV	153	K153DNV	156	L156JNH	159	L159JNH	161	L161JNH
151	K151DNV	154	K154DNV	157	L157JNH	160	L160JNH	162	L162JNH
152	K152DNV	155	L155JNH	158	L158JNH				

168-186

Volvo B10M-62 · Plaxton Premiére Interurban · DP51F · 1996-97

168	P168KBD	172	P172KBD	176	R176DNH	180	R180DNH	184	R184DNH
169	P169KBD	173	P173KBD	177	R177DNH	181	R181DNH	185	R185DNH
170	P170KBD	174	R174DNH	178	R178DNH	182	R182DNH	186	R186DNH
171	P171KBD	175	R175DNH	179	R179DNH	183	R183DNH		

301-326

Mercedes-Benz 709D · Alexander Sprint · B23F · 1996

301	N301XRP	307	N307XRP	312	N312XRP	317	N317XRP	322	N322XRP
302	N302XRP	308	N308XRP	313	N313XRP	318	N318XRP	323	N323XRP
303	N303XRP	309	N309XRP	314	N314XRP	319	N319XRP	324	N324XRP
304	N304XRP	310	N310XRP	315	N315XRP	320	N320XRP	325	N325XRP
305	N305XRP	311	N311XRP	316	N316XRP	321	N321XRP	326	N326XRP
306	N306XRP								

332-349

Mercedes-Benz 709D · Alexander Sprint · B25F · 1994

332	M332DRP	337	M337DRP	341	M341DRP	344	M344DRP	347	M347DRP
334	M334DRP	338	M338DRP	342	M342DRP	345	M345DRP	348	M348DRP
335	M335DRP	339	M339DRP	343	M343DRP	346	M346DRP	349	M349DRP
336	M336DRP	340	M340DRP						

350-383

Mercedes-Benz 709D · Alexander Sprint · B25F* · 1992-93 · *351-66 are B21F

350	K350ANV	357	K357ANV	364	L364JBD	371	L371JBD	378	L378JBD
351	K351ANV	358	K358ANV	365	L365JBD	372	L372JBD	379	L379JBD
352	K352ANV	359	K359ANV	366	L366JBD	373	L373JBD	380	L380JBD
353	K353ANV	360	L360JBD	367	L367JBD	374	L374JBD	381	L381NBD
354	K354ANV	361	L361JBD	368	L368JBD	375	L375JBD	382	L382NBD
355	K355ANV	362	L362JBD	369	L369JBD	376	L376JBD	383	L383NBD
356	K356ANV	363	L363JBD	370	L370JBD	377	L377JBD		

401-422

Volvo B6-9.9M · Alexander Dash · B40F · 1993

401	L401JBD	406	L406JBD	411	L411JBD	415	L415JBD	419	L419JBD
402	L402JBD	407	L407JBD	412	L412JBD	416	L416JBD	420	L420JBD
403	L403JBD	408	L408JBD	413	L413JBD	417	L417JBD	421	L421JBD
404	L404JBD	409	L409JBD	414	L414JBD	418	L418JBD	422	L422MVV
405	L405JBD	410	L410JBD						

423	L423XVV	Volvo B6-9.9M	Alexander Dash	DP40F	1994
424	L424XVV	Volvo B6-9.9M	Alexander Dash	DP40F	1994
425	L425XVV	Volvo B6-9.9M	Alexander Dash	DP40F	1994
450	P450KRP	Dennis Dart	Alexander Dash	B40F	1996
451	P451KRP	Dennis Dart	Alexander Dash	B40F	1996
452	P452KRP	Dennis Dart	Alexander Dash	B40F	1996
500	LFR862X	Leyland National 2 NL106AL11/1R		B44F	1981	Ex Cumberland, 1993
501	LFR864X	Leyland National 2 NL106AL11/1R		B41F	1982	Ex Cumberland, 1993

559-568

Volvo Olympian · Alexander RL · H45/27F · 1997

559	R703DNH	561	R561DRP	563	R563DRP	565	R565DRP	567	R567DRP
560	R560DRP	562	R562DRP	564	R564DRP	566	R566DRP	568	R568DRP

600	F110NES	Leyland Olympian ON6LXCT/5RZ Alexander RL		H66/44F	1989	Ex East Midland, 1992

601-611

Leyland Olympian ONLXB/1R Eastern Coach Works H45/32F* 1981 *601 is DPH45/27F
*602/5/6 are DPH41/27F

601	ARP601X	604	ARP604X	606	ARP606X	608	ARP608X	610	ARP610X
602	ARP602X	605	ARP605X	607	ARP607X	609	ARP609X	611	ARP611X

612	WLT528	Leyland Olympian ONLXB/1RV	Alexander RL	H43/34F	1987	Ex Bluebird, 1991
613	D383XRS	Leyland Olympian ONLXB/1RV	Alexander RL	H43/34F	1987	Ex Bluebird, 1991
614	WLT512	Leyland Olympian ONLXB/1RV	Alexander RL	H47/34F	1987	Ex Bluebird, 1991
615	685DYE	Leyland Olympian ONLXB/1RV	Alexander RL	H47/34F	1987	Ex Bluebird, 1991
616	GSO6V	Leyland Olympian ONLXB/1RV	Alexander RL	H47/34F	1987	Ex Bluebird, 1991
617	GSO7V	Leyland Olympian ONLXB/1RV	Alexander RL	H47/34F	1987	Ex Bluebird, 1991
618	GSO2V	Leyland Olympian ONLXB/1RV	Alexander RL	H47/34F	1986	Ex Bluebird, 1994

620-649

Leyland Olympian ONLXB/2RZ Alexander RL H51/36F* 1988-89 *635-644 are H51/34F
*645-9 are DPH51/31F

620	F620MSL	626	F626MSL	632	F632MSL	638	F638YRP	644	G644EVV
621	F621MSL	627	F627MSL	633	F633MSL	639	G639EVV	645	G645EVV
622	F622MSL	628	F628MSL	634	F634MSP	640	G640EVV	646	G646EVV
623	F623MSL	629	F629MSL	635	F635YRP	641	G641EVV	647	G647EVV
624	F624MSL	630	F630MSL	636	F636YRP	642	G642EVV	648	G648EVV
625	F625MSL	631	F631MSL	637	F637YRP	643	G643EVV	649	G649EVV

654	H654VVV	Leyland Olympian ON2R56G13Z4 Alexander RL	H51/34F	1990		

655-670

Leyland Olympian ON2R50G13Z4 Northern Counties Palatine H47/29F 1992

655	K655UNH	658	K658UNH	661	K661UNH	664	K664UNH	668	K668UNH
656	K656UNH	659	K659UNH	662	K662UNH	665	K665UNH	669	K669UNH
657	K657UNH	660	K660UNH	663	K663UNH	667	K667UNH	670	K670UNH

671-685

Volvo Olympian YN2RV18Z4 Northern Counties Palatine H47/29F 1993

671	L671HNV	674	L674HNV	677	L677HNV	680	L680HNV	683	L683HNV
672	L672HNV	675	L675HNV	678	L678HNV	681	L681HNV	684	L684HNV
673	L673HNV	676	L676HNV	679	L679HNV	682	L682HNV	685	L685JBD

686-692

Volvo Olympian YN2RV18Z4 Alexander RL H51/36F 1996

686	P686JBD	688	P688JBD	690	P690JBD	691	P691JBD	692	P692JBD
687	P687JBD	689	P689JBD						

693-703

Volvo Olympian Alexander RL H45/27F 1997

693	R693DNH	695	R695DNH	697	R697DNH	699	R699DNH	702	R702DNH
694	R694DNH	696	R696DNH	698	R698DNH	701	R701DNH		

708	J808WFS	Leyland Olympian ON2R56C13Z4 Alexander RL	H47/32F	1992	Ex Fife Scottish, 1994
709	K709ASC	Leyland Olympian ON2R56C13Z4 Alexander RL	H47/32F	1992	Ex Fife Scottish, 1994
710	K710ASC	Leyland Olympian ON2R56C13Z4 Alexander RL	H47/32F	1992	Ex Fife Scottish, 1994
713	K713ASC	Leyland Olympian ON2R56C13Z4 Alexander RL	H47/32F	1992	Ex Fife Scottish, 1994
714	J620GCR	Leyland Olympian ON2R56G13Z4 Alexander RL	H51/34F	1991	Ex Bluebird, 1994
715	J621GCR	Leyland Olympian ON2R56G13Z4 Alexander RL	H51/34F	1991	Ex Bluebird, 1994
716	J622GCR	Leyland Olympian ON2R56G13Z4 Alexander RL	H51/34F	1991	Ex Bluebird, 1994

Opposite, top:- **Coachlinks names are used by United Counties for their express services, many of which use the M1 in their schedule. However, when photographed, 159, L159JNH was heading for Daventry on school duties.   Thirteen Interurbans were delivered in 1993 with a further fifteen in the last year or so. These are likely to be the last for a while as none of the type feature in the 1998 delivery programme.** *Malc McDonald*
Opposite, bottom:- **Northern Counties have been the second-string bodybuilder of double-deck buses for Stagecoach with all the deliveries carrying the original Palatine body styling. For United Counties, the 1993 delivery carried this body, represented by 671, L671HNV, the first of the batch.** *Malc McDonald*

721-740 Bristol VRT/SL3/6LXB   Eastern Coach Works   H43/31F   1980-81 Ex Devon General, 1988-89

721	LFJ862W	726	LFJ855W	734	FDV812V	736	LFJ865W	739	LFJ869W
722	LFJ863W	727	LFJ879W	735	LFJ864W	738	FDV835V	740	FDV832V
724	LFJ852W								

744	LFJ878W	Bristol VRT/SL3/6LXC	Eastern Coach Works	H43/31F	1981	Ex Devon General, 1989
752	FAO419V	Bristol VRT/SL3/6LXB	Eastern Coach Works	H43/31F	1980	Ex Cumberland, 1992
862	RRP862R	Bristol VRT/SL3/6LXB	Eastern Coach Works	H43/31F	1976	
863	RRP863R	Bristol VRT/SL3/6LXB	Eastern Coach Works	H43/31F	1976	
901	BAU179T	Bristol VRT/SL3/6LXB	Eastern Coach Works	H43/31F	1978	Ex East Midland, 1993

912-967 Bristol VRT/SL3/6LXB   Eastern Coach Works   H43/31F   1978-81 919/61 are DPH41/27F

912	FRP912T	923	LBD923V	937	SNV937W	945	URP945W	962	VVV962W
914	HBD914T	930	SNV930W	939	URP939W	949	VVV949W	963	VVV963W
915	HBD915T	931	SNV931W	940	URP940W	950	VVV950W	965	VVV965W
916	HBD916T	935	SNV935W	941	URP941W	952	VVV952W	966	VVV966W
920	LBD920V	936	SNV936W	944	URP944W	961	VVV961W	967	VVV967W
921	LBD921V								

970	KRU843W	Bristol VRT/SL3/6LXB	Eastern Coach Works	H43/31F	1980	Ex Hampshire Bus, 1988
971	KRU845W	Bristol VRT/SL3/6LXB	Eastern Coach Works	H43/31F	1980	Ex Hampshire Bus, 1988
973	KRU847W	Bristol VRT/SL3/6LXB	Eastern Coach Works	H43/31F	1980	Ex Hampshire Bus, 1988
974	KRU852W	Bristol VRT/SL3/6LXB	Eastern Coach Works	H43/31F	1980	Ex Hampshire Bus, 1988

		Leyland Titan TNLXB2RR	Leyland		H44/27F	1982	Ex East London, 1998
...	NUW554Y	...	NUW568Y	...	NUW584Y	...	NUW595Y	...	NUW608Y
...	NUW557Y	...	NUW576Y	...	NUW588Y	...	NUW602Y	...	NUW610Y
...	NUW565Y	...	NUW579Y	...	NUW590Y	...	NUW605Y		

Special event vehicles

703u	HVS937	AEC Routemaster R2RH	Park Royal	H36/28R	1961	Ex London Buses, 1988
708u	CUV192C	AEC Routemaster R2RH	Park Royal	H36/28R	1965	Ex London Buses, 1988

Previous Registrations:

647DYE	C85PRP		
685DYE	D379XRS	HVS937	WLT682
A728ANH	A800TGG, 4009SC, A332SNH, WLT908	VLT255	B357KNH, Malawi ?,
A729ANH	A798TGG, 7878SC, A320SNH, 647DYE	WLT512	D384XRS
GSO2V	C472SSO	WLT528	D382XRS
GSO6V	D376XRS	WLT682	C81PRP
GSO7V	D377XRS	WLT908	C82PRP

The number of Bristol VRs remaining with United Counties is declining, and further inroads are expected when the transfer of fourteen Leyland Titans from East London has been completed. Pictured in Northampton is 734, FDV812V, which was one of many transferred from Devon General as that operation introduced large numbers of minibuses.
Malc McDonald

Allocations:-

Bedford (St Johns)

Outstations - Biggleswade; Huntingdon and Northampton

Mercedes-Benz	302	304	317	318	319	320	321	322
	323	324	325	326	332	334	335	336
	337	338	350	369	370	371	372	373
Tiger	120	121	122					
Volvo B6	402	403	404	405	406	407	408	409
	410	411	412	413	414	415	416	417
	418	419	420	421	422			
National	500							
Volvo B10M coach	130	131	132	133	134	144	145	148
	149	150	151	152	153	154	168	169
	170	171	172	173				
Bristol VR	722	726	738					
	916	920	921	923	930	931	936	937
	944	950	961	962	967	974		
Olympian	559	560	561	562	563	564	565	566
	567	568	600	612	613	614	615	616
	617	618	621	622	623	624	629	630
	631	632	634	635	636	637	638	639
	640	641	642	644	655	661	662	663
	664	665	708	709	710	713	714	715
	716							

Corby (Station Road)

Outstation - Uppingham

Mercedes-Benz	351	352	353	354	355	356	357	358
	359	360	361	362	363	364	365	366
	367	368						
Tiger	81	82	85					
Bristol VR	721	739	912	914	915	941	945	949
	952	963	970	971	973			
Olympian	604	607	608	609	620			

Kettering (Northampton Road)

Outstations - Chown's Mill; Desborough; Thrapston and Wellingborough

Mercedes-Benz	306	307	308	309	310	311	312	313
	314	315	316	339	340	341	342	343
	344	345	346	347	348	349	383	
Expressliners	92	93	94	95	96			
Volvo B10M coach	135	174	175	176	177	178	179	180
	181	182	183	184	185	186		
Bristol VR	724	727	736	740	744	752	939	940
	961	965	966					
Olympian	625	626	627	628	633	643	645	646
	647	648	649	654	667	668	669	670

United Counties operate one of the three tri-axle Leyland Olympians as its 600, F110NES. The vehicle seats 110 passengers and was marketed as the Megadecker for a time. Stagecoach took a further batch of the model for use in Hong Kong which are now operating with Citybus while twenty of the comparable Dennis Product, the Dragon, were supplied to Kenya Bus, though these are reported to be due to return to the UK during 1998. *Malc McDonald*

Northampton (Rothersthorpe Avenue)

Outstations - Buckingham; Chown's Mill; Daventry; Husbands Bosworth and Milton Keymes

Mercedes-Benz	301	303	305	374	375	376	377	378
	379	380	381	382				
Volvo B6	401	423	424	425				
Dennis Dart	450	451	452					
National	501							
Volvo B10M coach	107	146	147	155	156	157	158	159
	160	161	162					
Bristol VR	734	735	739	935	937	962		
Olympian	601	602	605	606	610	611	656	657
	658	659	660	671	672	673	674	675
	676	677	678	679	680	681	682	683
	684	685	686	687	688	689	690	691
	692	693	694	695	696	697	698	699
	701	702						

Unallocated or delicenced

Tiger	116	
Volvo B10M	125	126
Routemaster	703	708

Opposite, top: The striking livery of Cumberland's Coachline operation is shown on this picture of Cumberland 111, VRR447. Here, the Plaxton Paramount body is based on a Volvo B10M chassis.
Opposite, bottom:- United Counties' 630, F630MSL is one of the longer variants of the Leyland Olympian, though retaining standard window sizes, Alexander use a small central bay to account for the additional length. The vehicle is seen heading for Bedford where the vehicle is currently allocated. *Malcolm Flynn*

WESTERN

Western Buses Ltd; A1 Service Ltd,
Sandgate, Ayr, KA7 1DD

001-035

Mercedes-Benz 709D   Alexander Sprint   B25F   1995-96

001	N601VSS	007	N607VSS	021	N621VSS	026	N626VSS	031	N631VSS
002	N602VSS	008	N608VSS	022	N622VSS	027	N627VSS	032	N632VSS
003	N603VSS	009	N609VSS	023	N623VSS	028	N628VSS	033	N633VSS
004	N604VSS	010	N610VSS	024	N624VSS	029	N629VSS	034	N634VSS
005	N605VSS	011	N611VSS	025	N625VSS	030	N630VSS	035	N635VSS
006	N606VSS	012	N612VSS						

038-046

Mercedes-Benz L608D   Reeve Burgess   B20F   1986-87 Ex Cumberland, 1997

038	RBZ3427	039	RBZ3428	042	RBZ4209	043	RBZ3429	046	RBZ4241

052-058

Mercedes-Benz L608D   Reeve Burgess   B20F   1986   Ex Cumberland, 1997

052	RBZ4245	053	RBZ4281	054	RBZ4359	055	RBZ5459	058	RBZ5491

060	M395KVR	Mercedes-Benz 709D	Alexander Sprint	B27F	1995	Ex AA, Ayr, 1997
061	M396KVR	Mercedes-Benz 709D	Alexander Sprint	B27F	1995	Ex AA, Ayr, 1997
064	E499TSJ	Mercedes-Benz 609D	Devon Conversion	C23F	1988	Ex AA, Ayr, 1997
065	J460YDT	Mercedes-Benz 709D	Reeve Burgess Beaver	B27F	1991	Ex AA, Ayr, 1997
066	J277OSJ	Mercedes-Benz 709D	Reeve Burgess Beaver	B25F	1992	Ex AA, Ayr, 1997
067	M397KVR	Mercedes-Benz 709D	Alexander Sprint	B27F	1995	Ex AA, Ayr, 1997
080	RBZ5492	Mercedes-Benz L608D	Reeve Burgess	B20F	1986	Ex Ribble (B&P), 1997
081	RBZ5493	Mercedes-Benz L608D	Sparshatts	B20F	1986	Ex Ribble (B&P), 1997
082	RBZ5494	Mercedes-Benz L608D	Sparshatts	B20F	1986	Ex Ribble (B&P), 1997
083	RBZ5495	Mercedes-Benz L608D	Sparshatts	B20F	1986	Ex Ribble (B&P), 1997

084-089

Mercedes-Benz 811D   Carlyle   B29F   1991   Ex Bluebird Buses, 1998

084	H106HDV	086	H986FTT	087	H987FTT	088	H180GTA	089	H789GTA
085	H107HDV								

103-121

Volvo B10M-62   Plaxton Première Interurban DP51F   1997

103	R103LSO	104	R104LSO	105	R105LSO	119	R119OPS	121	R121OPS

122-128

Volvo B10M-62   Plaxton Premiére Interurban DP51F   1994   Ex Stagecoach South, 1996

122	M160CCD	124	M162CCD	126	M164CCD	127	M165CCD	128	M166CCD
123	M161CCD	125	M163CCD						

129	WLT416	Volvo B10M-60	Plaxton Paramount 3500 III	C51F	1989	Ex Cambus (Premier), 1996
130	YSV730	Volvo B10M-60	Plaxton Paramount 3500 III	C53F	1990	Ex Cambus (Premier), 1996
131	YSV735	Volvo B10M-60	Plaxton Paramount 3500 III	C53F	1991	Ex Cambus (Premier), 1996
132	J917LEM	Volvo B10M-61	Plaxton Paramount 3500 III	C53F	1991	Ex Bluebird Buses, 1997
133	J919LEM	Volvo B10M-61	Plaxton Paramount 3500 III	C53F	1991	Ex Bluebird Buses, 1997
135	VLT104	Volvo B10M-60	Plaxton Expressliner	C53F	1990	Ex Bluebird Buses, 1995
136	WLT794	Volvo B10M-60	Plaxton Expressliner	C53F	1990	Ex Bluebird Buses, 1995
137	WLT809	Volvo B10M-60	Plaxton Expressliner	C53F	1990	Ex Dorset Travel, 1995
138	WLT720	Volvo B10M-60	Plaxton Expressliner	C53F	1990	Ex Dorset Travel, 1995
139	WLT727	Volvo B10M-60	Plaxton Expressliner	C53F	1990	Ex Ribble, 1995
140	WLT830	Volvo B10M-60	Plaxton Expressliner	C53F	1990	Ex Ribble, 1995
141	IIL3507	Volvo B10M-60	Plaxton Paramount 3500 III	C51F	1989	Ex Ribble, 1995

Opposite, top:- **Western Buses 136, G387GNV has been re-registered WLT794 since this picture was taken. The vehicle, though in corporate livery was built as an Expressliner to the requirements of National Express contracts.** *Murdoch Currie*
Opposite, bottom:- **The principal service between Kilmarnock and Ayr is now worked by Volvo Olympians which carry the colour of the former A1 operation, with fleet names in the same font as the main Stagecoach name. Pictured heading east is 931, N865VHH.** *Billy Nicol*

Clyde Coaster livery is carried by six Western Buses vehicles including 453, H455RGG, a former AA Buses vehicle. This Alexander PS was one of pair bought from dealer stock before the early 1990s recession caused dealers to reduce their stock holding of new vehicles considerably. Clyde Coaster service requires eight buses with its initial allocation being two from Clydeside, three from A1 Service and three from AA Buses. Once vehicles have been integrated the expectation is that A1 Service blue livery will be carried by Olympians operating on service 11 while AA Buses green and cream livery will be worn on vehicles required to operate Troon local service, the Ayr to Ardrossan link and Irvine local services. *Phillip Stephenson*

620	TMS404X	Leyland Leopard PSU3G/4R	Alexander AYS	B53F	1982	Ex Fife, 1996
621	TMS405X	Leyland Leopard PSU3G/4R	Alexander AYS	DP49F	1982	Ex Fife, 1996
622	TMS407X	Leyland Leopard PSU3G/4R	Alexander AYS	DP51F	1982	Ex Fife, 1996
623	XMS423Y	Leyland Leopard PSU3G/4R	Alexander AYS	B53F	1982	Ex Fife, 1996
624	WFS136W	Leyland Leopard PSU3F/4R	Alexander AYS	B53F	1980	Ex Bluebird Buses, 1995
625	YSF98S	Leyland Leopard PSU3D/4R	Alexander AYS	B55F	1977	Ex Bluebird Buses, 1995
626	YSF100S	Leyland Leopard PSU3E/4R	Alexander AYS	B53F	1977	Ex Bluebird Buses, 1995
627	NPA229W	Leyland Leopard PSU3E/4R	Plaxton Supreme IV Express	C49F	1981	Ex Bluebird Buses, 1995
628	TBC1X	Leyland Leopard PSU3F/4R	Plaxton Supreme IV Express	C53F	1981	Ex Busways, 1997
629	GMS285S	Leyland Leopard PSU3E/4R	Alexander AYS	B53F	1978	Ex Kelvin Scottish, 1987
630	GMS292S	Leyland Leopard PSU3E/4R	Alexander AYS	B55F	1978	Ex Kelvin Scottish, 1987
631	WFS147W	Leyland Leopard PSU3F/4R	Alexander AYS	B53F	1980	Ex Fife Scottish, 1997
632	CSF163W	Leyland Leopard PSU3E/4R	Alexander AYS	DP49F	1981	Ex Fife Scottish, 1997
633	GCS33V	Leyland Leopard PSU3E/4R	Alexander AY	B53F	1980	Ex Clydeside Scottish, 1989
634	OSJ636R	Leyland Leopard PSU3C/3R	Alexander AY	O49F	1977	Ex Bluebird Buses, 1996

637-680

							Leyland Leopard PSU3E/4R*		Alexander AY		B53F*		1977-80	*637 is DP49F; 636 is O49F

Leyland Leopard PSU3E/4R*   Alexander AY   B53F*   1977-80 *637 is DP49F; 636 is O49F
                                                              *667/70/1/6/8-80 are PSU3D/4R;

637	GCS37V	648	GCS48V	658	GCS58V	667	TSJ67S	676	TSJ76S
638	GCS38V	649	GCS49V	660	GCS60V	669	GCS69V	678	TSJ78S
641	GCS41V	651	GCS51V	661	GCS61V	670	TSJ70S	679	TSJ79S
645	GCS45V	653	GCS53V	662	GCS62V	671	TSJ71S	680	TSJ80S
647	GCS47V	657	GCS57V	665	GCS65V				

681	TMS406X	Leyland Leopard PSU3G/4R	Alexander AYS	DP49F	1982	Ex Fife Scottish, 1996
682	GSO82V	Leyland Leopard PSU3E/4R	Alexander AYS	DP49F	1980	Ex Fife Scottish, 1996
683	GSO83V	Leyland Leopard PSU3E/4R	Alexander AYS	DP49F	1980	Ex Fife Scottish, 1996
684	GSO84V	Leyland Leopard PSU3E/4R	Alexander AYS	DP49F	1980	Ex Fife Scottish, 1996

685	TSJ85S	Leyland Leopard PSU3D/4R		Alexander AY		B53F	1978		
686	XMS422Y	Leyland Leopard PSU3G/4R		Alexander AYS		B53F	1982	Ex Fife Scottish, 1996	
687	WFS138W	Leyland Leopard PSU3F/4R		Alexander AYS		B53F	1980	Ex Fife Scottish, 1996	
688	WFS142W	Leyland Leopard PSU3F/4R		Alexander AYS		B53F	1980	Ex Fife Scottish, 1996	
689	GSO77V	Leyland Leopard PSU3E/4R		Alexander AYS		B55F	1980	Ex Highland Country, 1996	

691-699

Leyland Leopard PSU3E/4R* Alexander AY B53F 1977-80 695-7 ex Clydeside Scottish, 1989
*691-3 are PSU3D/4R; 692/6 are B55F

691	TSJ31S	693	TSJ33S	696	BSJ896T	698	BSJ930T	699	BSJ931T
692	TSJ32S	695	BSJ895T	697	BSJ917T				

701	UIB3541	Leyland National 11351A/1R			B48F	1979	Ex Kelvin Central, 1989

702-706

Leyland National 11351A/3R B48F 1978-79 Ex British Airways, Heathrow, 1993

702	UIB3542	703	UIB3543	704	OIW7024	705	OIW7025	706	UIB3076

707	GMB654T	Leyland National 10351B/1R (Gardner)		B40F	1978	Ex AA Buses, Ayr, 1997
708	YSJ14T	Leyland National 11351A/1R		B52F	1979	Ex AA Buses, Ayr, 1997
710	KMA399T	Leyland National 11351A/1R(Gardner)		B51F	1979	Ex A1 Service, 1995
721	703DYE	Bedford YMT	Duple Dominant II Express	C49F	1981	Ex Arran Coaches, 1994
729	FSU739	Bedford Venturer YNV	Plaxton Paramount 3200 III	C57F	1987	Ex Arran Coaches, 1994
756	DBV834W	Leyland National 2 NL106L11/1R		B44F	1980	Ex Cumberland, 1997
757	RRM383X	Leyland National 2 NL116AL11/1R		DP52F	1981	Ex Cumberland, 1997
758	SHH393X	Leyland National 2 NL116AL11/1R		B52F	1982	Ex Cumberland, 1997
759	KHH378W	Leyland National 2 NL116L11/1R		B52F	1980	Ex Cumberland, 1997
760	HHH372V	Leyland National 2 NL116L11/1R		B52F	1980	Ex Cumberland, 1997
761	FSD687V	Leyland National 2 NL116L11/1R		B52F	1980	Ex AA Buses, Ayr, 1997
762	JSD595W	Leyland National 2 NL116L11/1R		B52F	1980	Ex AA Buses, Ayr, 1997
763	LSD732W	Leyland National 2 NL116AL11/1R		B52F	1981	Ex AA Buses, Ayr, 1997
764	LSJ871W	Leyland National 2 NL116AL11/1R		B52F	1981	Ex AA Buses, Ayr, 1997
765	LSJ872W	Leyland National 2 NL116AL11/1R		B52F	1981	Ex AA Buses, Ayr, 1997
766	NSJ550X	Leyland National 2 NL116AL11/1R		B52F	1981	Ex AA Buses, Ayr, 1997
767	USJ491Y	Leyland National 2 NL116TL11/1R		B52F	1983	Ex AA Buses, Ayr, 1997
768	A306YSJ	Leyland National 2 NL116TL11/1R		B52F	1984	Ex AA Buses, Ayr, 1997
769	A523YSD	Leyland National 2 NL116HLXCT/1R		B52F	1984	Ex AA Buses, Ayr, 1997
770	C112GSJ	Leyland National 2 NL116HLXCT/1R		B52F	1985	Ex AA Buses, Ayr, 1997

771-791

Leyland National 2 NL116L11/1R B52F* 1980-81 Ex Kelvin Scottish, 1988
*774/5/85/9-91 are B48F

771	WAS771V	775	MDS865V	781	MSO18W	786	SNS826W	790	YFS310W
773	RFS583V	779	RFS579V	783	NLS983W	788	WAS768V	791	YFS309W
774	YFS304W	780	YFS308W	785	NLS985W	789	NLS989W		

During 1997 Western changed the fleet name style to match the other Scottish operations. The result is seen on Alexander PS-bodied Volvo 590, M790PRS. The vehicle is now based at Kilmarnock.
Billy Nicol

792	KRS540V	Leyland National 2 NL106L11/1R		B41F	1980	Ex Bluebird, 1993
793	KRS542V	Leyland National 2 NL106L11/1R		B41F	1980	Ex Bluebird, 1993
795	MSO10W	Leyland National 2 NL106L11/1R		B41F	1980	Ex Bluebird, 1993
796	NLP388V	Leyland National 2 NL116L11/3R		B48F	1980	Ex British Airways, Heathrow, 1993
797	JTF971W	Leyland National 2 NL116AL11/1R		B48F	1981	Ex Mitchell, Plean, 1994
801	UNA863S	Leyland Atlantean AN68A/1R	Park Royal	H43/32F	1978	Ex GM Buses, 1991
802	WVM884S	Leyland Atlantean AN68A/1R	Park Royal	H43/32F	1978	Ex GM Buses, 1991
804	ANA211T	Leyland Atlantean AN68A/1R	Northern Counties	H43/32F	1978	Ex GM Buses, 1991
806	RJA702R	Leyland Atlantean AN68A/1R	Northern Counties	H43/32F	1977	Ex GM Buses, 1991
807	UNA772S	Leyland Atlantean AN68A/1R	Northern Counties	H43/32F	1977	Ex GM Buses, 1991
809	VBA161S	Leyland Atlantean AN68A/1R	Northern Counties	H43/32F	1978	Ex GM Buses, 1992
810	UNA824S	Leyland Atlantean AN68A/1R	Park Royal	H43/32F	1977	Ex GM Buses, 1992
812	WVM888S	Leyland Atlantean AN68A/1R	Park Royal	H43/32F	1978	Ex GM Buses, 1992
819	KSD62W	Leyland Atlantean AN68B/1R	Alexander AL	H45/33F	1980	Ex A1 Service, 1995
833	UWV607S	Bristol VRT/SL3/6LXB	Eastern Coach Works	CO43/31F	1977	Ex Bluebird Buses, 1996
834	XSJ656T	Leyland Fleetline FE30AGR	Northern Counties	O44/31F	1978	
835	HDS566H	Daimler Fleetline CRG6LX	Alexander D	O44/31F	1970	Ex Clydeside Scottish, 1989
836	GHV948N	Daimler Fleetline CRG6	Park Royal	O44/27F	1974	Ex Stagecoach Selkent, 1995
837	GHV102N	Daimler Fleetline CRG6	Park Royal	O44/27F	1975	Ex Stagecoach Selkent, 1995
838	ASJ207T	Leyland Fleetline FE30AGR	Alexander AL	H45/33F	1979	Ex AA Buses, Ayr, 1997
839	ASJ206T	Leyland Fleetline FE30AGR	Alexander AL	H45/33F	1979	Ex AA Buses, Ayr, 1997
840	ULS660T	Leyland Fleetline FE30AGR	Eastern Coach Works	H43/32F	1979	Ex Kelvin Central, 1989
843	ASA23T	Leyland Fleetline FE30AGR	Eastern Coach Works	H43/32F	1978	Ex Northern Scottish, 1987
847	ASA27T	Leyland Fleetline FE30AGR	Eastern Coach Works	H43/32F	1978	Ex Northern Scottish, 1987

851-889

Leyland Fleetline FE30AGR   Northern Counties   H44/31F   1978-79 859-6/9/80/9 ex Clydeside, 1988-89

851	XSJ651T	857	XSJ657T	866	XSJ666T	870	BCS870T	882	ECS882V
853	XSJ653T	859	XSJ659T	867	XSJ667T	878	ECS878V	888	BCS865T
854	XSJ654T	860	XSJ660T	868	XSJ668T	879	ECS879V	889	BCS869T
855	XSJ655T	862	XSJ662T	869	XSJ669T	880	ECS880V		

892	A308RSU	Volvo Citybus B10M-50	East Lancashire	H47/36F	1983	Ex A1 Service, 1995
893	B24CGA	Volvo Citybus B10M-50	Alexander RV	H47/37F	1985	Ex A1 Service, 1995
894	E864RCS	Volvo Citybus B10M-50	Alexander RV	DPH41/25F	1987	
895	E865RCS	Volvo Citybus B10M-50	Alexander RV	DPH45/35F	1987	
896	E866RCS	Volvo Citybus B10M-50	Alexander RV	DPH45/35F	1987	
897	E867RCS	Volvo Citybus B10M-50	Alexander RV	DPH43/33F	1987	

901-906

Leyland Olympian ONLXB/1R   Roe   H47/29F   1982-83 Ex A1 Service, 1995

901	HSB698Y	903	CUB73Y	904	EWY74Y	905	EWY75Y	906	EWY76Y
902	CUB72Y								

907	C800HCS	Leyland Olympian ONLXB/1R	Eastern Coach Works	H45/32F	1986	Ex A1 Service, 1995
908	F41XCS	Leyland Olympian ONCL10/1RZ	Leyland	H47/31F	1989	Ex A1 Service, 1995
909	F524WSJ	Leyland Olympian ONCL10/1RZ	Leyland	H47/31F	1989	Ex A1 Service, 1995
910	F149XCS	Leyland Olympian ONCL10/1RZ	Leyland	H47/31F	1989	Ex A1 Service, 1995
911	PJI4983	Leyland Olympian ONTL11/2RSp	Eastern Coach Works	CH45/24F	1985	Ex Cleveland Transit, 1995

912-932

Volvo Olympian YN2RC16V3   Alexander RL   H47/32F   1995

912	M490ASW	917	N851VHH	921	N855VHH	925	N859VHH	929	N863VHH
913	M491ASW	918	N852VHH	922	N856VHH	926	N860VHH	930	N864VHH
914	M492ASW	919	N853VHH	923	N857VHH	927	N861VHH	931	N865VHH
915	N849VHH	920	N854VHH	924	N858VHH	928	N862VHH	932	N866VHH
916	N850VHH								

933-942

Leyland Titan TNLXB2RRSp   Park Royal   H44/26D*   1978-80 Ex East London, 1995
*Lower deck seating varies; 934-6 ex Selkent, 1995

933	EYE236V	935	CUL179V	937	WYV5T	939	WYV29T	941	EYE246V
934	CUL189V	936	CUL209V	938	WYV27T	940	CUL197V	942	EYE248V

943-949

Leyland Titan TNLXB2RRSp   Leyland   H44/26D*   1981-83 Ex East London, 1995
*Lower deck seating varies

943	GYE252W	945	GYE273W	947	OHV684Y	948	A833SUL	949	A876SUL
944	GYE254W	946	GYE281W						

Leyland Titans, in both closed and open formats, are entering service with all the Scottish operations. By the start of the summer season ten open-top Titans should have entered service and displaced the various earlier types with one common model. Closed-top versions are also displacing older double-decks. Shown working A1 duties is 939, WYV29T. *Tony Wilson*

950-960

		Leyland Titan TNLXB2RRSp		Leyland		H44/26D*	1983	Ex Stagecoach Selkent, 1996	
								*Lower deck seating varies	

950	A824SUL	952	OHV710Y	954	OHV728Y	957	OHV800Y	959	NUW618Y
951	OHV700Y	953	OHV714Y	956	OHV780Y	958	OHV809Y	960	NUW674Y

964	WYV49T	Leyland Titan TNLXB2RRSp	Park Royal	H44/22D	1979	Ex Stagecoach Selkent, 1995
965	WYV56T	Leyland Titan TNLXB2RRSp	Park Royal	H44/26D	1979	Ex Stagecoach Selkent, 1995
966	CUL208V	Leyland Titan TNLXB2RR	Leyland	H44/26D	1980	Ex Stagecoach Selkent, 1995
967	KYV410X	Leyland Titan TNLXB2RR	Leyland	H44/24D	1982	Ex Stagecoach Selkent, 1995
968	A77THX	Leyland Titan TNLXB2RR	Leyland	H44/26D	1984	Ex Stagecoach East London, 1997
969	A918SYE	Leyland Titan TNLXB2RR	Leyland	H44/24D	1984	Ex Stagecoach East London, 1997

Special event vehicles - traditional liveries

1059	UCS659	Albion Lowlander LR3	Alexander	H40/31F	1963	
1074	YYS174	Bedford C5Z1	Duple Vista	C21FM	1960	Ex David MacBrayne, 1970
1081	YSD350L	Leyland Leopard PSU3/3R	Alexander AY	B41F	1972	
1082	RCS382	Leyland Titan PD3A/3	Alexander	L35/32RD	1961	

Opposite, top:- **Bluebird Buses and Western retain a small fleet of special event vehicles, most of which originate from one of the former operations. Photographed at Brodick Castle is Bedford 1074, YYS174. The vehicle is liveried in David MacBrayne colours.** *Tony Wilson*
Opposite, bottom:- **Many of the vehicles which operated the AA Buses duties at the time the business was acquired were leased and have been replaced by a batch of ten Dennis Dart SLF buses which have been placed in service in AA Buses cream and green livery while the AA Buses name is in Stagecoach's font. Photographed shortly after delivery is 464, R464LSO.** *Western Buses*

Previous Registrations:

13CLT	D317SBG	RBZ5497	D107NUS
283URB	E561UHS	RBZ5498	D108NUS
295UB	B421CMC	RBZ5503	D113NUS
439UG	B422CMC	UIB3076	EGT458T
495FFJ	B193CGA	UIB3541	EGB89T
5796MX	B106REL	UIB3542	EGT451T
703DYE	MCS138W	UIB3543	WGY589S
896HOD	B192CGA	UM7681	A317ONE
BYJ919Y	XUF534Y, 404DCD	VCS376	G529LWU
CSO386Y	ASA10Y, TSV780	VCS391	B191CGA
D131UGB	D219NCS, VLT73	VLT54,	G262EHD
ESU435	GGE127X, FSU737, TOS550X	VLT104	G386PNV
F149XCS	F523WSJ	VLT154	NCS121W, WLT415, WGB646W
FSU737	D217NCS	WDZ2104	C104KDS
FSU739	E849AAO	WDZ4138	D118NUS
HDS566H	SMS402H, 703DYE	WDZ6951	D136NUS
HSB698Y	CUB50Y	WDZ6962	D130NUS
IIL3507	F410DUG	WDZ6974	D121NUS
KRS540V	GSO6V	WDZ6975	C594SHC
KRS542V	GSO8V	WLT415	D218NCS
M151FGB	M1ABO	WLT416	F252OFP, XDU599, C84PRP
MIL4693	C351FVV	WLT439	G569ESD
MSU466	D526ESG	WLT447	D220NCS
OIW7024	GLP433T	WLT465	B196CGA
OIW7025	GLP427T	WLT501	D221NCS
PJI4983	B577LPE	WLT526	D216NCS
RBZ3427	D38UAO	WLT538	E159XHS
RBZ3428	D39UAO	WLT546	D318SGB
RBZ3429	D43UAO	WLT697	B197CGA
RBZ4209	D42UAO	WLT720	G345FFX
RBZ4241	D46UAO	WLT727	H149CVU
RBZ4245	D520RCK	WLT774	E158XHS
RBZ4281	D530RCK	WLT794	G387PNV
RBZ4359	D534RCK	WLT809	G344FFX
RBZ5459	D525RCK	WLT830	H150CVU
RBZ5491	D558RCK	WLT874	G528LWU
RBZ5492	C80OCW	WLT978	B195CGA
RBZ5493	D81UFV	XDU599	C84PRP
RBZ5494	D82UFV	YSV730	H403DEG
RBZ5495	D83UFV	YSV735	H406GAV
RBZ5496	C101KDS		

Allocations:-

AA Buses (Wagon Road, Ayr)

Mercedes-Benz	058	060	061	064	065	066	067	
Dart	400	401	463	464	465	466	467	468
	469	470	471					
Leopard	621							
National	708	756	757	759	760	766	767	770
	771	774	788	791				

Ardrossan (Harbour Road)

Mercedes-Benz	022	024	025	026	027	029	032	038
	052	054	209	210	215	217	224	227
	230	234	266	270	271	272		
MetroRider	244							
Volvo Interurban	103	119	121	122	126	146	147	148
	149	154						
Volvo Coach	141	191						
Dart	303	307	308	310				
B10M Bus	427	431	597	598	599			
Volvo B10B	501							
Atlantean	819							
Fleetline	866	867						
Citybus DD	893							
Olympian	901	902	903	904	905	906	907	908
	909	910	912	913	914	915	916	917
	918	919	920	921	922	923	924	

Arran (Brodick)

Mercedes-Benz	203	221	246	282	
MetroRider	237	288			
Volvo B10M PS	508	509	510	511	
Leopard	625	630	689	692	696
Dorchester	421				
Bedford	729				

Ayr (Waggon Road) -

Outstation - Girvan

Mercedes-Benz	002	003	004	005	006	007	008	009
	010	011	012	021	214	222	225	
Volvo B6	312	313	325	326	332	333	334	335
	336	353	354	355	356	357	358	
Leopard	622	623	626	631	637	638	647	653
	658	660	665	669				
Tiger	169							
National	710	785	786	793	795	796		
Volvo B10M PS	565	566	567	580	581	582		
Volvo Interurban	123	124	125	127	128	150	151	
	152	153	188	189	190			
Coach	129							
Artic	198							
Fleetline	854	860	878	880				
B10M Citybus	892	894	895	896	897			
Titan	941							

Cumnock (Ayr Road)

Mercedes-Benz	245	247	256	257				
Dodge	296							
Leopard	620							
Tiger	165	179	180					
Volvo Interurban	104	155	156	157	158			
Volvo Coach	137	138	139	140	197			
Volvo B10M PS	570	571	572	573	574	575	576	577
	578	579						
Artic	199							
Titan	939	958						
Olympian	911							

Irvine is the location for this picture of Roe-bodied Leyland Olympian 906, EWY76Y. One of six acquired from A1 members, they are all based at Ardrossan.
Murdoch Currie

Dunoon (Argyll Road)

Mercedes-Benz	269	279				
Dart	301	302	304	305	306	399
Dorchester	416					
Volvo B10M PS	568	569				
National	792					
Atlantean	801	809	812			

Dumfries (Eastfield Road)

Outstations - Annan and Kircudbright

Volvo Interurban	105	142	143	144	145			
Volvo coach	130	131	196					
Mercedes-Benz	208	248	249	250	251	252	253	254
	259	260	261	262	263	264	265	267
	268							
Talbot	274	277						
Dart	309	390	391	392	393	394	395	396
	397	398						
Volvo B10M PS	505	512	583	594				
Leopard	633	641	649	651	657	670	680	681
	682	683	684	688				
Fleetline	851	868	888					

Kilmarnock (Mackinlay Place)

Mercedes-Benz	001	028	030	031	034	035	039	042
	043	053	055	081	083	216	223	229
	231	258	281	283	284	285		
Volvo B6	318	319	320	321	322	323	324	327
	337	338	339	340	341	351	352	
Leopard	627	628	629	632	648	687	691	
Tiger	168	172	173					
Volvo coach	184							
National	701	703	780	781	797			
Volvo B10M PS	503	506	507	584	585	586	587	588
	589	590	591	592	593	595	596	
Volvo Interurban	159							
Fleetline	840	843						
Olympian	925	926	927	928	929	930	931	932
Titan	933	934	936	937	938	940	942	943
	944	945	946	948	949	950	951	953
	957	959	960	968	969			

Rothsay (Pointhouse)

Mercedes-Benz	023	232	280				
Dorchester	420						
National	702	704	705	706	773	775	783
Bedford	721						

Stranraer (Lewis Street)

Outstations - Drummore and Whithorn

Mercedes-Benz	200	219	297					
Leopard	624	671	678	685	686	693	695	697
National	779	789	790					
Tiger	181							
Volvo Coach	132	133	136	174	175	183	186	187
	194	195						
Volvo Interurban	160							
Expressliner	616	617						
Fleetline	847	869	882					

Stagecoach
Overseas operations

STAGECOACH AUSTRALIA

Stagecoach Australia Pty Ltd, 13 Bartlett Road, Noosaville, Queensland, Q 4566, Australia

Depots:- Booval, Caloundra; Cairns; Ipswich; Noosaville.

013DVI	Volvo B59		B41F	1978	
018CYX	Volvo B59		B38F	1977	
019CYX	Volvo B59		B38F	1977	
021BNH	MAN		B43F	1976	
	MAN SL200		B43D	1979	
030CTE	032CTE	034CTE		035CTE	036CTE
031CTE	033CTE				
050CIV	MAN SL200		B43D	1976	
061EGR	Leyland Tiger TRCTL11/3R		B63F	1989	
076DZS	Volvo B59		B43F	1977	
078BMN	MAN		B43D	1976	
092BMN	MAN		B51D	1976	
102BVL	Asia Combi		M18	1987	
133CJB	MAN		B51D	1977	
134CJB	MAN		B43D	1978	
135CJB	MAN		B43D	1978	
136CJB	MAN		B43D	1978	
140EDB	Volvo B59		B43D	1977	
141EDB	Volvo B59		B43D	1977	
142EDB	Volvo B59		B43D	1977	
143EDB	Volvo B59		B43D	1977	
144EDB	Volvo B59		B43D	1977	
151EDB	Mercedes-Benz		C51F	1977	
184BJQ	Leyland National 10951/2R/ckd		B48D	1975	Ex Canberra (ZIB313)
213DAV	MAN		B43F	1978	
222PUR	Bedford		B48D	1975	Ex Canberra (ZIB313)
228BPV	Leyland		B51F	1986	
230BPV	Mercedes-Benz		B51F	1986	
233CUR	Mercedes-Benz 1418		B57	1994	
233CUR	Mercedes-Benz 1418		B57	1994	
234CUR	Mercedes-Benz 1418		B57	1994	
235CUR	Mercedes-Benz 1418		B57	1995	
236CUR	Mercedes-Benz 1418		B57	1994	
248CUR	Mercedes-Benz 1418		B57	1995	
	Volvo B59		B43D	1977	
261DBA	263DBA	265DBA		267DBA	268DBA
262DBA	264DBA	266DBA			
266DRL	MAN		B43D	1986	
275CYR	Mercedes-Benz 1418		B57	1994	
276CYR	Mercedes-Benz 1418		B57	1995	
277CYR	Mercedes-Benz 1418		B57	1995	
282BHZ	AEC 5P5R		B41D	1978	
283BHZ	AEC 5P5R		B41D	1978	
301DSL	MAN		AB80D	1979	
312PZC	Leyland		B41D	1978	
361EDD	Volvo B59		B43D	1978	
366EDD	Volvo B59		B43D	1978	
367BPF	MAN		B43D	1976	
438DZS	Isuzu		B38D	1977	
445AFV	AEC 5PR		B41D	1978	
463AIV	Leyland		B41D	1978	
489EDB	Volvo B59		B43D	1978	
490EDB	Volvo B59		B43D	1978	
491EDB	Volvo B59		B43D	1978	

491DAV	Volvo B59	B43D	1978	
496DIZ	MAN		AB80D	1979
500EAE	Volvo B59		B43D	1977
501EAE	Volvo B59		B43D	1977
502EAE	Volvo B59		B43D	1977
503EAE	Volvo B59		B43D	1977
504DSN	Bedford		B48D	1978
504EAE	Volvo B59		B43D	1977
518PTA	Leyland		B61D	1986
526DSN	Bedford		B48D	1978
529CGO	Leyland Leopard PSU3E/2R		B43D	1975
530CGO	Leyland Leopard PSU3E/2R		B43D	1975
531CGO	Leyland Leopard PSU3E/2R		B43D	1975
531AZX	Leyland Leopard PSU3A/2R		B43D	1971
578PXY	MAN		B43D	1976
608DTQ	Leyland Tiger TRCTL11/3R		B63D	1989
609DTQ	Leyland Tiger TRCTL11/3R		B63D	1989
613DEV	Volvo/Fuji		B64D	1984
621AEX	Asia AM805		M18	1987
623DFK	Volvo/Fuji		B64D	1984
671CUR	Volvo B59		B43D	1978
672CUR	Volvo B59		B43D	1978
673CUR	Volvo B59		B43D	1978

	Leyland Leopard		B57F	1984
674PKX	676PKX	678PKX	680PKX	682PKX
675PKX	677PKX	679PKX	681PKX	

688PKX	Leyland Tiger		B57F	1984
719AAO	Bedford		B48D	1976
744BWH	Volvo B59		B43D	1978
747BWH	Volvo B59		B43D	1978
749BWH	Volvo B59		B43D	1978
750BWH	Volvo B59		B43D	1978
760POG	Leyland Leopard		B61F	1986
765BYF	Volvo B59		B43D	1977
773ADW	Volvo B59		B43D	1977
780OSK	Benning		B48D	1977
784ACD	Volvo B59		B43D	1977
834ECA	Volvo B59		B43D	1978
835EDB	Volvo B59		B43D	1978
836ECA	Volvo B59		B38D	1978
837ECA	Volvo B59		B43D	1978
838ECA	Volvo B59		B38D	1978
856CWA	MAN		B43D	1980
857CWA	MAN		B43D	1980
858CWA	MAN		B43D	1980
874CJR	Mercedes-Benz O307		B43D	1977
877AZR	Isuzu		B48D	1989
889CWM	Volvo B59		B38D	1978
891CWM	Volvo B59		B38D	1978
892CWM	Volvo B59		B38D	1978
893CWM	Volvo B59		B38D	1978
894CWM	Volvo B59		B38D	1978
895CWM	Volvo B59		B38D	1978
896CWM	Volvo B59		B38D	1978
897CWM	Volvo B59		B38D	1978
898CWM	Volvo B59		B38D	1978
899CWM	Volvo B59		B38D	1978
900CWM	Volvo B59		B38D	1978
901CWM	Volvo B59		B38D	1978
902CWM	Volvo B59		B38D	1978
919CJR	Mercedes-Benz O307		AB80D	1977
929CJR	Mercedes-Benz O307		B43D	1977
946DOL	Leyland		B41D	1978
994AII	Leyland		B57D	1974
997CQJ	Volvo B6		B38D	1983
ORD650	Bedford		B48D	1976
PYR667	Albion		B48D	1972

KENYA BUS

Kenya Bus Services Ltd, General Waruingi Street, Eastleigh,
P O Box 41001, Nairobi, Kenya.

Depots: Mombasa and Nairobi.

201-220		Dennis Dragon 1820		AVA		H115F*	1995-96		
						*206-11 seat 99, 213-15 seat 103; 220 seats 78			
201	KAG544H	206	KAG542J	209	KAG060M	213	KAG470T	215	KAG472T
202	KAG931E	208	KAG544J	211	KAG602M	214	KAG471T	220	KAH560B
203	KAG292E								

301-320		ERF Trailblazer 6LXB		Suleman		B47D	1983-85		
301	KUW565	304	KUY289	310	KWE764	319	KWQ732	320	KWT363
303	KUY279	305	KUY829						

321-331		ERF Trailblazer 6LXB		Labh Singh		B49D*	1986-88 *325 is B51F; 331 is B46D		
321	KXQ484	324	KXR388	327	KYW205	329	KYV457	331	KYW206
322	KXR065	325	KYD116	328	KYV458				

334	KYH176	ERF Trailblazer 6LXB	Suleman	B47D	1987		
336	KYM857	ERF Trailblazer 6LXB	Suleman	B47D	1987		
337	KYN019	ERF Trailblazer 6LXB	Suleman	B47D	1987		
338	KYS305	ERF Trailblazer 6LXB	Suleman	B47D	1988		

341-396		ERF Trailblazer 6LXB MkII		Labh Singh		B45D*	1993-94 *347 is B46D, 378 is B48D		
341	KAC649X	352	KAD528A	363	KAD447C	374	KAD407E	385	KAD199J
342	KAC929X	353	KAD526A	364	KAD553D	375	KAD860F	386	KAD386J
343	KAC023Y	354	KAD619A	365	KAD743D	376	KAD147G	387	KAD378J
344	KAC022Y	355	KAD841A	366	KAD737D	377	KAD117G	388	KAD659K
345	KAC021Y	356	KAD902A	367	KAD779D	378	KAD194G	389	KAD822K
346	KAC287Y	357	KAD535D	368	KAD826D	379	KAD233G	390	KAD899Y
347	KAC290Y	358	KAD126C	369	KAD899D	380	KAD589H	391	KAD902Y
348	KAC289Y	359	KAD127C	370	KAD994D	381	KAD641H	392	KAD937Y
349	KAC288Y	360	KAD158C	371	KAD021E	382	KAD846H	393	KAD938Y
350	KAD527A	361	KAD225C	372	KAD261E	383	KAD947H	396	KAD688A
351	KAD521A	362	KAD368C	373	KAD360E	384	KAD075J		

Kenya Bus operate over roads which would not suit the current British models, so appropriate vehicles are required. Pictured before the vehicle entered service, 401 is a ERF Trailblazer II with Gardner engine and bodywork by local builder Labh Singh.
Andrew Jarosz

400-450

ERF Trailblazer 6LXB MkII — Labh Singh* — B52D — 1994-95
*424/9/35/41/3-7/9/50 are bodied by Choda

400w	KAE660C	410	KAE061G	420	KAE164L	430	KAE098Q	442	KAE959R
401w	KAE026D	411	KAE991E	421	KAE981M	431	KAE375Y	443	KAE112W
402	KAE975C	412	KAE793H	422	KAE985M	432	KAE285S	444	KAE838X
403	KAE977C	413	KAE792H	423	KAE018P	433	KAE286S	445	KAG241C
404	KAE137D	414	KAE697K	424	KAE109P	435	KAE716T	446	KAG920B
405	KAE138D	415	KAE696K	425	KAE183P	436	KAE793T	447	KAG818D
406	KAE609E	416	KAE698K	426	KAE287P	437	KAE052S	448	KAG819D
407	KAE011G	417	KAE699K	427	KAE351P	438	KAE053S	449	KAG751D
408	KAE992E	418	KAE856K	428	KAE394P	439	KAE749T	450	KAG927D
409	KAE012G	419	KAE857K	429	KAE023Q	441	KAE821V		

451	KAG641G	ERF Trailblazer 6LXB MkII	Choda	B51D	1995

452-459

ERF Trailblazer 6LXB MkII — Labh Singh — B52D — 1995

452	KAG722J	454	KAG287K	456	KAG661L	458	KAG684L	459	KAG716L
453	KAG052K	455	KAG288K	457	KAG683L				

460	KAG756L	ERF Trailblazer 6LXB MkII	Choda	B52D	1995

461-484

ERF Trailblazer 6LXB MkII — Labh Singh — B52D* — 1995-96 *Seating varies

461	KAG842N	468	KAG654S	473	KAG173V	477	KAG174V	481	KAG864X
462	KAG094P	469	KAG672S	474	KAG008Y	478	KAG962W	482	KAG053Y
465	KAG179P	470	KAG394T	475	KAG244V	479	KAG789X	483	KAG092Y
466	KAG334P	471	KAG582U	476	KAG291V	480	KAG848X	484	KAG094Y
467	KAG181R	472	KAG859U						

485-494

ERF Trailblazer 6LXB MkII — Choda — B49D* — 1996 *Seating varies

485	KAG095Y	487	KAG333Y	489	KAG749Z	491	KAH097A	493	KAH368H
486	KAG287Y	488	KAG341Y	490	KAH096A	492	KAH367A	494	KAH616B

495	KAH781B	ERF Trailblazer 6LXB MkII	Labh Singh	B49D	1996
496	KAH881B	ERF Trailblazer 6LXB MkII	Choda	B49D	1996
497	KAH962B	ERF Trailblazer 6LXB MkII	Labh Singh	B49D	1996

498-502

ERF Trailblazer 6LXB MkII — Choda — B49D — 1996

498	KAH717C	499	KAH747C	500	KAH768C	501	KAH769C	502	KAH930C

503-518

ERF Trailblazer 6LXB MkII — Labh Singh — B49D* — 1996 *Seating varies

503	KAH049D	507	KAH184G	510	KAH291G	513	KAH764H	516	KAH207J
504	KAH389D	508	KAH185G	511	KAH293G	514	KAH951H	517	KAH238J
505	KAH392D	509	KAH270G	512	KAH763H	515	KAH129J	518	KAH199L
506	KAH049G								

519	KHA201L	ERF Trailblazer 6LXB MkII	Choda	B49D	1996

523-530

ERF Trailblazer 6LXB MkII — Labh Singh — B49D — 1996

523	KAH635M	525	KAH687M	526	KAH887M	527	KAH894M	530	KAH259N

531	KAH309N	ERF Trailblazer 6LXB MkII	Choda	B49D	1996
532	KAH646P	ERF Trailblazer 6LXB MkII	Labh Singh	B49D	1996
533	KHA647P	ERF Trailblazer 6LXB MkII	Choda	B49D	1996

534-542

ERF Trailblazer 6LXB MkII — Labh Singh — B49D — 1997

534	KAH673R	536	KAH031S	538	KAH835T	540	KAH924T	542	KAH107Y
535	KAH674R	537	KAH032S	539	KAH832T	541	KAH132U		

601	KAA128N	DAF TB2100DHT	Labh Singh	B47D	1990
602	KAA351N	DAF TB2100DHT	Labh Singh	B47D	1990
603	KAA330N	DAF TB2100DHT	Labh Singh	B47D	1990
604	KAA313Q	DAF TB2100DHT	Labh Singh	B47D	1990

605-616

DAF TB2100DHT · Labh Singh · B43D · 1992

605	KAC145H	607	KAC252H	611	KAC592J	613	KAC865J	615	KAC519L
606	KAC146H	608	KAC253H	612	KAC672J	614	KAC887J	616	KAC243K

620-640

ERF Trailblazer 6LXB MkII · Labh Singh · B45D* · 1994-96 *626-8 are B52F; 630 is B55F

620	KAD105Z	624	KAE919A	627	KAG095P	635	KAH350L	638	KAH686M
621	KAD135Z	625	KAE649T	628	KAG096P	636	KAH351L	639	KAH051N
622	KAE689A	626	KAE750T	630	KAH172L	637	KAH352L	640	KAH258N
623	KAE918A								

701-777

Leyland Victory J MkII · Labh Singh · B49D* · 1979-82
713,797 are B48D; 731 is B41D; 755 is B59D

701	KVR629	714	KVT857	724	KVV957	736	KSJ265	763	KTK846
707	KVR995	717	KVU018	725	KVW013	749	KSW894	764	KTM915
708	KVS025	721	KVU237	727	KVX664	755	KTF528	768	KTQ004
713	KVT703	723	KVV809	731	KVY237	757	KTF834	777	KTT617

797-824

Leyland Victory J MkII · Labh Singh · B49D* · 1980-82 *Seating varies

797	KTW268	803	KUG560	809	KUG938	815	KUJ874	820	KUJ890
798	KTW190	804	KUH104	810	KUG978	816	KUJ638	821	KUM688
799	KTY110	805	KUG585	811	KUH141	817	KUJ998	822	KUM870
800	KUF144	806	KUJ641	812	KUH254	818	KUJ889	823	KUM534
801	KUG599	807	KUG850	813	KUH275	819	KUK083	824	KUK271
802	KUG474	808	KUG860	814	KUJ561				

831-850

Leyland Victory J MkII · Labh Singh · B49D* · 1983-84 *Seating varies

831	KUY105	835	KWA577	839	KWB295	843	KWK134	847	KWM059
832	KWA562	836	KWA574	840	KWC826	844	KWK144	848	KWM145
833	KWA575	837	KWB994	841	KWE920	845	KWL823	849	KWM189
834	KWA576	838	KWB286	842	KWE971	846	KWL923	850	KWN536

851-874

Leyland Victory J MkII · Labh Singh · B49D* · 1984-85 *870 is B45D

851	KWP262	856	KWR077	861	KWS725	866	KWT169	871	KWX948
852	KWQ584	857	KWR105	862	KWS971	867	KWT337	872	KWY155
853	KWQ808	858	KWR140	863	KWS985	868	KWV976	873	KWY371
854	KWQ914	859w	KWS524	864	KWT030	869	KWX587	874	KXA037
855	KWQ946	860	KWS690	865	KWT146	870	KWX892		

876-900

Leyland Victory J MkII · Labh Singh · B49D* · 1985-86 *Seating varies

876	KXD797	881	KXG262	886	KXH624	891	KXJ173	896	KXM065
877	KXK017	882	KXG278	887	KXH875	892	KXJ369	897	KXN855
878	KXK503	883	KXH320	888	KXH896	893	KXJ474	898	KXN982
879	KXD761	884	KXH321	889	KXH993	894	KXK610	899	KXP038
880	KXD781	885	KXH623	890	KXJ010	895	KXK708	900	KXP187

901-930

ERF Trailblazer 6LXB MkII · Labh Singh · DP66F* · 1995-96 *901 is DP67F

901	KAE837V	907	KAE640Z	913	KAG816G	919w	KAH804B	925	KAH010G
902	KAE109W	908	KAG291A	914	KAG173H	920	KAH891B	926	KAH021G
903	KAE385W	909	KAG056C	915	KAG373H	921	KAH876C	927	KAH294G
904	KAE002Y	910	KAG817D	916	KAG869Z	922	KAH177D	928	KAH762H
905	KAE230Y	911	KAG820D	917	KAH215A	923	KAH835E	929	KAH005J
906	KAG260A	912	KAG092E	918w	KAH617B	924	KAH882E	930	KAH130J

Opposite:- **At the end of 1997 the first withdrawals of the Dennis Dragons are taking place. The type is illustrated in the 1997 edition and these are being prepared for operation at one of the English units later in 1998. The ERF Trailblazer (upper picture) is the standard chassis now being used for Kenya buses which is replacing the Guy Victory (lower picture). Pictured while heading for the Likoni Post Office is 393, KAD938Y and parked at the depot is 766, KTN216, a Guy Victory that has since been withdrawn.** *Andrew Jarosz*

The dominant bodybuilder in Kenya is Labh Singh and one of his bodies is seen on Kenya Bus 804, KUH104. The city depots are Eastleigh and Riruta while the coutry services also run out of Eastleigh.
Andrew Jarosz

931	KAH985K	ERF Trailblazer 6LXB MkIII	Choda	DP66F	1996
932	KAH979K	ERF Trailblazer 6LXB MkIII	Banbros	DP66F	1996
933	KAH645K	ERF Trailblazer 6LXB MkIII	Labh Singh	DP66F	1996
934	KAH162L	ERF Trailblazer 6LXB MkIII	Banbros	DP66F	1996
935	KAH200L	ERF Trailblazer 6LXB MkIII	Labh Singh	DP66F	1996
936	KAH549K	ERF Trailblazer 6LXB MkIII	Labh Singh	DP66F	1996
961	KUF067	Leyland Victory J	Labh Singh	B49D	1982 Rebuild
962	KUG695	Leyland Victory J	Labh Singh	B45D	1982 Rebuild
963	KUT967	Leyland Victory J	Labh Singh	B49D	1983 Rebuild
966	KZF894	Leyland Victory J MkIII	Labh Singh	B49D	1988
968	KQD250	Leyland Victory J	Labh Singh	B48D	1975 Rebuild
969	KPW753	Leyland Victory J	Labh Singh	B48D	1974 Rebuild
970	KPW294	Leyland Victory J	Labh Singh	B45D	1974 Rebuild
971	KUR801	Leyland Victory J II	Labh Singh	B45D	1983 Rebuild
972	KUR881	Leyland Victory J II	Labh Singh	B42D	1983 Rebuild

991-997

| | | Leyland Victory J MkIII | Labh Singh | B49D* | 1979 | *991 is B43D |

| 991 | KZC129 | 993 | KZA013 | 995 | KYZ546 | 996 | KZD894 | 997 | KZB481 |
| 992 | KZC481 | 994 | KZF416 | | | | | | |

Operational units:
Country 201-3/6/8/9/11/3-5/20, 630. 902-17/20-36
City Remainder

STAGECOACH PORTUGAL

Stagecoach Portugal, Rua Capitão Rey Vilar No383, Alvide, 2750 Cascais, Portugal

Depots: Aboboda and Adroana

Tram operation:-
The first stretch of line between Banzão and Praia das Maçãs was reopened on 16th September 1997 with the next stage between Banzão and Ribeira opened on 30th October 1997. The mayoress of Sintra has pledged the final extension back to Sintra now she has won the recent elections. Pictured on one of the early journeys are closed car tram 3 and open trailer 9.

Motor Cars

1	Brill	Open Car	32 seats	1903	original bodywork
2	Brill	Closed Car	24 seats	1903	rebuilt in 1947 in Lisbon style
3	Brill	Closed Car	17 seats	1903	original bodywork
4	Brill	Closed Car	24 seats	1903	rebuilt in 1947 in Lisbon style
5	Brill	Closed Car	24 seats	1903	rebuilt in 1947 in Lisbon style
6	Brill	Open Car	32 seats	1903	original bodywork
7	Brill	Open Car	32 seats	1903	original bodywork

Trailer Cars

8	Brill	Closed Car	17 seats	1903	original bodywork
9	Brill	Open Car	32 seats	1903	original bodywork
10	Brill	Closed Car	17 seats	1903	original bodywork
11	Brill	Open Car	32 seats	1903	original bodywork
12	Brill	Open Car	32 seats	1903	original bodywork
13	Brill	Open Car	32 seats	1903	original bodywork
14	Brill	Open Car	32 seats	1903	original bodywork of tram 5 adapted for use as a trailer
15	Brill (Truck removed)	Closed Car	20 seats	1903	not known if this ever ran as a trailer

Bus fleet

101-150   Scania L113CLB   Marcopolo   B37D   1996

101	51-47-GM	111	64-86-GV	121	62-41-HA	131	20-02-HF	141	20-14-HF
102	80-96-GP	112	64-87-GV	122	90-78-HA	132	20-05-HF	142	20-15-HF
103	80-99-GP	113	64-88-GV	123	90-79-HA	133	20-06-HF	143	20-16-HF
104	80-98-GP	114	64-89-GV	124	90-80-HA	134	20-07-HF	144	20-17-HF
105	80-97-GP	115	64-90-GV	125	90-81-HA	135	20-08-HF	145	49-66-HG
106	80-93-GP	116	62-36-HA	126	90-82-HA	136	20-09-HF	146	49-67-HG
107	80-94-GP	117	62-37-HA	127	90-83-HA	137	20-10-HF	147	49-68-HG
108	80-95-GP	118	62-38-HA	128	90-84-HA	138	20-11-HF	148	49-69-HG
109	64-84-GV	119	62-39-HA	129	20-03-HF	139	20-12-HF	149	49-70-HG
110	64-85-GV	120	62-40-HA	130	20-04-HF	140	20-13-HF	150	49-71-HG

183	EL-44-91	UTIC-AEC U2055	A Caetano(1987)	B42D	1972	Ex Rodoviária de Lisboa, 1996
189	DE-62-73	UTIC-AEC U2055	UTIC(1990)	B42D	1972	Ex Rodoviária de Lisboa, 1996
191	GC-62-04	UTIC-AEC U2055	A Caetano(1987)	B42D	1972	Ex Rodoviária de Lisboa, 1996

201-210   Scania L113CLB   Marcopolo   DP51F   1997

201	33-66-HL	203	33-68-HL	205	33-70-HL	207	32-90-HP	209	32-92-HP
202	33-67-HL	204	33-69-HL	206	32-89-HP	208	32-91-HP	210	32-93-HP

219	IM-97-87	UTIC-AEC U2055	UTIC(1990)	B42D	1974	Ex Rodoviária de Lisboa, 1996
301	EU-37-57	Volvo B10R-55	CAMO	B34D	1980	Ex Rodoviária de Lisboa, 1996
302	FS-09-78	Volvo B10R-55	CAMO	B40D	1980	Ex Rodoviária de Lisboa, 1996

534-551   Volvo B10R-59   CAMO   DP48D*   1979-80   Ex Rodoviária de Lisboa, 1996
*551 is DP49D

534	IS-98-38	535	NP-75-76	536	HS-59-99	537	HS-70-33	551	ES-83-85

During 1998 the MAN chassis is being introduced into the British fleets while in New Zealand a shorter version of the model has been supplied to Stagecoach since 1994. After a batch of fifty-four were received in 1994 ans 1995 a low floor version arrived. Illustrated here is the first of the low floor units 601, TJ2541. Bodywork on the type is supplied by Designline. *Stagecoach New Zealand*

417-478

		Leyland Leopard PSU3E/2R			Hawke Coachwork		B40D	1978-79 479/80 ex Goldstar, Frankton, 1992		
417	IU9434	429	IX3807	443	JC2506	454	JF1908		466	KP7998
418	IU9433	430	IX3808	444	JC2568	455	JF1910		468	LH1322
419	IU9432	432	PA6877	445	JC2569	456	JF1911		469	JA1184
420	IU9431	433	IX7765	446	JC2570	457	JF1913		470	JA1197
421	IX7733	434	IX7763	447	JD184	458	JF1914		472	JC2505
423	IX3304	435	IU9931	448	JD183	459	IX3806		474	JD181
424	IX3302	436	IU9932	449	JD182	461	IX3815		475	JC2520
425	IX3781	438	JC2431	451	JD197	462	IX7767		476	JD199
426	IX3660	439	JC2430	452	JF1903	463	IX7766		477	JF1902
427	IX3783	440	JA1187	453	JF1909	464	TD5442		478	JF1912
428	IX3782	441	JA1185							

479	IX3303	Leyland Leopard PSU3E/2R	Hawke Coachwork	B46D	1979	Ex Goldstar, Frankton, 1992
480	IX7734	Leyland Leopard PSU3E/2R	Hawke Coachwork	B46D	1979	Ex Goldstar, Frankton, 1992
481	LA5234	Leyland Leopard PSU3E/2R	Hawke Coachwork	B49D	1983	Ex Invercargill, 1992
482	JT684	Leyland Leopard PSU3E/2R	Hawke Coachwork	B47D	1982	Ex Cesta Travel, 1993

501-520

		MAN 11.190 HOCL			Designline		B39D	1994-95		
501	SS5537	505	TB6105	509	SY1641	513	TA2667	517	TB6042
502	SS5538	506	SW4400	510	SY1631	514	TA2691	518	TB6050
503	ST7109	507	SW4435	511	SZ5917	515	TA2714	519	TB6056
504	SX7724	508	SW4436	512	SZ5918	516	TB6023	520	TB6057

521-554

		MAN 11.190 HOCL			Designline		B39D	1995		
521	TB6106	528	TE2325	535	TG5856	542	TG5879	549	TJ2515
522	TB6107	529	TE2326	536	TG5857	543	TG5896	550	TJ2516
523	TD2564	530	TE2327	537	TG5871	544	TG5897	551	TR1643
524	TD2593	531	TF6235	538	TG5872	545	TG5898	552	TR1644
525	TD2594	532	TF6236	539	TG5876	546	TG5899	553	TR1645
526	TD2630	533	TF6237	540	TG5877	547	TH5837	554	TR1646
527	TD2631	534	TG5855	541	TG5878	548	TH5838		

601-626

MAN 11.190 HOCL — Designline — B39D — 1995-96

601	TJ2541	607	UB490	612	UB496	617	UB483	622	UF5846
602	TJ2542	608	UB491	613	UB500	618	UB482	623	UF5847
603	UB487	609	UB492	614	UB499	619	UB484	624	UF5850
604	UB488	610	UB497	615	UB498	620	UB485	625	UF5851
605	TU1498	611	UB495	616	UF5845	621	UF5849	626	UF5852
606	UB489								

627-658

MAN 11.190 HOCL — Designline — B39D — 1996

627	UF5853	634	UH7205	641	UH7218	647	UL5044	653	UL5060
628	UF5854	635	UH7206	642	UH7212	648	UL5045	654	UL5042
629	UF5855	636	UH7207	643	UH7219	649	UL5046	655	UO9429
630	UF5856	637	UH7208	644	UH7220	650	UL5051	656	UO9427
631	UF5857	638	UH7215	645	UH7213	651	UL5052	657	UO9433
632	UF5858	639	UH7216	646	UH7214	652	UL5053	658	UT5625
633	UH7204	640	UH7217						

5907	1055IC	Hino BG300	Emslie	C41F	1980
6009	JZ6948	Bedford NFM/6BD1	NZ Motor Bodies	B37D	1981
6890	MI8415	Hino RK176	Coachwork International	B45D	1985

7193-7253

Hino RK176 — Coachwork International — B47D* — 1987-88 — *6890/7193/7-7200 are B45D

7193	NA6078	7201	NK8507	7237	NA7358	7245	NL7826	7250	NL7831
7197	NA6060	7231	NA7353	7238	NA7359	7246	NL7827	7251	NA7832
7198	NA6947	7232	NA7350	7239	NA7361	7247	NL7828	7252	NA7833
7199	NA6946	7233	NA7351	7242	NL7824	7248	NL7829	7253	NL7834
7200	NA6945	7236	NA7357	7244	NL7825	7249	NL7830		

7255-7556

Hino RK177 — Coachwork International — B47D — 1988-89

7255	NL7823	7266	NL8272	7278	NX9487	7538	OB4207	7547	OE7912
7256	NL7790	7267	NL7793	7279	NX9488	7539	OB4208	7548	OE7917
7258	NL7796	7268	NL8264	7532	NX9510	7540	OB4215	7549	OG5328
7259	NL7797	7269	NL8265	7533	NX9509	7542	OB4213	7551	OG5327
7260	NL7799	7270	NL8266	7534	NX9507	7543	OB4212	7553	OG5341
7261	NL7794	7271	NL8273	7535	NX9508	7544	OB4214	7554	OG5342
7263	NL7791	7273	NL8267	7536	NX9516	7545	OE7913	7555	OG5343
7264	NL7792	7274	NL8268	7537	NX9517	7546	OE7916	7556	OG5344
7265	NL7798	7276	NX9485						

	ex KWA215W	Bristol VRT/SL3/6LXC	Eastern Coach Works	H43/31F	1981	Ex Bluebird Buses, 1998
	ex KWA216W	Bristol VRT/SL3/6LXC	Eastern Coach Works	H43/31F	1981	Ex Bluebird Buses, 1998

Kelburn Cable Car

1		Habegger	Habegger	S28D	1979
2		Habegger	Habegger	S28D	1979

Previous Registrations:

HQ3930	PW8450	MQ9796	SK700
KP7998	IU9929	PA6897	NT9388
LH1322	JA1186	SC2911	MO1390

Opposite:- **The pictures received from Stagecoach's Wellington operation give an impression of blue sky and clear air whatever the location. Representing the fleet in this year's colour section are Hawke-bodied Leyland Leopard 418, IU9433, and MAN 522, TB6107. During 1997 several of the stored Leopards were re-instated into service, while new Mercedes-Benz 709 minibuses with Alexander Sprint bodywork from the main British order have displaced the L608 versions exported two years ago from Stagecoach South. As we go to press two Bristol VRs from Bluebird Buses are en route to New Zealand where they will feature in a new service in the capital.** *Stagecoach Wellington*

SWEBUS

Swebus AB, Kungsgatan 29, 111 56 Stockholm

Swebus operate around 3300 vehicles in Sweden, 322 in Finland, 247 in Norway and 127 in Denmark. Vehicles are allocated to the 24 districts. The list produced below is the latest information available and was believed correct to January 1998. Unfortunately, seating configurations are not yet available, though most are thought to have high-back seating. The publishers would welcome any additional details, including seating configurations and liveries or photographs.

17	MXC222	Volvo B10M-60	Van Hool Alizée	1986	
19	EZS682	Volvo B10M-60	Van Hool Alizée	1987	
25	LXJ717	Volvo B10M-65	Säffle	1984	
34	OAT766	Volvo B10M-60	Säffle	1989	
99	GZT311	Scania CN113CLB	Scania	1991	Aqcuired 1997
101	AFG231	Scania CN113	Scania	1990	Aqcuired 1997
102	AHS261	Scania CN113	Scania	1990	Aqcuired 1997
105	AZA245	Volvo B10R-65	Säffle	1982	Aqcuired 1997
106	BAZ404	Volvo B10M-65	Säffle	1982	Aqcuired 1997
108	BSP963	Volvo B10M-65	Säffle	1987	Aqcuired 1997
109	BXO873	Volvo B10R-65	Säffle	1987	Aqcuired 1997
115	CFK923	Volvo B10M-65	Säffle	1987	Aqcuired 1997
118	CFL623	Volvo B10M-65	Säffle	1987	Aqcuired 1997
121	CRN411	Scania CN113	Scania	1990	Aqcuired 1997
123	CRP431	Scania CN113	Scania	1990	Aqcuired 1997
129	DZB021	Scania CN113	Scania	1990	Aqcuired 1997
131	EAO201	Scania CN113	Scania	1990	Aqcuired 1997
132	EPF709	Volvo B10R-60	Säffle	1985	Aqcuired 1997
136	EPZ350	Scania CR112	Scania	1982	Aqcuired 1997
150	EWT539	Volvo B10R-60	Säffle	1985	Aqcuired 1997
151	EWZ959	Volvo B10R-60	Säffle	1985	Aqcuired 1997
156	FBP999	Volvo B10R-60	Säffle	1985	Aqcuired 1997
159	FBT549	Volvo B10R-60	Säffle	1985	Aqcuired 1997
174	GCH689	Scania CR112	Scania	1984	Aqcuired 1997
180	GCO709	Scania CN112	Scania	1984	Aqcuired 1997
181	GFB709	Scania CN112	Scania	1984	Aqcuired 1997
189	GYO091	Scania CN113	Scania	1991	Aqcuired 1997
192	KWW890	Volvo B10M-60	Van Hool	1982	
193	KXO980	Volvo B10M-60	Van Hool	1982	
199	GZE745	Scania N113CLB	Scania	1988	
201	GZF515	Scania CN113CLB	Scania	1988	
203	GZZ111	Scania CN113	Scania	1991	
204	HCC865	Scania N113CLB	Scania	1988	
212	HDH121	Scania CN113	Scania	1991	
222	LKK878	Volvo B10M-60	Van Hool	1983	
248	HFN066	Scania N113CLB	Scania	1988	
249	KSN342	Volvo B10M-60	Säffle	1981	Aqcuired 1997
250	LRK131	Mercedes-Benz 0303/9	Mercedes-Benz	1983	
253	LRP491	Mercedes-Benz 0303/9	Mercedes-Benz	1983	
254	LRZ391	Mercedes-Benz 0303/9	Mercedes-Benz	1983	
256	LCU577	Volvo B10M-65	Van Hool Alizée	1983	
265	LBY697	Volvo B10M-60	Van Hool Alizée	1983	
271	KFR401	Volvo B10M-65	Alpus 260S	1984	
279	LOY587	Volvo B10M-65	Alpus 260S	1984	
280	LPO727	Volvo B10M-65	Alpus 260S	1983	
281	LPP737	Volvo B10M-65	Alpus 260S	1983	

284-288		Volvo B10M-70B		Van Hool Alizée			1984		
284	GMF091	**285**	HXB391	**286**	GZX311	**287**	HFP341	**288**	GNL001

289-298 — Volvo B10M-65 — Alpus 260S* — 1984 *299/300 are Alpus 260SR

289	GYU331	291	DMA814	296	FRL794	297	DPA514	298	GBA564

306	ATX260	Volvo B10M-70B	Van Hool Alizée	1984
312	BSH340	Volvo B10M-70B	Van Hool Alizée	1984
314	GPS481	Volvo B10M-70B	Van Hool Alizée	1984

321-348 — Volvo B10M-65 — Alpus 260SR* — 1984-85 *333-6 are 260S

321	GOW406	330	EYF200	338	GYB543	343	JMG703	346	JYP613
323	GEK166	331	GAC190	340	LBC873	344	HCG773	347	LAW613
324	GMB196	335	GPZ196	341	LET823	345	JGX763	348	LFJ983
327	GOU196	336	GLC136	342	LBB863				

349	AWG978	Volvo B10M-70B	Van Hool Alizée	1985
350	AXD918	Volvo B10M-70B	Van Hool Alizée	1985
351	AEG908	Volvo B10M-70B	Van Hool Alizée	1985

352-363 — Volvo B10M-65 — Alpus 260S* — 1985

352	FDB030	355	CLT921	357	CME731	360	BHA863	362	BEC703
354	CTB961	356	CZM841	358	DFB761	361	ABP883	363	AAG603

364	MPD326	Volvo B10M-70B	Van Hool Alizée	1985
365	MPE026	Volvo B10M-70B	Van Hool Alizée	1985
366	MOP116	Volvo B10M-65	Alpus 260SR	1985
368	EMG263	Mercedes-Benz O303/9	Mercedes-Benz	1985
369	EFU173	Mercedes-Benz O303/9	Mercedes-Benz	1985
370	FBB053	Mercedes-Benz O303/9	Mercedes-Benz	1985
371	FWE373	Mercedes-Benz O303/9	Mercedes-Benz	1985

372-389 — Volvo B10M-60 — Van Hool Alizée — 1985

372	GOF598	375	GZG618	378	GUU568	382	CXE911	388	FWO150
373	GPC918	376	HMA668	380	HNT838	387	CPZ941	389	FXM340

391	LAX543	Volvo B10R-59	Säffle	1983
393	LCO981	Volvo B10R-59	Säffle	1983
394	MXA086	Scania K112CLS	Alpus 260SR	1986

395-411 — Volvo B10M-65 — Alpus 260SR — 1985-86

395	MON266	399	MMY066	403	MPL076	406	MOT146	409	MPF106
396	MNU016	400	MLR356	404	MPR026	407	MOY246	410	MOM326
397	MNU186	401	MLU386	405	MPW126	408	MOX306	411	MON026
398	MMP176	402	MLP276						

412-420 — Volvo B10M-70B — Van Hool Alizée — 1986-87 419-25 are B10M-60

412	MPF400	415	MMZ243	418	MJJ585	419	MNL373	420	MNK293
414	MNJ433	416	MJE545						

421	LCS782	Volvo B10R-59	Säffle	1983

423-430 — Volvo B10M-70B — Van Hool Alizée — 1986-87 423-25 are B10M-60

423	MNF023	425	MNN153	427	MHZ845	429	MDJ775	430	LJU794
424	MND243	426	MME283						

431	LPW291	Scania CN112	Scania	1984
433	LXH450	Mercedes-Benz		1983
434	MUM715	Scania CN112	Scania	1986
435	MUR685	Scania CN112	Scania	1985

436-444   Volvo B10M-65   Alpus 260S   1987

436	KAF010	438	JUM210	440	JJC390	442	JPU440	444	JMN160
437	KAW100	439	JNL110	441	JUT410	443	JXD290		

445	NWG985	Volvo B9M-46	Alpus	1987
446	NWB935	Volvo B9M-46	Alpus	1987
448	EBA201	Volvo B10M-50B	Van Hool Alizée	1987
449	DZL361	Volvo B10M-50B	Van Hool Alizée	1987
450	MWA313	Scania CN112	Scania	1986
451	HEU823	Volvo B10M-70B	Van Hool Alizée	1987

452-460   Volvo B10M-70B   Van Hool Alizée   1987

452	JJF563	454	KME603	456	JPU993	459	HFU963	460	JBY993
453	JOC663	455	JGH923	458	HGP993				

461	MWB013	Scania CN112	Scania	1986
462	NRG808	Renault Master	Renault	1988
464	NSF493	Mercedes-Benz	. Mercedes-Benz	1991
465	OCM525	Scania SC	Van Hool Alizée	1990
466	OTN805	Auwaerter Neoplan N116	Auwaerter Cityliner	1990

467-475   Volvo B10M-65R   Alpus 260S   1988

467	NEE179	469	NKR320	471	NMM312	473	NMJ082	475	NLW482
468	NKN390	470	NLW242	472	NMN322	474	NML162		

476	NOM959	Volvo B10M-70B	Van Hool Alizée	1988
477	NOC739	Volvo B10M-70B	Van Hool Alizée 310	1988
478	NOA959	Volvo B10M-70B	Van Hool Alizée	1988
479	NNS629	Volvo B10M-70B	Van Hool Alizée	1988
480	NDK389	Volvo B10M-65	Alpus 260SR	1988
481	ASR794	Scania K113CLB	Van Hool Alizée	1988
482	AOC764	Scania K113CLB	Van Hool Alizée	1988

483-488   Volvo B10M-60   Van Hool Alizée   1988

483	NDR093	485	NEB273	486	NDU193	487	NEO043	488	NDL043
484	NEE063								

489	NEA333	Volvo B10M-58B	Van Hool Alizée 310	1988
490	NEF383	Volvo B10M-58B	Van Hool Alizée 310	1988
491	NED433	Volvo B10M-70B	Van Hool Alizée	1988
492	NEG223	Volvo B10M-70B	Van Hool Alizée	1988
494	NEN103	Volvo B10M-70B	Van Hool Alizée	1988
495	KSO416	Volvo B10M-65	Van Hool Alizée	1988
496	KON186	Volvo B10M-65	Van Hool Alizée	1988
497	OTN975	Auwaerter Neoplan N116	Auwaerter Cityliner	1990

498-508   Volvo B10M-65   Alpus 260SR   1989

498	OOL259	500	OOD299	502	ONJ039	503	ONT329	504	ONT499
499	OOH479	501	OOP059						

505	OBT252	Volvo B10M-70B	Alpus 260SR	1989
506	OBK342	Volvo B10M-70B	Alpus 260SR	1989
507	OCB102	Volvo B10M-70B	Alpus 260SR	1989
508	ODE132	Volvo B10M-70B	Alpus 260SR	1989

509-514   Volvo B10M-70B   Säffle   1989

509	OSK141	511	OSM301	512	OSH371	513	OSN171	514	ORZ191
510	OSE271								

515	OZW174	Volvo B10M-70B	Alpus 260SR	1989
516	OZR454	Volvo B10M-70B	Alpus 260SR	1989
517	OZR074	Volvo B10M-70B	Alpus 260SR	1989
518	OZM344	Volvo B10M-70B	Alpus 260SR	1989
519	OBC955	Volvo B10M-65	Alpus 260SR	1989
520	OBL785	Volvo B10M-65	Alpus 260SR	1990
521	OBH525	Volvo B10M-65	Alpus 260SR	1990

New in 1984, Swebus 324 is a Volvo B10M-65 with Alpus 260R bodywork. It is seen in Karlstad. The type are used as regional vehicles in a similar way to the British interurban model is used.
Malcolm Tranter

522-529
Volvo B10M-65 — Van Hool Alizée — 1989

522	ODD143	**524**	ODG483	**526**	ODB363	**528**	OOR314	**529**	ODM353
523	ODO443	**525**	ODJ403	**527**	ODM113				

530	OBU402	Volvo B10M-58B	Van Hool Astral	1989
531	OBH262	Volvo B10M-58B	Van Hool Astral	1989

532-539
Volvo B10M-65* — Van Hool Alizée — 1989 — *Models varey

532	OZT474	**534**	OZH244	**536**	OBB635	**538**	OZE454	**539**	OZU314
533	OAD454	**535**	OZW004	**537**	OBB565				

540	OZJ014	Volvo B10M-70B	Alpus 260SR	1989
541	OJF918	Volvo B10M-65	Alpus 260SR	1990

542-546
Volvo B10M-70B — Säffle — 1990

542	OHS708	**543**	OJG618	**544**	OHZ828	**545**	OHT958	**546**	OJG858

547	OHX738	Volvo B10M-70B	Alpus 260SR	1990
548	OHR558	Volvo B10M-70B	Alpus 260SR	1990
550	OFC929	Volvo B10M-56B	Van Hool Astral	1990

551-556
Volvo B10M-65 — Alpus 260SR — 1989

551	OFX679	**553**	OFN919	**554**	OGA809	**555**	OFX509	**556**	OFN849
552	OFD939							

| 557 | OFZ699 | Volvo B10M-70B | Alpus 260SR | | 1990 | | |
| 558 | OTO675 | Auwaerter Neoplan N3 | Auwaerter | | 1990 | | |

559-564 Volvo B10M-70B Säffle 1988

| 559 | NCY059 | **561** | NTG311 | **562** | NCX382 | **563** | NEH334 | **564** | NER315 |
| 560 | NXL420 | | | | | | | | |

576	BCW148	Volvo B10M-65	Ajokki 5000	1982
577	CZO348	Volvo B10M-65	Ajokki 5000	1982
580	CML338	Volvo B10M-65	Ajokki 5000	1982
590	MLH159	Volvo B10R-59	Säffle	1986
591	MLD429	Volvo B10R-59	Säffle	1986
593	BRZ164	Volvo B10M-65	Säffle	1987
594	BJP194	Volvo B10M-65	Säffle	1987

595-599 Scania CN113 Scania 1988-89

| 595 | NLL725 | **596** | NON755 | **597** | NLH635 | **598** | OYT369 | **599** | OZK119 |

600	OMH191	Volvo B10M-55L	Säffle		1989
601	OMB131	Volvo B10M-55L	Säffle		1989
609	HEX494	Volvo B10M-70B	Kutter 9		1986
610	OLU361	Volvo B10M-55L	Säffle		1989
611	OMC141	Volvo B10M-65	Säffle		1989
612	OCO163	Volvo B10M-55L	Säffle		1989
613	MTD280	Volvo B9M-46	Säffle		1986
614	JLG216	Scania K93	West		1991
615	FCG295	Scania K93	West		1991
616	OAH555	Scania K113	West		1990
617	DUY143	Hino RB145	Hino		1990
618	MAU092	Hino RB145	Hino		1990
619	AXY446	Scania K93	Helmark		1989
620	FXF239	Mercedes-Benz 1120/L42	Delta Star 21	B21F	1987
621	MJX735	Mercedes-Benz 1120/L42	Delta Star 21	B21F	1987
622	MAC461	Scania CN112	Scania		1986
623	LXS400	Scania CN112	Scania		1987
624	HRY061	Scania CN113	Scania		1990
625	FPX025	Scania K113	Ajokki Victor		1991
626	FPS475	Scania K113	Ajokki Victor		1991
628	PXA535	Scania K113	Ajokki Victor		1993
629	GBB659	Scania CN112	Scania		1984
631	CLU681	Scania CR112	Scania		1983
632	DMF497	Volvo B10R-59	Säffle		1982
633	FXH183	Scania CR112	Scania		1982
636	LWA195	Scania CR112	Scania		1983
638	BRO798	Volvo B10M-60	Van Hool Alizée		1985
639	HGE199	Scania CN112	Scania		1985
640	MKC258	Scania K112	Van Hool Alizée		1986
641	AHH250	Scania CN112	Scania		1987
642	MAM609	Volvo B10M-60	Van Hool Alizée		1987
643	NHE292	Volvo B9M-46	Ajokki Victor		1988
644	CTD185	Scania K113	Ajokki Victor		1991
646	ANW945	Scania CN113	Scania		1992
647	MFX091	Scania CN112	Scania		1986
648	OAP273	Volvo B10M-60	Delta Star 501		1990
649	MAM061	Scania CN112	Scania		1986
650	OHP896	Scania CN113	Scania		1990
651	OZP602	Mercedes-Benz 0410	Mercedes-Benz	C49F	1989
653	KOP337	Volvo B9M-46	Ajokki Victor		1990
654	CMW575	Scania K113T	Ajokki Regal		1992
655	JKA519	Scania CN113	Scania		1992
656	PFG603	Volvo B10M-65	Ajokki Regal		1992

Opposite, top:- **Photographed in Karlstad wearing Värmlands livery is Swebus 0468, NKN390, a Volvo B10M with Alpus 260 SR bodywork.** *Malcolm Tranter*
Opposite, bottom:- **During 1997 the Sewbus fleet has been augmented with many coaches, including four-axle Neoplan Megaliners for express services and Mercedes-Benz O404 coaches. One of the latter, 4098, FCN765, is illustrated here.** *Nigel Hunt*

659	OUN340	Volvo B10M-70B	Ajokki Royal		1989
660	PJW623	Auwaerter Neoplan N116	Auwaerter Cityliner		1992
664	PFH853	Volkswagen Kombi	Volkswagen	M9	1992
665	PET873	Volkswagen Kombi	Volkswagen	M9	1992
666	AKA090	Scania CN112	Scania		1987
667	HXZ031	Scania CN113	Scania		1990
668	MKJ505	Scania K112	Ajokki City		1987
669	MXE088	Scania K112	Ajokki City		1986
670	DLF708	Scania K113	Ajokki		1989
671	LAN768	Scania K112	Ajokki 6000		1983
672	AWU194	Volvo B10M-	Säffle		1983
674	LGE913	Volvo B10M-	Säffle		1983
675	LHM839	Volvo B10M-	Säffle		1983
676	LJL659	Volvo B10M-	Säffle		1983
678	LLY082	Volvo B10M-	Säffle		1983
679	LHL874	Volvo B10M-	Säffle		1983
680	LET627	Volvo B10M-	Säffle		1983
681	LHK680	Volvo B10M-	Säffle		1983
682	LHU751	Volvo B10M-	Säffle		1983
683	PLU317	Volvo B10M-	Säffle		1993
684	PME357	Volvo B10M-	Säffle		1993
685	OXY253	Volvo B10M-	Säffle		1991
686	OXU303	Volvo B10M-	Säffle		1991
687	OWE303	Volvo B10M-	Säffle		1991
688	NAE796	Volvo B10M-	Säffle		1988
689	NPT924	Volvo B10M-	Säffle		1988
690	NTL956	Volvo B10M-	Säffle		1988
691	NSH907	Volvo B10M-	Säffle		1988
692	NPL828	Volvo B10M-	Säffle		1988
693	NPN789	Volvo B10M-	Säffle		1988
694	NPW510	Volvo B10M-	Säffle		1988
695	KDJ385	Volvo B10M-	Säffle		1991
696	KEC465	Volvo B10M-	Säffle		1991
697	PHF207	Volvo B10M-	Säffle		1993
698	PLR387	Volvo B10M-	Säffle		1993
699	EYL310	Volvo B10M-	Säffle		1996
700	ETD120	Volvo B10M-	Säffle		1996
703	MCJ705	Scania K112T	Ikarus Club		1986
706	CXM462	Scania K112	Kutter 9 Clipper		1984
711	LSM034	Scania K112	Ajokki 6000		1983
712	PGA435	Renault Master	Renault		1994
713	PFA655	Renault Master	Renault		1991
714	MPA120	Renault Master	Renault		1988
715	PJJ106	Renault Trafic	Renault		1993
716	PHK127	Renault Trafic	Renault		1993
717	ASB084	Renault Trafic	Renault		1991
718	OEK362	Volvo B10M-	Säffle		1991
719	OJK032	Volvo B10M-	Säffle		1991
720	OJH192	Volvo B10M-	Säffle		1991
722	EWZ381	Scania K112T	Wiima K202		1987
726	DYM019	Volvo B10M-50B	Carrus Star 602		1996
728	DXG614	Scania K112	Ajokki City		1985
729	ETE789	Scania K112	Ajokki City		1985
730	LRE443	Scania K112	Ajokki		1984
731	LUA413	Scania K112	Ajokki		1984
732	OZT996	Scania CN113	Scania		1990
733	OZX776	Scania CN113	Scania		1990
734	PHN965	Scania CN113	Wiima		1992
735	PHN585	Scania CN113	Wiima		1992
736	LBB028	Volvo B10M-	Säffle		1991
737	ONU480	Volvo B10M-	Säffle		1989
738	MGD129	Volvo B10M-60	Lahti 450 Eagle		1986
742	PAE988	Ontario II	Ontario II		1989
744	LHY235	Volvo B10M-65	Säffle		1983
745	LJE185	Volvo B10M-65	Säffle		1983
746	DEW648	Volvo B10M-65	Säffle		1984
747	DPU898	Volvo B10M-65	Säffle		1984
748	LXB658	Scania K112	Delta Plan 200		1984
749	LXG538	Scania K112	Delta Plan 200		1984
750	BBG571	Volvo B10M-70B	Van Hool Alizée		1985
751	DWR510	Scania K112	Ajokki Express		1985
752	MNK301	Volvo B9M-46	Säffle		1986
755	NUL865	Volvo B10M-70	Säffle		1988

756	NUN885	Volvo B10M-70	Säffle			1988		
757	GYA416	Volvo B10M-65	Säffle			1988		
758	GYR146	Volvo B10M-65	Säffle			1988		
759	HFY386	Volvo B10M-65	Säffle			1989		
760	JFL136	Volvo B10M-65	Säffle			1989		
761	OHN249	Volvo B10M-70B	Säffle			1989		
762	OLP451	Volvo B10M-65	Säffle			1989		
763	OMF131	Volvo B10M-65	Säffle			1989		
764	OYK025	Scania CK113	Scania			1990		
765	OYN295	Scania CK113	Scania			1990		
766	PMG420	Volvo B10M-70B	Säffle 2000			1992		
767	FBD010	Scania CR112	Scania			1982		
768	LEJ446	Scania CR112	Scania			1983		
769	AGF075	Scania CN112	Scania			1985		
770	JKA016	Scania CN113	Scania			1989		
771	OSY815	Neoplan N4007NF	Neoplan			1990		
772	LJM385	Volvo B10M-60	Van Hool Alizée			1983		
773	LHS564	Volvo B10M-70B	Van Hool Alizée			1984		
774	MDU200	Volvo B10M-60	Van Hool Alizée			1986		
775	NUY725	Volvo B10M-60	Van Hool Alizée			1988		
776	OFT608	Volvo B10M-60	Van Hool Alizée			1990		
777	OGS598	Volvo B10M-58B	Van Hool Alizée			1990		
778	BCL426	Kässbohrer Setra S210H	Kässbohrer			1985		
781	MLW701	Mercedes-Benz 711D				1989		
785	MKR695	Scania CN112	Scania			1987		
786	DEW195	Scania CN113	Scania			1991		
787	DGZ165	Scania CN113	Scania			1991		
788	PJW766	Scania CN113	Scania			1993		
789	PJW696	Scania CN113	Scania			1993		
790	FYZ319	Volvo B10R-59	Säffle			1987		
791	GUF339	Volvo B10R-59	Säffle			1987		
792	GRO089	Volvo B10R-59	Säffle			1987		
793	HNM019	Scania CN112	Scania			1985		
794	HEB129	Scania CN112	Scania			1985		
795	OHS816	Scania CK113	Scania			1990		
796	OJB536	Scania CK113	Scania			1990		
797	PWE320	Auwaerter Neoplan N3	Auwaerter			1994		
798	OFY181	Volvo B10M-60	Vest Ambassador			1989		

800-805		Ontario II	Ontario			1989		
800w	PAM894	**801**	PAM893	**802**	PAM923	**803**	PAM922	**805**	PAU007

806	JDS371	Volvo B10M-65	Ajokki Express			1990
807	EDB023	Volvo B10M-65	Ajokki Express			1990
812	HPU386	Scania L113	Aabenraa			1991
813	HLS165	Kässbohrer Setra SG219	Kässbohrer			1991

824-828		Scania K113	Ajokki Express			1992		
824	PKB972	**825**	PKP992	**826**	PXF504	**827**	PWZ584	**828**	PWS604

829-833		Volvo B10M-70	Säffle 2000			1992		
829	PLN934	**830**	PLJ904	**831**	PLK764	**832**	PLL844	**833**	PLN554

834-838		Volvo B10M-65	Säffle 2000			1992		
834	PLB864	**835**	PLS664	**836**	PLD644	**837**	PLG814	**838**	PLC944

864	HJU582	Volkswagen Kombi	Volkswagen	M9	1984
866	FSP536	Volvo B10M-65	Skandia Meteor		1983
869	CHK595	Volvo B10M-65	Alpus 260S		1983
870	MPE196	Volvo B10M-70B	Van Hool Alizée		1986
871	AXD821	Volvo B10L-55L	Säffle		1985
872	AJG891	Volvo B10L-55L	Säffle		1985
874	FXU974	Volvo B10M-65	Alpus 260S		1984
875	FSG276	Volvo B10M-65	Alpus 260S		1984
876	FTU047	Volkswagen Caravelle	Volkswagen		1985
877	MTX143	Scania K112T	Ajokki Express		1987
878	MTY223	Scania K112T	Ajokki Express		1987
879	MOM186	Volvo B10M-70B	Van Hool Alizée		1986
880	MTO013	Scania K112T	Ajokki Express		1987
881	MUB143	Scania K112T	Ajokki Express		1987

882	MTU373	Scania K112T	Ajokki Express	1987					
883	MTL083	Scania K112T	Ajokki Express	1987					
884	AUE738	Volvo B10M-70B	Van Hool Alizée	1985					
885	DWF989	Volvo B10M-70B	Van Hool Alizée	1985					
886	DMZ589	Volvo B10M-70B	Van Hool Alizée	1985					
887	FWM440	Volvo B10M-65	Alpus 260SR	1984					
888	BET673	Volvo B10M-65	Alpus 260SR	1985					
889	MHW715	Volvo B10M-65	Wiima	1987					
890	MUE173	Scania K112T	Ajokki Express	1987					
891	MHC905	Volvo B10M-65	Wiima	1987					
892	MHN825	Volvo B10M-65	Wiima	1987					
893	EML421	Volvo B10M-70	Wiima	1987					
894	MHO905	Volvo B10M-65	Wiima	1987					
895	MHY735	Volvo B10M-65	Wiima	1987					
896	MJH656	Volvo B10M-65	Wiima	1987					
897	MML066	Volvo B10M-65	Alpus 260SR	1985					
899	KLL224	Kässbohrer Setra SG221UL	Kässbohrer	1988					
900	NDE757	Scania CN112	Scania	1988					
901	NDJ627	Scania CN112	Scania	1988					
902	NCW717	Scania CN112	Scania	1988					
903	NLG393	Scania CN112	Scania	1988					
904	EHP915	Scania K112T	Ajokki Express	1988					
905	HHZ598	Scania K112T	Ajokki Express	1988					

906-911		Volvo B10M-65		Alpus 260SR		1987-88			
906	JLP110	**907**	JLP350	**909**	NDM239	**910**	NEE489	**911**	NDZ479

912	OTG344	Scania K113	Aabenraa	1989					
913	OUY091	Scania CK113	Scania	1989					
914	OKY093	Volvo B10M-70	Säffle	1989					
915	DJA948	Scania CK113	Scania	1990					
916	OKE667	Scania CN113A	Scania	1990					
917	OKM797	Scania CN113A	Scania	1990					
918	OKG757	Scania CN113A	Scania	1990					
919	OLR094	Kässbohrer Setra SG219SL	Kässbohrer	1990					
920	OLN134	Kässbohrer Setra SG219SL	Kässbohrer	1990					
921	OLN374	Kässbohrer Setra SG219SL	Kässbohrer	1990					
922	OUG441	Scania CK113	Scania	1989					
923	OWF454	Scania CK113	Scania	1989					
924	OZB405	Scania CK113	Scania	1989					
925	ORL491	Volvo B10M-65	Säffle	1989					
926	OPP151	Volvo B10M-65	Säffle	1989					
927	OOA040	Scania K113	Ajokki Express	1989					
928	OKB261	Scania K113	Ajokki Express	1989					
929	OKB021	Scania K113	Ajokki Express	1989					
930	OKG071	Scania K113	Ajokki Express	1989					
931	OLD173	Volvo B10M-70	Säffle	1989					
932	OCA302	Scania K113T	Ajokki Express	1989					
933	OBG222	Scania K113T	Ajokki Express	1989					
934	OJG013	Scania K113T	Ajokki Express	1989					
935	OKP343	Volvo B10M-65	Säffle	1989					
936	OUJ221	Scania CK113	Scania	1989					
937	OUZ001	Scania CK113	Scania	1989					
938	OUJ391	Scania CN113	Scania	1989					
939	OUS431	Scania CN113	Scania	1989					
940	OUZ171	Scania CN113	Scania	1989					
941	OKE361	Scania K113T	Ajokki Express	1989					
942	OJZ341	Scania K113T	Ajokki Express	1989					
943	OKH151	Scania K113T	Ajokki Express	1989					
944	ORL181	Volvo B10M-70	Säffle	1989					
945	OYH325	Scania CK113	Scania	1990					
946	OJU481	Scania K113T	Ajokki Express	1989					
947	OKK231	Scania K113T	Ajokki Express	1989					
948	OUY471	Scania CK113	Scania	1989					
949	OYJ335	Scania CK113	Scania	1990					
950	OYT102	Scania K113T	Aabenraa	1989					
952	OKS320	Scania K112T	Ajokki Express	1988					
954	JGJ171	Volvo B10M-65	Ajokki Victor	1990					
955	HZY201	Volvo B10M-65	Ajokki Victor	1990					
956	JGX241	Volvo B10M-65	Ajokki Victor	1990					
957	PKP512	Scania K113	Carrus Fifty	1992					
960	MKO686	Volvo B9M-46	Helmark	1986					

962	DXR222	Volvo B10M-60	Van Hool Alizée	1987
963	GJG216	Scania K112T	Ajokki Royal	1988
964	OJF483	Scania K113T	Ajokki Royal	1989
965	ONZ380	Scania K113	Ajokki Express	1989
966	BKD548	Scania K113	Ajokki Victor	1989
967	OOF470	Scania K113	Ajokki Express	1989
968	OJN443	Scania K113T	Ajokki Royal	1989
974	OEK333	Volvo B10M-70B	Ajokki Express	1989
975	ODU423	Volvo B10M-70B	Ajokki Express	1989
976	OEM283	Volvo B10M-70B	Ajokki Express	1989
977	OED453	Volvo B10M-70B	Ajokki Express	1989
978	GJT097	Volvo B10M-65B	Delta Star 501	1989
979	CDL490	Volvo B10M-70	Aabenraa	1991
980	CFM060	Volvo B10M-70	Aabenraa	1991
981	DHF053	Volvo B10M-70	Aabenraa	1990
982	DGR383	Volvo B10M-70	Aabenraa	1990
983	DGX323	Volvo B10M-65	Aabenraa	1990
984	DDD293	Volvo B10M-65	Aabenraa	1990
985	AZT082	Volvo B10M-65	Säffle	1990
986	AWA012	Volvo B10M-55L	Säffle	1990
987	AUF222	Volvo B10M-55L	Säffle	1990
988	ASS422	Volvo B10M-55L	Säffle	1990
989	AWC272	Volvo B10M-55L	Säffle	1990
990	BDC462	Volvo B10M-55L	Säffle	1990
991	DGC363	Volvo B10M-55L	Aabenraa	1990
992	KCX062	Volvo B10M-65	Aabenraa	1990
993	MBY392	Volvo B10M-65	Aabenraa	1990
994	DDM193	Volvo B10M-65	Aabenraa	1990
998	CCN218	Scania K113	Ajokki Victor	1991
1001	DFL678	Scania K113	Ajokki Victor	1989
1003	CRL078	Scania K113T	Delta Star 701	1991
1004	CRN168	Scania K113T	Delta Star 701	1991
1006	DYJ092	Scania K112T	Van Hool Astrobel	1987
1007	EKN372	Scania K92	Van Hool Alizée	1987
1008	MKO877	Auwaerter Neoplan N212	Auwaerter Jetliner	1987
1010	BDU101	Volvo B10M-65	Skandia Meteor	1984
1014	AJY751	Volvo B10M-55L	Säffle	1985
1015	EEY159	Volvo B10M-55L	Säffle	1991
1020	DGM839	Volvo B10M-60	Säffle	1985
1021	BKX929	Volvo B10M-60	Säffle	1985
1022	NTN845	Volvo B10M-60	Säffle	1987
1023	NLH472	Volvo B10M-60	Säffle	1990
1024	DRW283	Volvo B10M-60	Säffle	1990
1025	DPF293	Volvo B10M-60	Säffle	1990
1026	NLX725	Renault Master FB30	Renault	1988
1027	NGO624	Renault Master FB30	Renault	1988
1029	NSB715	Volvo FL6.14	Helmark Meteor	1988
1031	BNH199	Scania B86	Ajokki 5000D	1981
1035	LBJ870	Volvo F4.08	Skandia	1983
1036	HJW651	Volvo B10M-45	Skandia Meteor	1985
1037	DUN002	Volvo B9M-46	Van Hool Alizée	1987
1038	FLO762	Volvo B9M-46	Van Hool Alizée	1987
1039	OLT111	Volvo B9M-46	Vest Ambassadör	1989
1040	NSZ737	Auwaerter Neoplan N214SH	Auwaerter Jetliner	1988
1053	JXW182	Volvo B10M-60	Van Hool Alizée	1984
1055	MMS785	Volvo B10M-60	Van Hool Alizée	1987
1056	OBA313	Volvo B10M-60	Van Hool Alizée	1989
1057	BLZ609	Volvo B10M-60	Van Hool Alizée	1987
1058	BDX690	Volvo B10M-50B	Van Hool Astral	1988
1059	NNM201	Volvo B10M-60	Van Hool Alizée	1988
1060	NFO442	Volvo B10M-50B	Van Hool Astral	1988
1061	OUL250	Volvo B10M-60	Van Hool Alizée	1989
1062	APF301	Volvo B10M-60	Van Hool Alizée	1990
1063	NGH012	Auwaerter Neoplan	Auwaerter	1988
1064	AOP390	Auwaerter Neoplan N116	Auwaerter Cityliner	1991
1066	PSW685	Auwaerter Neoplan N117/3	Auwaerter Spaceliner	1993
1067	AJJ228	Auwaerter Neoplan	Auwaerter	1991
1068	PRD602	Auwaerter Neoplan N117/3	Auwaerter Spaceliner	1993
1069	MGJ377	Auwaerter Neoplan	Auwaerter	1989
1070	PRJ652	Auwaerter Neoplan N117/3	Auwaerter Spaceliner	1992
1071	EKZ594	Auwaerter Neoplan N117/3	Auwaerter Spaceliner	1989
1072	ANS100	Auwaerter Neoplan N116	Auwaerter Cityliner	1991
1075	OSB189	Volvo B10M-60	Van Hool Alizée	1989

Photographed during 1997 in Stockholm is 1327, GDG959, a Scania CN112 with bodywork also by Scania. The vehicle dates from 1984, and an interesting feature is the installation of curtains to the windows. *Andrew Jarosz*

1078	LPU809	Scania CR112	Scania	1984
1079	LRJ547	Scania CR112	Scania	1984
1080	HWW240	Scania K92	Scania	1987
1084	FCA101	Auwaerter Neoplan N116	Auwaerter Cityliner	1991
1085	ANA238	Auwaerter Neoplan N117/3	Auwaerter Spaceliner	1991
1090	NTM402	Auwaerter Neoplan N117/3	Auwaerter Spaceliner	1988
1092	PSB935	Auwaerter Neoplan N117/3	Auwaerter Spaceliner	1993
1110	PDY027	Auwaerter Neoplan N117/3	Auwaerter Spaceliner	1994
1111	POU540	Auwaerter Neoplan N116/3	Auwaerter Cityliner	1994
1117	PKN760	Auwaerter Neoplan N116/3	Auwaerter Cityliner	1993
1118	FJJ305	Auwaerter Neoplan N213	Auwaerter Jetliner	1991
1124	FLR331	Volvo B10R-59	Säffle	1984
1125	PKJ970	Auwaerter Neoplan N116/3	Auwaerter Cityliner	1993
1129	GBM757	Volvo B10R-59	Säffle	1985
1130	GGB717	Volvo B10R-59	Säffle	1985
1131	MKZ098	Volvo B10M-50B	Van Hool Astral	1986
1132	AEB535	Volvo B12-61B	Van Hool Alizée	1992
1133	MBM478	Volvo B10R-59	Säffle	1986
1139	MBG298	Volvo B10M-60	Säffle	1986

1140-1160		Volvo B10R-59	Säffle	1987-90

1140	MBW802	**1148**	NTN013	**1152**	ORG866	**1155**	ORF546	**1158**	OCY935
1142	MBB543	**1149**	NTC333	**1153**	ORF926	**1156**	OBW945	**1159**	OCG765
1144	MBD644	**1150**	NTG373	**1154**	ORH636	**1157**	OBO995	**1160**	OCU605
1147	NTN183							

1162	NGK250	Mercedes-Benz 0303		Mercedes-Benz		1987			
1164	AWU265	Scania CN112A		Scania		1985			
1165	MYL286	Scania CN112A		Scania		1986			
1166	MYX106	Scania CN112A		Scania		1986			
1167	OUK042	Scania K113T		Van Hool Alizée		1991			
1168	ATT105	Renault Master FB30		Renault		1996			
1169	PDR106	Renault Master FB30		Renault		1994			
1170	MFO087	Mercedes-Benz		Mercedes-Benz		1986			
1171	CWJ668	Renault Master FB30		Renault		1997			

1176-1188 — Scania CR112 — Scania — 1982

1176	EHO314	1182	FFA252	1186	LGY359	1187	LFS420	1188	LHJ261
1177	EFY355								

1189	EAB013	Hino RB145		Hino		1990			

1190-1197 — Volvo B10MA-55 — Säffle — 1986

1190	ALJ876	1192	BTA670	1194	MZH228	1196	MYW188	1197	MZU228
1191	FEA673	1193	ASD938	1195	MYU498				

1200	GMG935	Volvo B10M-60	Van Hool Alizée	1981
1201	OUN011	Scania CN113A	Scania	1989
1222	OUU381	Scania CN113A	Scania	1989
1229	OUX221	Scania CN113A	Scania	1989
1230	OUR041	Scania CN113A	Scania	1989
1233	MUA817	Volvo B10R-59	Säffle	1987
1234	MUD607	Volvo B10R-59	Säffle	1987
1235	MUG567	Volvo B10R-59	Säffle	1987
1236	MUG947	Volvo B10R-59	Säffle	1987
1237	OUO331	Scania CN113A	Scania	1989
1238	OUF361	Scania CN113A	Scania	1989
1239	OUN181	Scania CN113A	Scania	1989
1240	OUH211	Scania CN113A	Scania	1989

1241-1245 — Volvo B10R-59 — Säffle — 1991

1241	HXY336	1242	HZA076	1243	JAM006	1244	JCN056	1245	JEA466

1246	OUO401	Scania CN113A	Scania	1989
1247	OJA163	Scania CN113A	Scania	1989
1248	OHH473	Scania CN113A	Scania	1989
1249	OUT061	Scania CN113A	Scania	1990

1250-1259 — Auwaerter Neoplan N4014NF — Auwaerter — 1992

1250	PXU605	1252	PXZ565	1254	PXT905	1256	PYF895	1258	PXT525
1251	PXR985	1253	PYA605	1255	PXT765	1257	PXP595	1259	PXY935

1260	OUL293	Auwaerter Neoplan N4007	Auwaerter	1989
1261	OUW413	Auwaerter Neoplan N4007	Auwaerter	1989
1262	OWE393	Auwaerter Neoplan N4007	Auwaerter	1989
1274	ATU233	Scania CR112	Scania	1982
1275	LMX500	Scania CR112	Scania	1983
1283	LLW818	Scania CR112	Scania	1983
1290	MTC332	Scania CN112	Scania	1986
1291	MSO362	Scania CN112	Scania	1986

1292-1324 — Scania CR112 — Scania — 1982-84

1292	DLL222	1298	EUL250	1308	KOX975	1318	HHK569	1322	JDW569
1294	ELS294	1300	ERE215	1309	LUB616	1319	JJR589	1323	JYT779
1295	EHF355	1302	LWW789	1315	JMT529	1321	HYY719	1324	HJT999
1297	FJE338	1304	LWL721						

1325-1345 — Scania CN112 — Scania — 1984

1325	GOH809	1330	GES919	1334	BTO243	1338	LXK443	1342	LYN203
1326	GFL619	1331	GCB939	1335	BND373	1339	LZP123	1343	LZW473
1327	GDG959	1332	GDJ739	1336	LZE443	1340	LXO003	1344	LZJ003
1328	GPX579	1333	CBW253	1337	LZC353	1341	LXP183	1345	LYE473
1329	GJR509								

1346-1351 — Scania CN113A — Scania — 1993

1346	PKA916	1348	PKJ977	1349	PJX517	1350	PKF877	1351	PJO797
1347	PKE627								

1352-1369 — Scania CN112 — Scania — 1987

1352	MXE839	1356	MER678	1360	MTY939	1364	KTM090	1367	MTB579
1353	MEP598	1357	MFC558	1361	MTH609	1365	MTM879	1368	NSH875
1354	MEZ708	1358	MUE579	1362	MTN959	1366	MTB959	1369	NRU595
1355	MFE888	1359	MTY559	1363	MTG909				

1370	LOF658	Scania CR112	Scania		1984

1372-1382 — Scania CN112A — Scania — 1985-87

1372	FXW036	1375	GLC952	1377	GBM822	1379	GRD883	1381	GWB923
1373	GBS126	1376	FNA982	1378	FYY912	1380	GYB583	1382	GWY833
1374	GAR892								

1383	PKY615	Scania CN113A	Scania		1992
1384	PKW835	Scania CN113A	Scania		1992
1385	PKZ935	Scania CN113A	Scania		1992
1386	PKW905	Scania CN113A	Scania		1992
1387	OHJ808	Volvo B10M-55L	Säffle		1990
1388	OHE868	Volvo B10M-55L	Säffle		1990
1389	ORH343	Volvo B10M-55L	Säffle		1991
1390	OPO183	Volvo B10M-55L	Säffle		1991

1392-1397 — Volvo B10M-60 — Säffle — 1991

1392	DGE569	1394	BJN815	1395	BKB965	1396	BHN605	1397	BHM765
1393	BGJ845								

1407	GOK112	Volvo B10M-60	Säffle		1984

1408-1418 — Volvo B10M-55L — Säffle — 1990

1408	OHE798	1411	OGY918	1413	OGZ548	1415	OHC608	1417	OHD928
1409	OGY778	1412	OHM828	1414	OGX838	1416	OHA518	1418	OHM758
1410	OHN698								

1419-1456 — Volvo B10M-55L — Säffle — 1983-84

1428	LCF937	1444	LGR578	1447	LXZ907	1450	LZM947	1454	LXY517
1440	LGC798	1445	LYK717	1448	LZL937	1451	LYM667	1455	LYH637
1441	LGU988	1446	LYH947	1449	LZP977	1452	LYD697	1456	LXX987
1443	LGM538								

1458	BGB703	Volvo B10M-60	Säffle		1985

1488-1494 — Volvo B10M-55L — Säffle — 1983-84

1488	LPU968	1490	LOO303	1491	LPR463	1493w	LOG103	1494	LPN123

1495-1544 — Scania CN113 — Scania — 1986-90

1495	JWT156	1504	EAP698	1514	AEH658	1523	ABY598	1537	CRD508
1496	JOE346	1506	DXT728	1515	AEX598	1525	BAT898	1540	OMY967
1497	JAR256	1507	DCR588	1517	BSK538	1526	BXP648	1541	ONE817
1498	NLZ347	1508	EEP508	1518	BNR518	1528	CCH908	1542	ONG527
1499	BMA023	1511	DTZ988	1519	AAT978	1535	BCL868	1543	ONK857
1500	NMM317	1512	CHY598	1520	CKC958	1536	BBY898	1544	OMX957
1501	EJO578	1513	CTU588						

1545-1552 — Volvo B10MA-55 — Säffle — 1992

1545	PNB963	1546	PNG843	1547	PMT633	1549	PND743	1552	PMZ743

1556-1576 — Volvo B10MA-55 — Säffle — 1981-83

1556	KXW889	1559	KYT180	1568	APD137	1572	LKK999	1575	LCE549
1558	KYJ870	1566	KNC096	1569	DGC288	1574	LBZ539		

1578-1586 — Volvo B10MA-55 — Säffle — 1986

1578	GND508	1580	AFU699	1582	MHD913	1584	MHE853	1586	MRU794
1579	HJG538	1581	AUP716	1583	MHB513	1585	MSA794		

1588-1601 — Volvo B10MA-55 — Säffle — 1986-91

1588	MSK844	1596	OPE413	1599	OWW403	1600	OPR273	1601	OPR103
1590	NLS397	1597	OSU243						

1602	OZG826	Scania CN113	Scania	1990
1603	KJU495	Volvo B10M-..	Säffle	1991
1607	DMZ792	Volvo B10M-60	Säffle	1982

1608-1613 — Volvo B10M-60 — Säffle — 1993

1608	PJO406	1610	PJD036	1611	PJH076	1612	PHU316	1613	PLD466
1609	PHW246								

1616	ANO785	Volvo B10M-	Säffle	1984
1617	ADE765	Volvo B10M-	Säffle	1984
1618	ADG615	Volvo B10M-	Säffle	1984
1619	GGM083	Volvo B10M-	Säffle	1984
1620	GHU403	Volvo B10M-	Säffle	1984
1621	GDN153	Volvo B10M-	Säffle	1984
1622	GGE333	Volvo B10M-	Säffle	1984
1623	FXP023	Volvo B10M-	Säffle	1984
1624	FXN483	Volvo B10M-	Säffle	1984
1625	DSU494	Volvo B10M-	Säffle	1985
1626	DTD354	Volvo B10M-	Säffle	1985
1627	MLZ103	Volvo B10M-	Säffle	1986
1628	MLW483	Volvo B10M-	Säffle	1986
1629	MLN353	Volvo B10M-	Säffle	1986
1630	NLU393	Volvo B10M-	Säffle	1988
1631	NLO033	Volvo B10M-	Säffle	1988
1633	NLP113	Volvo B10M-	Säffle	1988
1634	NLK163	Volvo B10M-	Säffle	1988
1635	NLK093	Volvo B10M-	Säffle	1988
1636	NLL003	Volvo B10M-	Säffle	1988
1637	CNK574	Volvo B10M-	Säffle	1985
1639	GDH964	Volvo B10M-	Säffle	1985
1649	GGG584	Volvo B10M-	Säffle	1985
1654	FBW952	Volvo B10M-	Säffle	1987
1663	EXW602	Volvo B10M-	Säffle	1987
1664	EYF652	Volvo B10M-	Säffle	1987
1665	ETL532	Volvo B10M-	Säffle	1987
1666	GBW168	Volvo B10M-	Säffle	1989
1669	FWR298	Volvo B10M-	Säffle	1989
1670	FUE388	Volvo B10M-	Säffle	1989
1671	GFK088	Volvo B10M-	Säffle	1989
1673	JYR465	Volvo B10M-	Säffle	1991
1675	JYN435	Volvo B10M-	Säffle	1991
1680	JYH495	Volvo B10M-	Säffle	1991
1681	JYH325	Volvo B10M-	Säffle	1991
1692	JNG229	Volvo B10M-	Säffle	1991
1693	JKH229	Volvo B10M-	Säffle	1991
1695	JKW159	Volvo B10M-	Säffle	1991
1699	JHA209	Volvo B10M-	Säffle	1991
1704	OJK283	Volvo B10M-	Säffle	1989
1725	PWP611	Hino RB145	Hino	1992
1727	PNH864	Hino RB145	Hino	1992
1729	PRK625	Hino RB145SA	Hino	1992
1731	OJO463	Volvo B10M-	Säffle	1989
1732	OJE313	Volvo B10M-	Säffle	1989
1733	OJB073	Volvo B10M-	Säffle	1989

1761	PPP915	Volvo B10M-	Säffle					1992
1773	PPU715	Volvo B10M-	Säffle					1992
1774	PPU995	Volvo B10M-	Säffle					1992
1775	PRC595	Volvo B10M-	Säffle					1992
1776	PPL975	Volvo B10M-	Säffle					1992
1777	KML517	Volvo B10M-	Säffle					1992
1802	CEY860	Scania CR112	Scania					1980
1804	KDE977	Volvo B10M-	Säffle					1992
1805	KLH767	Volvo B10M-	Säffle					1992
1806	KHP947	Volvo B10M-	Säffle					1992
1813	HCR248	Volvo B10M-	Säffle					1995
1832	HDM038	Volvo B10M-	Säffle					1995

1843-1879 — Volvo B10M-65 — Säffle — 1981

1843	KNJ561	1849	KRM845	1871	KPG067	1876	KPB327	1878	KYX224
1844	KZM613	1863	KYO459	1872	FPR268	1877	KOS467	1879	KZE106

1887	HAP128	Volvo B10M-65	Säffle	1995

1889-1904 — Volvo B10M-65 — VBK — 1981

1889	KZK642	1900	KUB198	1901	KWL099	1902	KWR049	1904	KWS299

1922	KOW464	Scania CR112	Scania	1981
1923	KOU224	Scania CR112	Scania	1981
1928	HAU238	Volvo B10M-	Säffle	1995
1929	HCX048	Volvo B10M-	Säffle	1995
1934	FYM958	Scania CR112	Scania	1981
1949	MTN190	Volvo B9M-46	Säffle	1989
1950	OGM123	Volvo B9M-46	Säffle	1989

1956-1997 — Volvo B10M-65 — Säffle — 1982

1956	HWJ269	1965	FOP081	1970	JYX059	1978	FYN400	1996	BPR288
1957	FJM220	1966	ARC086	1971	GXE379	1980	BRS408	1997	BSX198
1961	FNP321	1968	FKD230	1977	FKB070	1991	CAK398		

2005	EKS838	Volvo B10M-65	VBK	1981
2007	EFZ658	Volvo B10M-65	VBK	1981
2014	ATP128	Volvo B10M-61	Van Hool Alizée	1982
2032	EMU432	Volvo B10M-65	Aabenraa	1982

2036-2071 — Volvo B10M-65 — Säffle — 1982-83

2036	LFN331	2044	LFY255	2048	LFJ301	2060	LFT082	2067	LFU302
2041	LEJ180	2045	LFT465	2054	LFB017	2063	LFJ471	2069	LEU310
2042	LFK161	2047	LFX005	2059	LFJ312	2064	LMG488	2071	LEX331
2043	LFS215								

2082	FAZ093	Volvo B10M-65	Säffle	1982

2089-2094 — Volvo B10M-65 — Aabenraa — 1982

2089	DYZ805	2090	CDL186	2091	GOR661	2093	EMR962	2094	FMY692

2095	LGX121	Scania CR112	Scania	1982
2096	LGU041	Scania CR112	Scania	1982
2097	LJC134	Scania CR112	Scania	1982
2098	LAD047	Scania CR112	Scania	1982

2100-2129 — Volvo B10M-55L — Van Hool Alizée — 1982

2100	LDU285	2114	LGT399	2120	LEU026	2125	LHC041	2129	LMM162
2113	LAF288								

2130-2137 — Neoplan N4007NF — Neoplan — 1991

2130	BXZ625	2132	BYS575	2134	BXD585	2136	FYH965	2137	NLZ182
2131	BZS545	2133	BXF745	2135	BYZ905				

2140	LKW055	Volvo B10M-60	Van Hool Alizée	1982
2148	LHU389	Volvo B10M-65	Säffle	1983
2157	DJC179	Volvo B10M-65	Aabenraa	1981

2159-2201   Scania CR112   Scania   1983

2159	LMY565	2170	LFJ587	2174	LAF641	2177	GMN994	2197	LSS975
2165	LMS651	2172	LAZ989	2175	LAJ682	2190	DJL554	2201	LSO945
2168	LMN574	2173	LAZ680	2176	LLJ873	2191	DJO609		

2207-2242   Volvo B10M-65   Säffle   1983

2207	LCW520	2212	LCD650	2218	LCX530	2227	LWP492	2238	LWB092
2208	LCP580	2213	LCC640	2219	LCJ910	2233	LUK222	2239	LWM152
2209	LCG510	2214	LCO640	2224	LWF342	2235	LUG372	2240	LWH292
2210	LCE590	2215	LCL850	2225	LWE262	2236	LUP342	2241	LWC482
2211	LCS670	2217	LCG990	2226	LWK062	2237	LWA222	2242	LWB232

2243-2262   Volvo B10M-65   Aabenraa   1983

2243	LNF123	2252	LWP313	2256	LUB313	2261	LSK033	2262	LTO283
2249	LOU323	2253	LWP003	2257	LWD483				

2263-2280   Volvo B10M-55L   Säffle   1983-84

2263	LZA374	2266	LYY464	2272	LYR034	2276	LZF184	2279	LYU374
2264	LYO014	2271	LYX144	2274	LYW444	2277	LYX454	2280	LYL464

2283	LWT765	Volvo B10M-55L	Van Hool Alizée	1983
2287	CAM625	Volvo B10M-55L	Van Hool Alizée	1983
2288	LXB855	Volvo B10M-65	Säffle	1983
2291	AWM525	Volvo B10M-65	Säffle	1983
2292	BUP705	Volvo B10M-65	Van Hool Alizée	1983
2294	LUH555	Volvo B10M-65	Van Hool Alizée	1983

2298-2308   Volvo B10M-70B   Van Hool Alizée   1984

2298	HAD928	2304	KRL688	2305	LPU758	2306	KGE838	2308	LZN720
2301	KZD798								

2314-2363   Volvo B10M-65   Säffle   1983-85

2314	LYZ839	2327	JWO025	2339	LOP295	2350	AJN075	2357	ABO235
2318	LNN640	2330	KJB155	2340	LPT295	2351	AGX315	2358	DHC165
2319	LNG830	2331	HXH055	2341	LFU195	2352	AGO425	2359	CXE125
2320	CSA402	2332	JSB475	2343	LMR195	2353	ANE475	2360	DAR195
2321	CKS222	2333	JMO055	2345	LZP095	2354	ACS235	2361	DGD105
2322	CLM172	2334	KYX395	2346	AHT295	2355	ACD215	2362	LBR095
2324	CRY492	2336	KCO455	2348	AON415	2356	ACK405	2363	DFE075
2326	CMB362	2338	LOW095	2349	AHZ235				

2367-2395   Volvo B10M-55L   Säffle   1984-85

2367	FLZ514	2373	GHU554	2380	DNK934	2386	FHH634	2391	LTU376
2368	DCP594	2374	FOP624	2381	DOJ834	2387	DOK764	2392	LUE246
2369	GND714	2375	DFX794	2382	DDE714	2388	ESS734	2393	LUO226
2370	DYS874	2376	ECX534	2383	FDU894	2389	LSO046	2394	LOY246
2371	FGZ834	2377w	EGD704	2384	DXF974	2390	LSZ196	2395	LRT256
2372	FTX894	2379	DKH534	2385	ELU974				

2402-2416   Volvo B10M-65   Van Hool Alizée   1984-85

2402	DHU403	2406	FBN591	2409	FGH811	2412	EWL701	2415	FHT941
2404	EMW881	2407	EHR791	2410	GNJ601	2413	FHU881	2416	FTP541
2405	FSR581	2408	GJW771	2411	GEU791	2414	FJX621		

2417-2424   Volvo B10M-60   Van Hool Alizée   1985

2417	DBG400	2419	CJA200	2421	DGB690	2422	CYO680	2424	DKL520
2418	CSY400	2420	DNM040						

2425-2440   Volvo B10M-70B   Van Hool Alizée   1985

2425	FLA602	2429	GGO792	2432	FRW622	2435	DYD409	2438	DPW209
2426	FZL952	2430	GFA632	2433	GMM662	2436	DLL179	2439	EAD269
2428	FWC732	2431	GDB912	2434	GGR572	2437	DSK499	2440	DUD489

2442-2468   Volvo B10M-70B   Säffle   1985

2442	EXD668	2449	FMB470	2457	CCS591	2461	CFN871	2465	CDJ591
2443	EOF688	2450	FJR170	2458	CGE871	2462	CCN791	2466	BGH811
2446	FJS010	2451	FEB160	2459	CGE701	2463	BHD841	2467	CHL651
2447	FDW150	2454	FDX160	2460	BGL521	2464	BCG681	2468	BYG871
2448	FLR290	2455	FTF430						

2469-2479   Volvo B10M-55L   Säffle   1985

2469	CDT483	2472	DPK093	2474	DCR173	2476	FKE463	2478	FPX383
2470	CHL493	2473	ECJ033	2475	DLC123	2477	FMU293	2479	FNN443
2471	DKC153								

2480-2530   Volvo B10M-65   Säffle   1985

2480	ETU502	2491	EXA552	2500	FDU973	2509	EEZ473	2522	FSA923
2481	EDS592	2492	EHB912	2501	GMW863	2510	FLZ493	2523	GNU523
2482	ECK732	2493	ETC853	2502	DWO084	2511	EOU173	2524	FCD723
2483	FBZ972	2494	GBS903	2503	EXB623	2512	DWP513	2525	FLG963
2484	FCA632	2495	FLM183	2504	EMU883	2513	DTY833	2527	GUO593
2486	EFZ892	2496	FDS443	2505	EFC803	2517	EXR893	2528	FXN923
2487	FBY652	2497	FGC353	2506	ESZ793	2518w	ESX773	2529	FSD573
2488	EAN922	2498	FGG393	2507	FMN303	2519	GJO963	2530w	GRE813
2489	EPO542	2499	EGR383	2508	EXH173				

2532-2562   Scania CN112   Scania   1985

2532	FMF055	2538	GCK479	2544	BCG578	2551	BLO748	2558	BGL175
2533	FZS415	2539	BEO578	2545	BOH568	2553	BZG668	2559	BSY495
2534	FTS215	2540	BGA808	2546	BNY688	2554	HLB399	2560	BSY325
2535	FTZ335	2541	AYH858	2547	AZO878	2555	GSD039	2561	ARJ425
2536	FMA175	2542	AYU618	2548	BAS698	2556	GJM279	2562	ARC085
2537	GPU145	2543	BGB508	2549	BAB968	2557	AEB095		

2563	LRO918	Scania K112	Aabenraa	1984
2567	CNY295	Scania K112	Aabenraa	1986
2568	EBN075	Scania K112	Säffle	1986

2569-2577   Scania K112   Aabenraa   1985-86

2569	DRL365	2570	BXS165	2571	DDE125	2574	GJO844	2577	CEC955

2579-2584   Volvo B10M-65   Säffle   1986

2579	DNN615	2581	DMM565	2582	CXD615	2583	DZE895	2584	DKW995
2580	DYU545								

2585	CYU615	Volvo B10M-55L	Säffle	1986
2586	CPX795	Volvo B10M-55L	Säffle	1986
2589	CKO615	Volvo B10M-55L	Säffle	1986

2591-2596   Volvo B10M-70B   Säffle   1985-86

2591	ESA825	2593	FPX785	2594	FSO905	2595	MWK096	2596	MWL176
2592	FPP595								

2599	MFZ173	Volvo B10M-60	Van Hool Alizée	1986
2600	MFX083	Volvo B10M-60	Van Hool Alizée	1986
2601	MGD483	Volvo B10M-60	Van Hool Alizée	1986
2602	MLY513	Volvo B10M-65	Van Hool Alizée	1986
2605	MLS713	Volvo B10M-65	Van Hool Alizée	1986
2606	MLZ903	Volvo B10M-65	Van Hool Alizée	1986

Number 3986, ESX347, in the Swebus fleet is Scania L113CLB with Carrus Fifty bodywork. It carries a green livery with red central band. *Nigel Hunt*

2607-2624   Volvo B10M-70B   Van Hool Alizée   1986

2607	MGH043	2611	MGC233	2615	MDN493	2619	MCR073	2622	MDB323
2608	MFP103	2612	MGE183	2616	MDK083	2620	MCM343	2623w	MCU483
2609	MFN323	2613	MGB153	2617	MDY163	2621	MDE353	2624	MCK013
2610	MFS053	2614	MFO023	2618	MDW213				

2627	MJK119	Volvo B10M-55L	Säffle	1986
2628	MJR489	Volvo B10M-55L	Säffle	1986
2629	MJN079	Volvo B10M-55L	Säffle	1986
2631	MJO159	Volvo B10M-55L	Säffle	1986
2632	MDC349	Volvo B10M-60	Säffle	1986
2633	MDB269	Volvo B10M-60	Säffle	1986
2634	MDB199	Volvo B10M-60	Säffle	1986

2635-2669   Volvo B10M-70B   Säffle   1986

2635	MMU059	2642	MNG329	2652	MNB449	2658	MXU240	2664	MJU091
2636	MNK109	2643	MXW480	2653	MXT090	2659	MJZ280	2665	MJO111
2637	MMW299	2645	MXG300	2654	MXC430	2660	MJP450	2666	MJR201
2638	MMW129	2646	MXR210	2655	MXJ320	2661	MKB410	2667	MKA481
2639	MNM059	2648	MNF249	2656	MXW310	2662	MJS141	2668	MJT151
2640	MNA439	2649	MMR269	2657	MXT300	2663	MKB491	2669	MHO103
2641	MND469								

2672-2702   Volvo B10M-65   Alpus 260SR   1986-87

2672	MLF412	2681	MLZ462	2687	MCM755	2693	MCY815	2698	MZT926
2673	MLA462	2682	MLR192	2688	MCW965	2694	MCX735	2699	MZS846
2675	MLR402	2683	MLL382	2689	MCS945	2695	MCN905	2700	MZS536
2677	MLL212	2684	MML042	2690	MCO535	2696	MCW655	2701	MZT546
2679	MLX372	2685	MDC745	2691	MDA965	2697	MCT885	2702	MZO506
2680	MLS272	2686	MCP785	2692	MCX665					

2703-2744   Volvo B10M-70   Säffle   1986

2703	MBN491	2711	MBR421	2722	MLN202	2730	MMB342	2738	MHH223
2704	MCB461	2712	MBZ241	2723	MLZ362	2731	MLY112	2739	MHG213
2705	MCC231	2713	MBX221	2724	MLX412	2732	MLN442	2740	MHM323
2706	MBK151	2714	MBT131	2725	MLR232	2733	MHP353	2741	MHB333
2707	MCD481	2718	MLT012	2726	MLH402	2734	MHU153	2742	MHR363
2708	MBX151	2719	MLX272	2727	MMT082	2735	MHK093	2743	MHO273
2709	MCB081	2720	MLO142	2728	MMS212	2736	MHO343	2744	MHT383
2710	MCE181	2721	MLT252	2729	MMR132	2737	MHP423		

2749	EHT149	Scania K112	Aabenraa	1987
2750	EEM179	Scania K112	Aabenraa	1987
2751	EYZ259	Scania K112	Aabenraa	1987
2754	EHK309	Scania K112	Aabenraa	1987
2755	EHC109	Scania K112	Askan	1987

2759-2770   Volvo B10M-70B   Van Hool Alizée   1987

2759	MPN885	2762	MPT905	2767	NTF645	2769	NTD625	2770	NST825
2760	MPY555								

2771	NTJ675	Volvo B10M-60	Van Hool Alizée	1987
2772	NST755	Volvo B10M-60	Van Hool Alizée	1987
2773	NSP725	Volvo B10M-60	Van Hool Alizée	1987

2774-2779   Volvo B10M-58B   Van Hool Alizée   1988

2774	NZD708	2776	NZG738	2777	NZE958	2778	NYL628	2779	NZB548
2775	NYM878								

2781	NSX775	Volvo B10M-65	Van Hool Alizée	1987

2782-2787   Volvo B10M-70B   Van Hool Alizée   1987

2782	NSS505	2784	NTH595	2785	NTD865	2786	NTE945	2787	NST995
2783	NTH975								

2788-2820   Volvo B10M-65*   Säffle   1987   *2797-820 are B10M-70B

2788	DAO603	2796	DBR693	2802	CCN201	2808	DMO362	2814	EJP272
2789	CJK703	2797	CDY251	2803	CFK421	2809	DJR122	2815	GSG523
2790	CSA553	2798	CCH191	2804	CGE381	2810	DDP092	2817	GER553
2792	CSK913	2799	CPL231	2805	DDB142	2811	DPP212	2818	GCW783
2793	DBS773	2800	CBJ201	2806	DDY122	2812	DHA422	2819	GAJ753
2794	CPL813	2801	CNF181	2807	DJJ232	2813	DZR292	2820	FTF663
2795	CZH793								

2821-2839   Volvo B10M-65   Alpus 260SR   1987-88

2821	DKC938	2832	NDX665	2834	NDY745	2836	NEM655	2838	NEM965
2822	BMC644	2833	NDF875	2835	NDS565	2837	NEL955	2839	NEH935

2840-2873   Volvo B10M-70   Säffle   1987-88

2840	NCF525	2846	CAX174	2853	NDE895	2861	NDL915	2869	NDW755
2841	NBS555	2847	BZF354	2854	NBZ985	2862	NDM545	2870	NDX835
2842	NCJ555	2849	NCC805	2855	NDY775	2865	NDZ615	2871	NEP545
2843	NBR855	2850	NBZ505	2856	NDK765	2866	NDJ765	2872	NER795
2844	ASY444	2851	NCA955	2859	NDO565	2867	NDO705	2873	NED785
2845	ASO234	2852	NDZ855	2860	NDG815	2868	NDY915		

2875-2884   Scania CK112   Scania   1988

2875	NCN566	2877	NYM676	2879	NYZ746	2881	NZA886	2883	NLR757
2876	NCY926	2878	NYF626	2880	NZB896	2882	NYL666	2884	NMF737

2885	NKJ827	Scania CN112	Scania	1988
2886	NKP947	Scania CN112	Scania	1988

2887-2891	Volvo B10M-70B		Säffle		1988		
2887 NMK737	2888	NML817	2889	NMS567	2890 NMN767	2891	NMW897

2895-2900	Volvo B10M-65		Säffle		1988		
2895 NHG528	2897	NHN648	2898	NHW538	2899 NHS688	2900	NHW848
2896 NHP668							

2901	NLO969	Scania K112T	Kutter 10	1988
2902	LGR980	Volvo B10M-60	Van Hool Alizée	1983
2906	NYX645	Scania K112T	Van Hool Alizée	1988
2907	NXC081	Volvo B10M-60	Van Hool Alizée	1988

2908-2923	Volvo B10M-55L		Säffle		1988		
2908 NAP243	2912	NBA113	2915	NXB192	2918 NXD112	2921	NNL242
2909 NBE393	2913	NAW283	2916	NXD282	2919 NXP112	2922	NOA152
2910 NAX053	2914	NBD073	2917	NXM322	2920 NXL482	2923	NNM252
2911 NAU283							

2924-2933	Volvo B10M-70B		Säffle		1988		
2924 NXM492	2926	NXC272	2928	NOW292	2930 FJF585	2932	NOF935
2925 NXH152	2927	NXL242	2929	FSU885	2931 FMR665	2933	NOX895

2934-2952	Volvo B10M-70		Säffle		1988		
2934 NAO303	2938	NAY203	2942	BLE835	2946 NAX293	2950	JLC934
2935 NAR493	2939	NAR323	2943	BGT935	2947 NBB123	2951	JGM614
2936 NBJ263	2940	NBF303	2944	BWW595	2948 NBD213	2952	JCN954
2937 NAS403	2941	BFB535	2945	BWH595	2949 JUF544		

2953-2959	Volvo B10M-65		Säffle		1988		
2953 DUX545	2955	NRZ615	2957	NRS595	2958 NNW985	2959	NKZ695
2954 FTX555	2956	NNT975					

2960	JBZ096	Volvo B10M-60	Säffle	1988
2961	FDO596	Volvo B10M-50	Säffle	1988

2962-2977	Volvo B10M-65		Alpus 260SR		1988		
2962 NMN163	2965	NMD323	2972	ABT605	2974 AYH705	2976	ART695
2963 NMC483	2971	AUM575	2973	ARS825	2975 ART525	2977	AWS815
2964 NMH363							

2978-2994	Scania CK113		Scania		1989		
2978 GAW545	2982	GFX815	2986	BMP996	2989 BEB988	2992	COU808
2979 GGE915	2983	MAR890	2987	CAX716	2990 BGM778	2993	NGT875
2980 GDB595	2984	MCN811	2988	BCX848	2991 BBS918	2994	NFW505
2981 GEF675	2985	BCY548					

2995	BYU112	Volvo B10M-65	Wiima	1985
2996	MEY322	Volvo B10M-60	Wiima Finlandia	1986
3000	OPM053	Volvo B10M-70B	Van Hool Alizée	1989
3001	MCZ859	Volvo B10M-58B	Van Hool Alizée	1989
3002	LTU899	Volvo B10M-70B	Van Hool Alizée	1989
3003	JKC909	Volvo B10M-60	Van Hool Alizée	1989
3004	JDE999	Volvo B10M-60	Van Hool Alizée	1989
3005	KJH559	Volvo B10M-60	Van Hool Alizée	1989
3006	MWU589	Volvo B9M-46	Säffle	1987
3007	HRX032	Renault Master	Renault	1990
3013	EEP513	Volvo B10M-60	Säffle	1982
3014	FNA021	Volvo B10R-59	Säffle	1984
3016	HCD843	Volvo B10R-59	Säffle	1987
3018	AAM826	Auwaerter Neoplan N213	Auwaerter Jetliner	1989

3019-3036 Volvo B10M-65 Säffle 1989

3019	OSG361	3023	OSE031	3027	OSC251	3031	OPH123	3034	OPD253
3020	OSF041	3024	OSD191	3028	ORY251	3032	OPC243	3035	OAH332
3021	OSN001	3025	OSJ141	3029	OSA091	3033	OPA153	3036	OAJ102
3022	OSO251	3026	OSK071	3030	ORO351				

3037-3042 Volvo B10M-55L Säffle 1989

3037	OAG174	3039	OAK264	3040	OAN434	3041	OZX254	3042	OZW484
3038	OAF164								

3043	OEL243	Volvo B10M-65	Säffle	1989
3044	OED043	Volvo B10M-65	Säffle	1989
3045	ODX333	Volvo B10M-65	Säffle	1989

3046-3051 Volvo B10M-65 Alpus 260SR 1989

3046	OHE074	3048	OHD374	3049	OGN384	3050	OHA414	3051	OHE214
3047	OGZ374								

3052	OAA362	Volvo B10M-70	Säffle	1989
3053	OAL112	Volvo B10M-70	Säffle	1989

3054-3059 Volvo B10M-70B Van Hool Alizée 1989

3054	OPA053	3056	OPF313	3057	OPB063	3058	OPS483	3059	OPM433
3055	OPD393								

3060	OWG181	Volvo B10M-60	Van Hool Alizée	1989
3061	OWD391	Volvo B10M-60	Van Hool Alizée	1989
3062	OPO453	Volvo B10M-60	Van Hool Alizée	1989

3063-3079 Scania CN113 Scania 1990

3063	OHW766	3067	OKL628	3071	OKF688	3074	OLA918	3077	OLD638
3064	OHL546	3068	OKH918	3072	OKH608	3075	OLC798	3078	OLA608
3065	OHN636	3069	OKF518	3073	OLC628	3076	OLB548	3079	EDE231
3066	OKN718	3070	OKG908						

3082	OCH595	Volvo B10M-70B	Van Hool Alizée	1989
3083	ODM105	Volvo B10M-60	Van Hool Alizée	1989

3084-3096 Volvo B10M-70B Säffle 1990

3084	OBO185	3087	OYZ745	3090	OYH575	3093	OYX895	3095	OYP535
3085	OBP195	3088	OYJ585	3091	OYL735	3094	OYJ655	3096	OYM675
3086	OBX145	3089	OYL595	3092	OYR855				

3101	HDC391	Volvo B10M-70B	Van Hool Alizée	1984
3102	GZJ723	Volvo B10M-65	Alpus 260SR	1985
3104	AUX778	Volvo B10M-70B	Van Hool Alizée	1985
3106	MPF020	Volvo B10M-70B	Van Hool Alizée	1985
3107	NJX607	Scania CN112	Scania	1988
3108	NKF897	Scania CN112	Scania	1988
3109	NJX777	Scania CN112	Scania	1988
3112	GNT759	Volvo B10M-65	Kutter	1984
3113	LDL707	Volvo B9M-60	Kutter	1983
3115	MLG698	Volvo B10M-58	Berkhof	1987
3117	MTC565	Volvo B10M-60	Van Hool Alizée	1987
3118	OUR299	Ford Transit VE6	Ford	1989
3119	OHB895	Volvo B10M-70B	Säffle	1990
3120	OGN995	Volvo B10M-70B	Säffle	1990
3121	OOP129	Volvo B10M-60	Lahti 450 Eagle	1989
3122	OSL331	Scania K113T	Lahti 450 Eagle	1989
3123	OOU184	Hino RB145SA	Hino	1989
3124	OOB545	Hino RB145SA	Hino	1989
3125	OWF749	Hino RB145SA	Hino	1990
3127	PAF264	Ontario II	Ontario	1989
3128	PAF334	Ontario II	Ontario	1989
3129	PAF337	Ontario II	Ontario	1989
3130	OWD659	Hino RB145	Hino	1990

3131	OUW929	Hino RB145		Hino				1990		

3132-3142 — Volvo B10M-55L — Säffle — 1990

3132	AKL170	**3135**	AER424	**3137**	AMG180	**3139**	ANL320	**3141**	ALF030
3133	AMK340	**3136**	ALX200	**3138**	AJS080	**3140**	AMX100	**3142**	ANL250
3134	AGC064								

3143	AKF370	Volvo B10M-70	Säffle	1990
3144	AGL220	Volvo B10M-70	Säffle	1990
3145	AET320	Volvo B10M-70	Säffle	1990
3146	AJN350	Volvo B10M-65	Säffle	1990
3147	BAU402	Volvo B10M-50	Säffle	1990
3148	BCG122	Volvo B10M-50	Säffle	1990
3149	AOE100	Volvo B10M-60	Säffle	1990
3150	ASJ142	Volvo B10R-59	Säffle	1990

3151-3159 — Volvo B10M-65 — Säffle — 1990

3151	ASC252	**3153**	ASW062	**3155**	BBA192	**3157**	AYU262	**3159**	AKD350
3152	AYA122	**3154**	AZG392	**3156**	BBZ022	**3158**	ANH230		

3160-3164 — Volvo B10M-70B — Säffle — 1990

3160	AYU332	**3161**	BDT402	**3162**	AYN132	**3163**	BBB412	**3164**	BCS282

3165	AAT224	Volvo B10M-60	Säffle	1990
3166	ABA234	Volvo B10M-60	Säffle	1990

3167	HYB302	Volvo B10M-65	Ajokki Express	1990
3169	HZL422	Volvo B10M-65	Ajokki Express	1990
3170	HUR242	Volvo B10M-65	Ajokki Express	1990
3171	HZM122	Volvo B10M-60	Van Hool Alizée	1990
3172	HUZ132	Volvo B10M-60	Van Hool Alizée	1990

3173-3183 — Volvo B10M-70B — Van Hool Alizée — 1990

3173	MHP112	**3176**	LUJ082	**3178**	MJZ392	**3180**	DGM313	**3182**	DGM173
3174	MGW492	**3177**	NDW092	**3179**	MAY492	**3181**	DDG363	**3183**	LLS232
3175	MGJ402								

3184	MSU515	Volvo B10M-50B	Van Hool Astral	1987
3185	MHP352	Volvo B10M-70B	Carrus	1990
3186	MJF412	Volvo B10M-70B	Carrus	1990
3187	LZC012	Volvo B10M-70B	Ajokki Express	1990
3188	DFG163	Volvo B10M-70B	Ajokki Express	1990
3191	OAG053	Volvo B10M-60	Lahti Eagle 451	1989

3192-3197 — Volvo B10M-70B — Säffle — 1990

3192	JFD213	**3194**	JDR423	**3195**	JHE193	**3196**	KPY165	**3197**	KLN105
3193	JKH483								

3198	AAU474	Volvo B10M-65	Säffle	1990
3199	ABB314	Volvo B10M-65	Säffle	1990
3200	DDP403	Volvo B10M-65	Van Hool Astral	1990
3202	FLJ455	Scania K113T	Ajokki Express	1990
3203	DDJ453	Volvo B10M-65	Van Hool Astral	1990
3204	DEO145	Scania CK113	Scania	1991
3205	DGS355	Scania CK113	Scania	1991
3206	DKW225	Scania CK113	Scania	1991
3207	DLM395	Scania CK113	Scania	1991
3209	GOJ385	Scania K113T	Ajokki Regal	1990
3210	GPE485	Scania K113T	Ajokki Regal	1990
3211	OMO381	Scania K113	Ajokki Victor	1989
3218	OHD880	Hino RB145	Hino	1990
3219	HGW163	Renault Trafic	Renault	1990
3220	OMS140	Ford Transit VE6	Ford	1991
3225	AFG036	Renault Master T35	Floby	1990
3226	AHG138	Renault Master T35	Floby	1990
3228	HRU001	Renault Master T35	Boggi	1991

3229	HNU301	Renault Master T35	Boggi	1991
3230	HPF011	Renault Master T35	Boggi	1991
3231	HPW411	Renault Master T35	Boggi	1991
3232	OSU173	Renault Master T35	Boggi	1991
3233	ORK423	Renault Master T35	Boggi	1991
3234	HNU492	Renault Master T35	Boggi	1990
3235	HSA192	Renault Master T35	Boggi	1990
3236	CFX128	Volvo B10M-55L	Säffle	1991
3237	CFZ388	Volvo B10M-55L	Säffle	1991
3238	BBU200	Volvo B10M-55L	Säffle	1991
3239	ATB350	Volvo B10M-65	Säffle	1991
3240	ARL390	Volvo B10M-65	Säffle	1991
3241	ARS040	Volvo B10M-65	Säffle	1991
3242	ASL050	Volvo B10M-65	Säffle	1991
3243	EBH351	Volvo B10M-70	Säffle	1991
3244	EDW391	Volvo B10M-70	Säffle	1991
3245	CPJ098	Volvo B10M-70B	Ajokki Express	1991
3246	CGF238	Volvo B10M-70B	Säffle	1991
3247	CRM468	Volvo B10M-70B	Ajokki Express	1991
3248	BBC250	Volvo B10M-65	Säffle	1991

3249-3253 — Volvo B10M-70B — Säffle — 1991

3249	CKY058	3250	AUN320	3251	APW090	3252	CLH178	3253	CGX408

3254	ABF120	Volvo B10M-70B	Ajokki Express	1991
3255	ABG370	Volvo B10M-70B	Ajokki Express	1991
3256	KAT461	Scania K113T	Ajokki Victor	1991
3257	JUW311	Scania K113T	Ajokki Victor	1991
3258	ABC260	Volvo B10M-70B	Ajokki Express	1991
3259	AAS390	Volvo B10M-70B	Ajokki Express	1991
3260	ELX150	Scania K113T	Ajokki Express	1991
3261	JYX031	Scania K113T	Ajokki Express	1991
3262	EAG061	Volvo B10M-70	Säffle	1991
3263	EAM171	Volvo B10M-70	Säffle	1991

3264-3269 — Volvo B10M-55L — Säffle — 1991

3264	CMD278	3266	CJC008	3267	CKZ208	3268	CJZ088	3269	CHO108
3265	CKT268								

3270-3277 — Volvo B10M-70B — Säffle — 1991

3270	AWN090	3272	CLE148	3274	CHS448	3276	ATG300	3277	ASX350
3271	ASE310	3273	CJZ468	3275	CJW438				

3278	CGK198	Volvo B10M-55L	Säffle	1991
3279	BCZ060	Volvo B10R-59	Säffle	1991
3280	AXT490	Volvo B10R-59	Säffle	1991
3281	BAF210	Volvo B10R-59	Säffle	1991
3282	JJF332	Hino RB145	Foreland	1990

3284-3292 — Volvo B10M-65 — Säffle — 1991

3284	BAS450	3286	AYR060	3288	AZA160	3290	ASS010	3292	ATN280
3285	AYL320	3287	AYZ400	3289	BBJ140	3291	ARZ090		

3293	ARE340	Volvo B10R-70	Säffle	1991
3294	AWB160	Volvo B10R-70	Säffle	1991
3295	FXR361	Volvo B10M-70B	Ajokki Express	1991
3297	OTN065	Renault Master T35	Floby	1989
3298	OLA284	Mercedes-Benz 709D	Backaryd	1990
3299	MPO332	Volvo B10M-60	Van Hool Alizée	1991
3300	MWE482	Volvo B10M-60	Van Hool Alizée	1991
3301	NCU252	Volvo B10M-50B	Van Hool Astral	1991
3302	MPO192	Volvo B10M-50B	Van Hool Astral	1991

3303-3310 — Volvo B10M-70B — Van Hool Alizée — 1991

3303	MRK292	3305	MXC292	3306	MPB492	3309	NBR182	3310	MZC302
3304	MOJ252								

3311-3316	Scania K113T	Ajokki Victor	1991						
3311	EGG070	3313	JZY251	3314	JJP051	3315	JNS441	3316	JKB491
3312	EHG420								

3317	PAR989	Volvo B10M-60	Van Hool Alizée	1989

3318-3325	Scania K113T	Van Hool Alizée	1991						
3318	COZ396	3320	CYS006	3322	CRZ196	3324	CSU446	3325	CTU106
3319	CMC136	3321	CSM096	3323	CTB146				

3328	CBD078	Renault Master T35	Floby	1991
3329	GGD875	Volvo B10M-65	Säffle 2000	1992
3330	DYU099	Mercedes-Benz 614D	Backaryd	1991
3331	GFG293	Mercedes-Benz 0303/15RHS	Mercedes-Benz	1991
3332	FPH093	Mercedes-Benz 0303/15RHS	Mercedes-Benz	1991
3334	HRS755	Volvo B10R-55L	Säffle	1992
3335	OJA820	Hino RB145	Hino	1990
3336	EHP913	Volvo B9M-46	Wiima	1991
3337	ETW723	Volvo B10M-70B	Ajokki Regal	1992
3338	ETC773	Volvo B10M-70B	Ajokki Regal	1992
3339	ETY743	Volvo B10M-70B	Ajokki Regal	1992
3340	ETJ733	Volvo B10M-70B	Ajokki Regal	1992
3341	GCG515	Volvo B10M-65	Wiima	1992
3342	GHG705	Volvo B10M-70	Säffle	1992
3343	GHS625	Volvo B10M-70	Säffle	1992
3344	GFX785	Volvo B10M-70	Säffle	1992
3345	GGG595	Volvo B10M-70	Säffle	1992
3346	JNZ766	Volvo B10M-50B	Van Hool Astral	1992

3347-3355	Volvo B10M-70B	Van Hool Alizée	1992						
3347	JMJ916	3349	JND866	3351	JOW706	3354	JMT516	3355	JNJ676
3348	JNS956	3350	JOD696	3352	JRN926				

3356	OOZ697	Scania K113T	Van Hool Alizée	1992
3357	ONW697	Scania K113T	Van Hool Alizée	1992
3358	KEY198	Volvo B10M-70B	Säffle	1991
3359	PEE260	Volvo B10M-70B	Ajokki Victor	1992
3360	PEH430	Volvo B10M-65	Säffle 2000	1992
3361	PEA460	Volvo B10M-65	Säffle 2000	1992
3362	OKT599	Volvo B12-61B	Ajokki Regal	1992
3363	HCH809	Volvo B10M-55L	Säffle 2000	1992

3364-3368	Volvo B10M-70B	Van Hool Alizée	1992						
3364	PRU963	3365	PRN763	3366	PRK593	3367	PRK973	3368	PRJ733

3369	PDP040	Volvo B10R-59	Säffle	1992
3370	HDT869	Volvo B10M-65	Säffle 2000	1992
3371	HDF549	Volvo B10M-65	Säffle 2000	1992
3372	HCM529	Volvo B10M-70B	Säffle 2000	1992
3373	PDZ320	Volvo B10M-70B	Ajokki Regal	1992
3374	PHX380	Volvo B10M-55L	Säffle 2000	1992
3375	EYB001	Hino RB145	Hino	1991
3376	PRR933	Volvo B10M-70B	Van Hool Alizée	1992
3377	PRJ803	Volvo B10M-70B	Van Hool Alizée	1992
3378	PRC843	Volvo B10M-70B	Van Hool Alizée	1992
3379	PRF563	Volvo B10M-70B	Van Hool Alizée	1992
3380	PEJ370	Volvo B10R-59	Säffle	1992
3381	PDZ010	Volvo B10R-59	Säffle	1992
3382	PEC480	Volvo B10R-59	Säffle	1992
3383	PRK803	Volvo B12-61B	Van Hool Alizée	1992
3384	HDL589	Volvo B10M-70	Säffle 2000	1992
3385	PRS943	Volvo B10M-50B	Van Hool Astral 460	1992
3386	HBB879	Volvo B10M-70	Säffle 2000	1992
3387	HBL619	Volvo B10M-70	Säffle 2000	1992
3388	HDD839	Volvo B10M-70	Säffle 2000	1992
3389	HED669	Volvo B10M-55L	Säffle 2000	1992

3390	HCO549	Volvo B10M-55L	Säffle 2000		1992			
3391	HCK819	Volvo B10M-55L	Säffle 2000		1992			
3392	PEJ200	Volvo B10M-70	Säffle 2000		1992			
3393	PEF340	Volvo B10M-70	Säffle 2000		1992			
3394	PEL070	Volvo B10M-70	Säffle 2000		1992			
3395	PEK130	Volvo B10M-70	Säffle 2000		1992			
3396	PDR120	Volvo B10M-70B	Säffle 2000		1992			
3397	PDP350	Volvo B10M-70B	Säffle 2000		1992			
3398	HDZ979	Volvo B10M-70	Säffle 2000		1992			
3399	HCZ839	Volvo B10M-70	Säffle 2000		1992			
3400	HCP939	Volvo B10M-70	Säffle 2000		1992			
3401	PZT662	Van Hool A508	Van Hool		1992			
3402	PZZ912	Van Hool A508	Van Hool		1992			
3404	PZE882	Van Hool A508	Van Hool		1992			
3405	PRN833	Volvo B10M-50B	Van Hool Astral 410		1992			
3406	PMJ831	Scania K113T	Ajokki Express		1992			
3407	MZG401	Van Hool A508	Van Hool		1991			
3408	HEF829	Volvo B10M-70	Säffle 2000		1992			
3409	HCZ909	Volvo B10M-70	Säffle 2000		1992			
3410	PFW569	Mercedes-Benz 0404	Mercedes-Benz	F	1993			
3411	PGW562	Mercedes-Benz 0404	Mercedes-Benz	F	1993			
3412	PEJ130	Volvo B10M-70B	Ajokki Victor		1992			
3413	PRX593	Volvo B10M-50B	Van Hool Astral 460		1992			
3414	PJL740	Volvo B10M-65	Säffle 2000		1992			
3415	PKW603	Renault Master T35	Renault		1992			
3418	PST842	Van Hool A508	Van Hool		1992			

3419-3424 Volvo B10M-65 Säffle 2000 1993

3419	PDO979	**3421**	PDO669	**3422**	PFD549	**3423**	PEU689	**3424** PFE629
3420	PDO809							

3425	PXB699	Volvo B10M-65	Carrus Fifty		1992			
3426	PXL509	Volvo B10M-65	Carrus Fifty		1992			
3427	PFA759	Volvo B10M-65	Säffle 2000		1993			
3429	PEN629	Volvo B10M-55L	Säffle 2000		1993			
3430	PER969	Volvo B10M-65	Säffle 2000		1993			
3431	PFB839	Volvo B10M-65	Säffle 2000		1993			
3432	PEM619	Volvo B10M-65	Säffle 2000		1993			
3433	PEP649	Volvo B10M-65	Säffle 2000		1993			

3434-3441 Volvo B10M-70 Säffle 2000 1992

3434	PEU999	**3436**	PFA519	**3438**	PFA689	**3440**	PFA999	**3441** PFC609
3435	PEY849	**3437**	PFE559	**3439**	PFD619			

3442	PEO949	Volvo B10M-55L	Säffle 2000		1992			
3443	PEW759	Volvo B10M-55L	Säffle 2000		1992			

3444-3448 Volvo B10M-70 Säffle 2000 1993

3444	PEN559	**3445**	PEZ619	**3446**	PEY919	**3447**	PEW829	**3448** PER899

3449	PZP969	Volvo B10M-65	Carrus Fifty		1993			

3450-3454 Volvo B10M-70B Carrus Fifty 1993

3450	PXK809	**3451**	PZY929	**3452**	PZS509	**3453**	PZY789	**3454** PZS749

3455	PSU968	Scania CN113CLL	Scania MAX Ci		1993			
3456	PSR938	Scania CN113CLL	Scania MAX Ci		1993			
3457	PSP618	Scania CN113CLL	Scania MAX Ci		1993			
3458	PKS222	Van Hool A508	Van Hool		1993			
3459	PKY402	Van Hool A508	Van Hool		1993			
3460	PPT635	Volvo B12-61B	Carrus Superstar		1992			
3461	PKR620	Auwaerter Neoplan N116/3	Auwaerter Cityliner		1993			
3462	PBF567	DAB 11-0860S	DAB		1992			
3463	PBF568	DAB 11-0860S	DAB		1992			
3464	PYD263	Auwaerter Neoplan N318	Auwaerter Transliner		1993			

3465-3470   Volvo B10M-65NG   Säffle 2000   1993

3465	PJZ397	3467	PHY487	3468	PHZ187	3469	PHY247	3470	PJU437
3466	PJC487								

3471	PTO004	Volvo B10M-70	Ajokki Victor	1993
3472	PJX102	Scania CN113	Scania	1993
3476	FTE149	Volvo B6F	Van Hool Alizée	1982
3477	CXC102	Volvo B10M-60	Van Hool Alizée	1984
3483	PUW086	Auwaerter Neoplan N128/4	Auwaerter Megaliner	1993
3484	PUM326	Auwaerter Neoplan N128/4	Auwaerter Megaliner	1993
3485	PUX166	Auwaerter Neoplan N128/4	Auwaerter Megaliner	1993
3486	PZK555	Volvo B10B-60	Säffle	1992
3487	PRC223	Volvo B10M-65	Säffle	1993
3488	PMH140	Auwaerter Neoplan N8008	Auwaerter Metroliner	1994
3489	PNA450	Auwaerter Neoplan N8008	Auwaerter Metroliner	1994
3490	PMP340	Auwaerter Neoplan N8008	Auwaerter Metroliner	1994
3491	PMW210	Auwaerter Neoplan N8008	Auwaerter Metroliner	1994
3492	PWH085	Volvo B10BLE-59	Säffle	1993
3493	PEC903	Volvo B10M-70B	Van Hool Alizée	1989
3494	PSG473	Auwaerter Neoplan N116/3	Auwaerter Cityliner	1993
3495	HAA985	Scania K113TLB	Ajokki Victor	1992
3496	CGY211	Volvo B10M-70B	Ajokki Victor	1993
3497	OKR403	Volvo B10M-70	Säffle	1994
3498	NUN103	Volvo B10M-70	Säffle	1993
3499	PWG059	Volvo B10M-70B	Carrus Regal	1993
3500	CCT201	Volvo B10M-70B	Carrus Regal	1994

3501-3512   Volvo B10M-70   Säffle 2000   1993-94

3501	OJN323	3504	JPK473	3506	JTD293	3508	JWT103	3510	DUE374
3502	NWY093	3505	JPW153	3507	JUA163	3509	JRZ393	3512	ECR024
3503	OMF143								

3514	AKY310	Scania L113CLB	Carrus Fifty	1994
3515	AND430	Scania L113CLB	Carrus Fifty	1994
3516	AKM490	Scania L113CLB	Carrus Fifty	1994

3518-3522   Scania CN113CLL   Scania MAX CI   1995

3518	EHD444	3519	EKF034	3520	EMO354	3521	EKY454	3522	ELS174

3523	BFD040	Scania L113CLB	Carrus Fifty	1995
3524	BEY100	Scania L113CLB	Carrus Fifty	1995
3525	BAN070	Scania L113CLB	Carrus Fifty	1995
3526	BAK110	Scania L113CLB	Carrus Fifty	1995

3527-3534   Volvo B10M-70B   Säffle   1994

3527	JRO483	3529	JRL213	3531	DSF341	3533	DML401	3534	DSD011
3528	JWD173	3530	JRU293	3532	DSA461				

3535-3539   Volvo B10M-65   Säffle   1994

3535	EED294	3536	EEY254	3537	EFN484	3538	EDB204	3539	EEC424

3540	PHC029	Volvo B10B-70	Wiima	1993

3541-3545   Volvo B10M-55L   Säffle   1994

3541	DWK224	3542	DUL184	3543	DZX304	3544	DUL254	3545	DUS384

3546	CUL404	Volvo B10BLE-59	Säffle	1992
3547	HLX495	Volvo B10BLE-59	Säffle	1993

3548	GPC355	Scania N113CLL	Carrus K204	1995
3549	JCB204	Volvo B12	Säffle 2000	1994
3554	BFE430	Scania K113TLB	Carrus Fifty	1994
3555	BDT410	Scania K113TLB	Carrus Fifty	1994
3556	BCE280	Scania K113TLB	Carrus Fifty	1994
3557	BBD440	Scania K113TLB	Carrus Fifty	1994
3558	BYS321	Scania L113CLB	Carrus Fifty	1994
3559	BAH340	Scania K113TLB	Carrus Regal	1994
3560	CML414	Volvo B10M-70	Säffle	1993
3561	CNZ324	Volvo B10M-70	Säffle	1994
3562	COC484	Volvo B10M-70	Säffle	1994
3563	COP254	Volvo B10M-70	Säffle	1994
3564	EAA044	Volvo B10M-55L	Säffle	1994
3565	DUD294	Volvo B10M-55L	Säffle	1994

3566-3572   Volvo B10M-70L   Säffle   1994

3566	CTJ284	3568	COK064	3570	CPP394	3571	COG114	3572	CSU134
3567	CRL014	3569	CPC454						

3573	CRZ024	Volvo B10M-70	Säffle	1994
3574	CNM324	Volvo B10M-70	Säffle	1994
3575	JOX193	Volvo B10M-55L	Säffle	1994
3576	JMZ003	Volvo B10M-55L	Säffle	1994
3577	JPL003	Volvo B10M-70	Säffle	1993
3578	DXK294	Volvo B10M-70B	Säffle	1994
3579	HPE295	Volvo B10M-70B	Säffle	1994
3580	BCO020	Scania K113TLB	Carrus Fifty	1994
3581	PUM019	Volvo B10M-65	Carrus Fifty	1993
3582	PWB009	Volvo B10M-65	Carrus Fifty	1993
3583	PUN199	Volvo B10M-65	Carrus Fifty	1993
3584	PUO109	Volvo B10M-65	Carrus Fifty	1993
3585	CGN231	Volvo B10M-70B	Carrus Fifty	1994
3586	CJR131	Volvo B10M-70B	Carrus Fifty	1994
3587	CEC371	Volvo B10M-70B	Carrus Regal	1994
3588	CHS241	Volvo B10M-70B	Carrus Regal	1994
3589	CEX331	Volvo B10M-70B	Carrus Regal	1994
3590	CCR111	Volvo B10M-70B	Carrus Fifty	1994
3591	EGB454	Volvo B10M-65	Säffle	1994
3592	ELK344	Scania CN113CLB	Scania	1994
3593	AOR100	Scania K113TLB	Carrus Vector	1994

3594-3615   Scania CN113CLL   Scania MAX CI   1994

3594	PTU488	3599	PTR078	3604	PTL490	3608	PST490	3512	PTF070
3595	PUF298	3600	PTL408	3605	PTD120	3609	PTH300	3513	PTD290
3596	PTY198	3601	PSA290	3606	PTK240	3510	PSX340	3514	PTG220
3597	PUE358	3602	PRY210	3607	PTH470	3511	PSZ120	3515	PSU330
3598	PTN288	3603	PTG390						

3616	EFD264	Volvo B10M-70	Säffle	1994
3617	EFF044	Volvo B10M-70	Säffle	1994
3618	EGH034	Volvo B10M-70	Säffle	1994
3619	ECA464	Volvo B10M-70	Säffle	1994
3620	DOO471	Volvo B10M-65	Säffle	1994
3621	DMM341	Volvo B10M-65	Säffle	1994
3622	DPK191	Volvo B10M-65	Säffle	1994
3623	PNL607	DAB 11-0860S	DAB	1994
3624	GEO102	Auwaerter Neoplan N318/3	Auwaerter	1994
3625	GCA142	Auwaerter Neoplan N318/3	Auwaerter	1994
3626	GGH402	Auwaerter Neoplan N318/3	Auwaerter	1994
3627	EGB384	Volvo B10M-70	Säffle	1994
3628	CDK121	Volvo B10M-70	Carrus Regal	1994
3629	PGK488	Volvo B6-45	Säffle 2000	1993
3630	PNH903	DAB 11-0860S	DAB	1994
3631	BGE193	Scania L113CLB	Carrus Fifty	1994
3632	BUP130	Auwaerter Neoplan N316SHD	Auwaerter Transliner	1994
3633	AAJ441	Auwaerter Neoplan N316SHD	Auwaerter Transliner	1994
3634	PUY150	Auwaerter Neoplan N316SHD	Auwaerter Transliner	1994
3635	JYE123	Auwaerter Neoplan N116/3	Auwaerter Cityliner	1994
3636	GDZ112	Auwaerter Neoplan N116/3	Auwaerter Cityliner	1994
3637	LST140	Scania K113TLA	Carrus Star 701	1995

3638-3642		Scania K113CLA		Carrus Star 602		1995		
3638	LLK450	3639	LPN390	3640	LOF050	3641	LLB310	3642	KDA232

3643-3647		Volvo B12-60		Carrus Star 602		1995		
3643	HWR018	3644	HUF358	3645	HWA078	3646	HSY358	3647	HWR258

3648-3652		Volvo B10M		Säffle 2000		1995		
3648	BFG080	3649	BBW250	3650	BFU470	3651	BCO410	3652	BDM460

3653-3657		Volvo B10M-70B		Säffle 2000		1995		
3653	KLJ045	3654	JDA194	3655	KOH115	3656	FDY195	3657	FDR075

3658	JHN018	Scania L113CLB	Carrus Fifty	1995
3659	JHT448	Scania L113CLB	Carrus Fifty	1995
3660	JKD228	Scania L113CLB	Carrus Fifty	1995
3661	KHW495	Volvo B10M-70B	Säffle	1996
3662	KGS405	Volvo B10M-70B	Säffle	1995
3663	KEA105	Volvo B10M-70	Säffle	1996
3664	CPG253	Scania CN113CLL	Scania MAX Ci	1995
3665	CNU463	Scania CN113CLL	Scania MAX Ci	1995
3666	KHT338	Auwaerter Neoplan N122/3	Auwaerter Skyliner	1995
3667	JTY259	Auwaerter Neoplan N116/3	Auwaerter Cityiner	1995
3668	KHA355	Volvo B10M-70	Säffle	1995
3669	KMD205	Volvo B10M-70	Säffle	1995
3670	KLF255	Volvo B10M-70	Säffle	1995
3671	BFG150	Volvo B10M-70B	Säffle	1995
3672	EBD005	Volvo B10M-65	Säffle	1995
3673	EAN325	Volvo B10M-65	Säffle	1995
3674	DXD205	Volvo B10M-65	Säffle	1995
3675	CZW300	Scania CN113CLL	Scania MAX Ci	1995
3676	KLM154	Scania CN113A	Scania	1995
3677	KKC274	Scania CN113A	Scania	1995
3678	JZY150	Volvo B10M-65	Carrus Fifty	1995
3679	JZC250	Volvo B10M-65	Carrus Fifty	1995
3680	BWT385	Scania K113T	Carrus Regal	1995
3681	JYY010	Volvo B10M-65	Carrus Fifty	1995
3682	DKD193	Scania K113	Carrus Victor	1995
3683	DJU463	Scania K113	Carrus Victor	1995
3684	GBH125	Volvo B10M-70B	Carrus Victor	1995
3685	DZP027	Volvo B10M-65	Säffle	1996
3686	ECE487	Volvo B10M-65	Säffle	1996
3687	HWN073	Volvo B10M-60	Carrus Star 502	1995
3688	CLZ372	Volvo B10M-50B	Carrus Star 602	1995
3689	FZL145	Volvo B10M-50B	Carrus Star 602	1996
3690	JWY278	Volvo B10M-70	Säffle	1996
3691	JTY088	Volvo B10M-70	Säffle	1996
3692	LLX062	Volvo B10M-70B	Säffle	1995
3693	JPH203	Auwaerter Neoplan N318SHD/3	Auwaerter Transliner	1995
3694	JRB383	Auwaerter Neoplan N318SHD/3	Auwaerter Transliner	1995
3695	KJF468	Auwaerter Neoplan N116/3	Auwaerter Cityliner	1995

3696-3703		Scania CN113CLL		Scania MAX Ci		1995		
3696	CFW083	3698	CGC003	3700	CLP243	3702	CKE423	3703	CFA323
3697	CKB013	3699	CEM283	3701	CLA213				

3704	OCZ392	Scania DAB	DAB	1995
3705	NSF032	Scania DAB	DAB	1995
3706	OXR002	Scania DAB	DAB	1995
3707	PPW092	Scania DAB	DAB	1995
3708	CPN133	Scania CN113CLL	Scania MAX Ci	1995
3709	JFL051	Auwaerter Neoplan N318SHD/3	Auwaerter Transliner	1995
3710	JEZ231	Auwaerter Neoplan N318SHD/3	Auwaerter Transliner	1995
3711	JCX101	Auwaerter Neoplan N318SHD/3	Auwaerter Transliner	1995
3712	JGG091	Auwaerter Neoplan N318SHD/3	Auwaerter Transliner	1995
3713	FFE255	Volvo B10M-70	Säffle	1996
3714	DWB005	Volvo B10M-70	Säffle	1995

3715-3723 Volvo B10M-70B Säffle 1995

3715	LTP172	**3717**	LER302	**3719**	LPP232	**3721**	LOO182	**3723**	LRS392
3716	LZG162	**3718**	LFB342	**3720**	LUY102	**3722**	LKE432		

3724	EBA167	Volvo B10MA-55	Säffle	1995
3725	DXD067	Volvo B10MA-55	Säffle	1995
3726	DYB417	Volvo B10MA-55	Säffle	1995
3727	DET206	Volvo B10M-65	Säffle	1995
3728	DFE496	Volvo B10M-65	Säffle	1995
3729	DCZ376	Volvo B10M-65	Säffle	1995
3730	DEL476	Volvo B10M-65	Säffle	1995
3731	CRH222	Volvo B10M-50B	Carrus Regal	1995
3732	GKL061	Volvo B10M-50B	Carrus Regal	1995
3737	CPF003	Scania CN113CLL	Scania MAX Ci	1995
3738	CPE473	Scania CN113CLL	Scania MAX Ci	1995
3739	CRZ193	Scania CN113CLL	Scania MAX Ci	1995
3740	DWW035	Volvo B10MA-70	Säffle	1996
3741	DZW045	Volvo B10MA-70	Säffle	1996
3742	DZF265	Volvo B10MA-70	Säffle	1995
3743	EEP367	Scania L113CLB	Carrus Fifty	1995
3744	LLM300	Scania L113CLB	Carrus Fifty	1995
3745	KZM290	Scania L113CLB	Carrus Fifty	1995
3746	LMR480	Scania L113CLB	Carrus Fifty	1995
3747	FPO275	Volvo B10M-70	Säffle	1995
3748	LUK402	Volvo B10L-60	Säffle	1995
3749	KJU225	Volvo B10L-60	Säffle	1995
3750	KKZ095	Volvo B10L-60	Säffle	1995
3751	JCH024	Volvo B10MA-55	Säffle	1995
3752	JAP114	Volvo B10MA-55	Säffle	1995
3753	HWD314	Volvo B10M-70	Säffle	1995
3754	HXX404	Volvo B10M-70	Säffle	1995

3755-3763 Auwaerter Neoplan N318K/3 Auwaerter Transliner 1995

3755	BCM312	**3757**	BFA012	**3759**	BTR013	**3761**	CBR143	**3763**	BZC433
3756	BBD062	**3758**	BXP403	**3760**	CCO023	**3762**	CBK183		

3764	ALF253	Volvo B10M-70B	Carrus Regal	1995
3765	AKW063	Volvo B10M-70B	Carrus Regal	1995
3766	DXD065	Volvo B10M-50	Säffle	1996
3767	CTG182	Volvo B10M-70B	Carrus Regal	1995
3768	COC302	Volvo B10M-70B	Carrus Regal	1995

3769-3773 Volvo B10M-65 Carrus Fifty 1995

3769	HCU336	**3770**	HBU126	**3771**	HCF176	**3772**	HBH056	**3773**	HAG386

3774	FFL445	Volvo B10M-70B	Säffle	1995
3775	FFE015	Volvo B10M-70B	Säffle	1995
3776	FCY295	Volvo B10M-70B	Säffle	1995
3777	FFM215	Volvo B10M-70B	Säffle	1995
3778	GBZ398	Volvo B10M-70B	Säffle	1996
3779	GCY118	Volvo B10M-70B	Säffle	1996

3780-3789 Volvo B10M-65 Säffle 1995

3780	DZP175	**3782**	DXO125	**3784**	DWH035	**3786**	DZK125	**3788**	DWU035
3781	DYN015	**3783**	EBN465	**3785**	EAX225	**3787**	DZH355	**3789**	DWO155

3790-3795 Volvo B12-70B Van Hool Alizée 360NL 1995

3790	CHP142	**3792**	EHF393	**3793**	ELN063	**3794**	EKR333	**3795**	ELX273
3791	EDR093								

3796	PTF193	Volvo B10M-60	Vest Ambassador	1995
3797	FZP188	Volvo B10M-70	Säffle	1996
3798	FZT118	Volvo B10M-70	Säffle	1996
3799	GBE265	Volvo B10M-70	Carrus Fifty	1996
3800	GAG455	Volvo B10M-70	Carrus Fifty	1996
3801	CPS243	Scania CN113CLL	Scania MAX Ci	1995

3802	CNL483	Scania CN113CLL	Scania MAX Ci	1995
3803	CMK023	Scania CN113CLL	Scania MAX Ci	1995
3804	EBL087	Volvo B10M-70B	Säffle	1996
3805	EAP437	Volvo B10M-70B	Säffle	1996
3806	DZU137	Volvo B10M-70B	Säffle	1996
3807	DYU237	Volvo B10M-70B	Säffle	1996
3808	ECY127	Volvo B10M-50	Säffle	1995

3809-3818 Volvo B10M-70B Säffle 1995

3809	LZZ032	3811	KLL365	3813	KLY055	3815	KMO055	3817	KJW395
3810	KJY485	3812	KKD195	3814	KMA415	3816	KPU225	3818	KKD265

3819	PSA076	Volvo B12-61B	Van Hool Altano	1995
3820	HGZ351	Volvo B12-61B	Van Hool Altano	1995
3821	HHL481	Volvo B12-61B	Van Hool Altano	1995
3822	PNR192	Scania DAB	DAB	1995
3823	PPT392	Scania DAB	DAB	1995
3824	JOT161	Volvo B10MA-55	Van Hool Alizée	1995

3825-3833 Volvo B10M-70B Säffle 1995

3825	LTH282	3827	LGN002	3829	LGC012	3831	LCH462	3833	DXL287
3826	LRH002	3828	LOC012	3830	LFD122	3832	LRN422		

3834	GAZ015	Scania L113	Carrus Fifty	1995
3835	FYO035	Scania L113	Carrus Fifty	1995
3836	FZP015	Scania L113	Carrus Fifty	1995
3837	GAB025	Scania L113	Carrus Fifty	1995
3838	HPT218	Auwaerter Neoplan N112/3	Auwaerter Skyliner	1995

3839-3844 Scania CN113CLB Scania 1995

3839	KDM394	3841	KFA404	3842	KDE264	3843	KGC414	3844	KCS064
3840	KES314								

3845	KMU024	Scania CN113A	Scania	1995
3846	KMH164	Scania CN113A	Scania	1995
3849	KDZ224	Scania CN113	Scania	1995
3850	KEW024	Scania CN113	Scania	1995
3851	KHS014	Scania CN113	Scania	1995

3852-3859 Volvo B10MA-55 Säffle 1995

3852	FKH035	3854	FOH185	3856	FTA405	3858	HGU238	3859	HEP258
3853	FNB224	3855	FOL405	3857	HFC388				

3862	KOF114	Scania CN113CLB	Scania	1995
3863	KGF424	Scania CN113CLB	Scania	1995
3864	KHM134	Scania CN113CLB	Scania	1995

3865-3872 Volvo B10MA-55 Säffle 1995

3865	HHR038	3867	HGR208	3869	HFC148	3871	HGO358	3872	HFE098
3866	HFA435	3868	HHX078	3870	HFF178				

3873-3877 Scania CN113CLB Scania 1996

3873	JLZ175	3874	JMZ145	3875	JKC435	3876	JKF085	3877	JMG345

3878-3884 Volvo B10MA-55 Säffle 1995-96

3878	EAT227	3880	DYH477	3882	JYP018	3883	BDL429	3884	BEL259
3879	DZZ097	3881	BBJ169						

3885	GBH055	Volvo B10M-50B	Carrus Regal	1996
3886	OSW269	Auwaerter Neoplan N8012	Auwaerter Metroliner	1996
3887	PSC261	Volkswagen Caravelle	Volkswagen	1995
3888	DBH462	Volkswagen Kombi	Volkswagen	1995
3889	BED265	Volkswagen Kombi	Volkswagen	1995
3890	JWT318	Volvo B10L-60	Säffle	1996
3891	EKL138	Scania N113CLL	Carrus K201L	1996

3892-3897 — Volvo B10M-65 — Säffle — 1996

3892	BDF693	**3894**	BDG753	**3895**	BDH563	**3896**	BDG933	**3897** BDH943
3893	BDG713							

3898	ANM721	Volvo B10M-70B	Carrus Regal	1996
3899	ANM811	Volvo B10M-70B	Carrus Regal	1996
3900	FRM070	Volvo B10M-70	Säffle	1996
3901	FSG480	Volvo B10M-70	Säffle	1996

3902-3915 — Volvo B10M-65 — Carrus Fifty — 1996

3902	HKE088	**3905**	HJU348	**3908**	ANB901	**3911**	ANL781	**3914**	ANM551
3903	HKO448	**3906**	HMG118	**3909**	ANC761	**3912**	ANL791	**3915**	HMS278
3904	HLU088	**3907**	ANB811	**3910**	ANC951	**3913**	ANL841		

3916	AZA672	Volvo B10M-70	Säffle	1996
3917	HTA230	Volvo B10M-70	Vest Ambassador 340	1996
3919	FPD030	Volvo B10M-70	Säffle	1996
3920	ELY090	Volvo B10M-70	Säffle	1996
3921	FOJ320	Volvo B10M-70	Säffle	1996
3922	AYD603	Scania L113CLB	Carrus Fifty	1996
3923	AYD743	Scania L113CLB	Carrus Fifty	1996
3924	AYD763	Scania L113CLB	Carrus Fifty	1996
3925	AYE733	Scania L113CLB	Carrus Fifty	1996
3926	DYG149	Volvo B10M-72B	Carrus Regal	1996
3927	AXK702	Volvo B10M-72B	Carrus Regal	1996
3928	AYC943	Scania K113TLA	Carrus Regal	1996
3929	BAL873	Volvo B12	Van Hool Alizée 360NL	1996

3930-3935 — Scania L113CLB — Scania — 1996

3930	BPW974	**3932**	BPX674	**3933**	BPY614	**3934**	BPY764	**3935** BPZ674
3931	BPX584							

3936	FOB280	Volvo B10M-70	Säffle	1996
3937	HTC180	Volvo B12	Van Hool Alizée	1996
3938	CGA060	Volvo B12-61	Neoplan N116/3 Cityliner	1996
3939	CGO080	Volvo B12-61	Neoplan N116/3 Cityliner	1996
3940	CFG360	Volvo B12-61	Neoplan N116/3 Cityliner	1996

3941-3965 — Scania CN113CLB* — Scania — 1996 — *3951-5/61-5 are CN113ALB

3941	GSF460	**3950**	GPU440	**3954**	GKG310	**3958**	GPE100	**3962**	GPG360
3942	GPK380	**3951**	GKE080	**3955**	GMW120	**3959**	GXE440	**3963**	BPZ894
3943	GRN210	**3952**	GGS140	**3956**	GSF390	**3960**	GWT010	**3964**	AOB532
3948	GSB420	**3953**	GGG080	**3957**	GMZ390	**3961**	GOF450	**3965**	ANJ622
3949	GOS210								

3966-3970 — Volvo B10M-65 — Säffle — 1996

3966	FXX535	**3967**	FXX725	**3968**	FXY585	**3969**	FXY635	**3970** FXY745

3971-3978 — Scania CN113CLB — Scania — 1996

3971	BRB484	**3973**	BRC804	**3975**	BRA914	**3977**	BRB774	**3978** BRB854
3972	BRC714	**3974**	BRA814	**3976**	BRB614			

3979	HUM060	Volvo B10M-62	Van Hool Alizée 360NL	1996
3980	HUC390	Volvo B10M-62	Van Hool Alizée 360NL	1996
3981	HXX470	Volvo B10M-62	Van Hool Alizée 360NL	1996
3982	HXO410	Volvo B10M-62	Van Hool Alizée 360NL	1996
3983	AUX632	Volvo B10L	Säffle	1996
3984	BDK753	Volvo B10M-65	Säffle	1996
3985	ETY327	Scania L113CLB	Carrus Fifty	1996
3986	ESX347	Scania L113CLB	Carrus Fifty	1996
3987	ESJ107	Scania L113CLB	Carrus Fifty	1996
3988	BDH963	Volvo B10MA-55	Säffle	1996
3989	FFH935	Volvo B10MA-55	Säffle	1997
3990	FFG875	Volvo B10MA-55	Säffle	1997
3991	AUX612	Volvo B10M-70	Säffle	1996
3992	AUX542	Volvo B10M-70	Säffle	1996
3993	AYY962	Volvo B10LA	Säffle	1996

3994	JEH436	Scania L113CLB	Carrus Fifty	1996
3995	JAX086	Scania L113CLB	Carrus Fifty	1996
3996	JCJ336	Scania L113CLB	Carrus Fifty	1996
3997	JDL486	Scania L113CLB	Carrus Fifty	1996
3998	BDJ573	Volvo B10M-50	Säffle	1996
3999	BDJ913	Volvo B10M-70	Säffle	1996
4000	BDJ953	Volvo B10M-70	Säffle	1996
4001	ESA367	Scania L113CLB	Carrus Fifty	1996
4002	EKO478	Scania L113CLB	Carrus Fifty	1996
4003	JET038	Scania L113CLB	DAB 1350L	1996
4004	BZR947	Volvo B10M-50	Säffle	1996
4005	BZS657	Volvo B10M-70	Säffle	1996
4006	BXY906	Volvo B10M-70	Säffle	1996
4007	BWM797	Volvo B10M-70	Carrus Fifty	1997
4008	BPY774	Scania N113	Scania	1996
4009	BPY874	Scania N113	Scania	1996
4010	BPY964	Scania N113	Scania	1996
4011	EKF975	Scania N113	Scania	1996
4012	EKG505	Scania N113	Scania	1996
4013	CNG976	Scania N113	Scania	1996
4014	CNG916	Scania SC	Scania	1996
4015	CNG806	Scania N113	Scania	1996
4016	AOB952	Volvo B10MA-55	Säffle	1996
4017	AOC682	Volvo B10MA-55	Säffle	1996
4018	AOC762	Volvo B10MA-55	Säffle	1996

4019-4029 — Volvo B10M-70 — Säffle — 1996

4019	BDO853	4022	DDJ509	4024	DDK769	4026	DDJ749	4028	DDJ629
4020	BDO843	4023	DDK979	4025	DDJ969	4027	DDJ689	4029	DDH879
4021	BEG923								

4030	BPZ744	Scania SC	Scania	1996	
4031	BPZ854	Scania SC	Scania	1996	
4032	AYC583	Scania K113TLB	Carrus Regal	1996	
4033	AKX522	Volvo B10M-72B	Carrus Regal	1996	
4034	DLL765	DAB	DAB	1992	Ex ?, 1996
4035	AYZ632	Volvo B10LA	Säffle	1996	
4036	EAK479	Volvo B10M-72B	Carrus Regal	1996	
4037	DLL755	DAB	DAB	1992	Ex ?, 1996
4038	DLL675	DAB	DAB	1993	Ex ?, 1996
4039	KPD469	Auwaerter Neoplan N122/3	Auwaerter Skyliner	1996	
4040	DLL665	DAB	DAB	1993	Ex ?, 1996
4041	BHS743	Volvo B10M-72B	Carrus Regal	1996	
4042	AYC563	Scania K113TLB	Carrus Regal	1996	
4043	BGA874	Volvo B10M-70B	Van Hool Alizée	1996	
4044	BGA864	Volvo B10M-70B	Van Hool Alizée	1996	

4045-4062 — Volvo B10M-70 — Säffle — 1996-97

4045	FFG895	4049	FNJ110	4053	FSZ040	4057	CJB658	4060	EGP555
4046	FFH645	4050	EGN855	4054	FFH785	4058	CJB678	4061	EGP635
4047	EZZ220	4051	EGO555	4055	FFH895	4059	EGP505	4062	EGP865
4048	FBN160	4052	EGO915	4056	CJB598				

4063	AXJ852	Volvo B10M-70B	Carrus Star 302	1996
4064	JAM478	Scania CN113CLL	Scania	1996
4065	HZJ358	Scania CN113CLL	Scania	1996
4066	AXK682	Scania L113CLB	Carrus Fifty	1996

4067-4071 — Volvo B10M-70 — Säffle — 1996

4067	FOM100	4068	FGD060	4069	FBX370	4070	FFA200	4071	AJF751

4072-4077 — Scania L113CLB — Carrus Fifty — 1996

4072	ESH337	4074	ETZ027	4075	FBE407	4076	EYL247	4077	ETN347
4073	EUE037								

4078	BXY516	Volvo B10M-70	Säffle	1996
4079	BXY716	Volvo B10M-70	Säffle	1996
4080	CXH829	Volvo B10M-70	Säffle	1997
4081	ASY552	Volvo B12	Van Hool Alizée	1996

4082	ATG962	Volvo B12		Van Hool Alizée	1996			
4083	ATH732	Volvo B12		Van Hool Alizée	1996			
4084	ATH852	Volvo B10MA-70B		Van Hool Alizée	1996			
4085	AYF773	Auwaerter Neoplan N128/4		Auwaerter Megaliner	1996			
4086	AYG962	Auwaerter Neoplan N128/4		Auwaerter Megaliner	1996			
4087	AYH543	Auwaerter Neoplan N128/4		Auwaerter Megaliner	1996			
4088	AYH583	Auwaerter Neoplan N128/4		Auwaerter Megaliner	1996			

4089-4094 DAB DAB 1992 Ex ?, 1996

4089	DFL565	4091	DFL675	4092	DFL685	4093	DFL695	4094 DFL795
4090	DFL665							

4095	CXG589	Volvo B10M-70	Säffle		1997
4096	CXG699	Volvo B10M-70	Säffle		1997
4097	CXG769	Volvo B10M-70	Säffle		1997
4098	FCN765	Mercedes-Benz O404	Mercedes-Benz	C	1997
4099	CYF940	Scania L113CLB	Carrus Fifty		1997
4100	CYE750	Scania L113CLB	Carrus Fifty		1997
4101	DTP680	Scania L113CLB	Carrus Fifty		1997
4102	FMG663	Auwaerter Neoplan	Auwaerter		1997
4103	FMG913	Auwaerter Neoplan	Auwaerter		1997
4104	FMH613	Auwaerter Neoplan	Auwaerter		1997
4105	FMH643	Auwaerter Neoplan	Auwaerter		1997
4106	DKH540	Scania CN113CLB	Scania		1996
4107	LZK995	Scania L113CLB	DAB		1998
4108	GWP746	Volvo B10M-70	Säffle		1997
4109	GWO636	Volvo B10M-70	Säffle		1997

4110-4115 Scania CN113CLB Scania 1997

4110	DKH620	4112	DKH830	4113	DKH840	4114	DKJ650	4115 DKK530
4111	DKH780							

4121	EUL843	Volvo B10M-70	Säffle	1997
4122	EUL943	Volvo B10M-70	Säffle	1997
4123	EUN763	Volvo B10M-70	Säffle	1997
4124	EUO643	Volvo B10M-70	Säffle	1997

4125-4130 Scania CN113CLB Scania 1997

4125	DEK769	4127	DEK699	4128	DEK539	4129	DEJ939	4130 DEJ839
4126	DEK739							

4131-4145 Volvo B10M-70 Säffle 1997

4131	ELO693	4134	EUD743	4137	EJC593	4140	EJD823	4143 EJE833
4132	ELO883	4135	EJA543	4138	EJD553	4141	EJE623	4144 EUK933
4133	EUO983	4136	EJA643	4139	EJD663	4142	EJE663	4145 EUL563

4146	DSN832	Scania SC	Scania	1997
4147	DEL559	Scania CN113CLB	Scania	1997
4148	DEK949	Scania CN113CLB	Scania	1997
4149	DEK799	Scania CN113CLB	Scania	1997
4150	JMT675	Volvo B10M-72B	Carrus Regal	1997
4151	JMS975	Volvo B10M-72B	Carrus Regal	1997
4152	JMU515	Volvo B10M-72B	Carrus Regal	1997
4153	JMT845	Volvo B10M-72B	Carrus Regal	1997
4157	DKK950	Scania CN113CLB	Scania	1997
4158	ELN953	Volvo B10LA	Säffle	1997
4159	ELN983	Volvo B10LA	Säffle	1997

4161-4166 Volvo B10M-72B Carrus Regal 1997

4161	ELD992	4163	ELD792	4164	ELD782	4165	ELC962	4166 ELC792
4162	ELD912							

4167	EWS744	Volvo B10M-70	Säffle	1997
4168	EWS764	Volvo B10M-70	Säffle	1997
4169	DEF749	Volvo B10M-72B	Carrus Regal	1997

4170	ENP963	Volvo B10M-72B	Carrus Regal	1997
4171	DKK960	Scania SC	Scania	1997
4172	JMR865	Volvo B10M-72B	Carrus Regal	1997
4173	EPB792	Scania CN113CLB	Scania	1997
4174	DKG990	Scania CN113CLB	Scania	1997

4175-4179 — Volvo B10L — Säffle — 1997

4175	GWM646	4176	GWP826	4177	GWP826	4178	GWO976	4179	GWM946

4180-4193 — Volvo B10M-70 — Säffle — 1997

4180	EJE933	4182	EJF603	4189	GNF606	4191	GNH526	4193	GND866
4181	EJF553	4188	GNG666	4190	GNG736	4192	GNE526		

4194	BOB794	Scania SC	Scania	1997
4195	CSR578	Scania SC	Scania	1997
4196	DSM972	Auwaerter Neoplan OVR	Auwaerter	1997
4200	DFH760	DAB	DAB	1997
4201	DFH620	DAB	DAB	1997
4202	DFH870	DAB	DAB	1997
4203	DFH830	DAB	DAB	1997
4204	DMH580	Scania CN113CLB	Scania	1997
4205	DKR670	Scania CN113CLB	Scania	1997
4206	DKR680	Scania CN113CLB	Scania	1997
4207	EMR722	Scania L113CLB	Carrus Fifty	1997
4208	EMR862	Scania L113CLB	Carrus Fifty	1997
4209	EMR882	Scania L113CLB	Carrus Fifty	1997
4210	EMR992	Scania L113CLB	Carrus Fifty	1997
4211	GNL896	Volvo B10M-70	Säffle	1998
4212	GWN786	Volvo B10M-70	Säffle	1998
4213	DKW881	Volvo B10M-72B	Carrus Regal	1997
4214	DDO879	Volvo B10LE	Säffle	1997
4215	DDP579	Volvo B10LE	Säffle	1997
4216	GCP676	Volvo B10M-70	Säffle	1997
4217	GCP776	Volvo B10M-70	Säffle	1997
4218	GCP886	Volvo B10M-70	Säffle	1997
4219	DMY961	Volvo B10M-72B	Vest	1997
4220	DMZ501	Volvo B10M-72B	Vest	1997
4221	EBS881	Volvo B10M-72B	Vest	1997
4222	JMR665	Volvo B10M-72B	Carrus Regal	1997
4223	DKX541	Volvo B10M-72B	Carrus Regal	1997
4225	ELC632	Volvo B10M-72B	Carrus Regal	1997
4226	ELB882	Volvo B10M-72B	Carrus Regal	1997
4227	GWN706	Volvo B10M-70	Säffle	1997
4228	GWN636	Volvo B10M-70	Säffle	1997
4236	DDB690	Mercedes-Benz O404	Mercedes-Benz	1997
4237	DDB950	Mercedes-Benz O404	Mercedes-Benz	1997

4238-4242 — Volvo B10M-70 — Säffle — 1997

4238	GWN846	4239	GWM586	4240	GWK846	4241	GWU666	4242	GWP526

4243	DKF950	Scania CN113CLB	Scania	1997
4244	DKE990	Scania CN113CLB	Scania	1997
4245	ENP903	Volvo B10M-72B	Carrus Regal	1997
4246	ELD872	Volvo B10M-72B	Carrus Regal	1997
4247	GWO756	Volvo B10M-70	Säffle	1997
4248	DKL900	Scania CN113CLB	Scania	1997
4249	DLK970	Scania CN113CLB	Scania	1997
4250	EMO632	Scania L113CLB	Carrus Fifty	1997
4251	EMP632	Scania L113CLB	Carrus Fifty	1997
4252	EMP752	Scania L113CLB	Carrus Fifty	1997
4253	EMR502	Scania L113CLB	Carrus Fifty	1997
4254	GNF996	Volvo B10M-70	Säffle	1997
4255	GNC996	Volvo B10M-70	Säffle	1997
4256	GND876	Volvo B10M-70	Säffle	1997
4257	GNH516	Volvo B10M-70	Säffle	1997
4258	CYF850	Scania K113CLB	Carrus Fifty	1997
4259	CYE850	Scania K113CLB	Carrus Fifty	1997
4260	EDZ741	Volvo B10M-72B	Carrus Regal	1997
4261	EDZ581	Volvo B10M-72B	Carrus Regal	1997

Stagecoach corporate livery has been applied to the newly introduced Swebus Express services from Stockholm to Oslo. Pictured ready for service is Neoplan Megaliner 4344, GWF586. *Swebus*

4262-4273 — Volvo B10LA — Säffle — 1997

4262	DRD901	4265	DRE791	4268	DRE881	4270	DRF761	4272	DRF861
4263	DRE731	4266	DRE821	4269	DRF541	4271	DRF811	4273	DRF921
4264	DRE751	4267	DRE871						

4274-4290 — Volvo B10L — Carrus Regal — 1997

4274	DDF550	4278	DDF990	4282	DDG730	4285	DDG990	4288	DDH950
4275	DDF610	4279	DDG500	4283	DDG770	4286	DDH760	4289	DDH960
4276	DDF700	4280	DDG580	4284	DDG790	4287	DDH860	4290	DDJ590
4277	DDF780	4281	DDG690						

4291	DDP759	Volvo B10LE	Säffle	1997
4292	DDP769	Volvo B10LE	Säffle	1997
4293	GNH616	Volvo B10M-70	Säffle	1997
4294	GND556	Volvo B10M-70	Säffle	1997
4299	DEF829	Volvo B10M-72B	Carrus Regal	1997
4300	DFW809	Volvo B10M-72B	Vest	1997
4301	DFW709	Volvo B10M-72B	Vest	1997
4302	DFW579	Volvo B10M-72B	Vest	1997
4303	DMX791	Volvo B10M-72B	Vest	1997

4304-4310 — Volvo B10MA-55 — Säffle — 1997

4304	DMO559	4306	DMM909	4308	DMN629	4309	DMN949	4310	DMN979
4305	DMM559	4307	DMM959						

4311-4325 — Scania L113CLB — Scania DAB — 1997

4311	DFS869	4314	DFT589	4317	DFS999	4320	DTK561	4323	DTL551
4312	DFS979	4315	DFU569	4318	DFT519	4321		4324	DTL501
4313	CPY654	4316	DFT759	4319	DFT689	4322	DTL871	4325	

| 4326 | BRB953 | Mercedes-Benz O404 | Mercedes-Benz | 1997 | | | · |

4327-4341

		Volvo B10M-65		Van Hool Alizée		1997		
4327	GRT566	4330	GRX586	4333	GRY556	4336	GSB776	4339	GRZ626
4328	GRT526	4331	GRT586	4334	GSA986	4337	GSA896	4340	GRY666
4329	GRW836	4332	GSA926	4335	GSA976	4338	GRX786	4341	GRY546

4343	GWF576	Auwaerter Neoplan OVR	Auwaerter	1997
4344	GWF586	Auwaerter Neoplan OVR	Auwaerter	1997
4345	DKM930	Scania CN113CLB	Scania	1997
4347	DKN690	Scania CN113CLB	Scania	1997
5026	GWD623	Scania K112TL	Delta Star 50	1987
5031	MLE439	Scania K112TL	Van Hool Alizée 260	1986
5263	LTZ662	Scania K112	Van Hool Alizée 210	1984
5269	AUJ517	Scania CN112	Scania	1985
5272	BJO917	Scania CN112	Scania	1985
5273	BMB927	Scania CN112	Scania	1985
5275	MLH089	Scania K112TL	Van Hool Alizée 260	1986
5276	MLH469	Scania K112TL	Van Hool Alizée 260	1986
5279	MWF053	Scania CN112	Scania	1986
5280	MUZ333	Scania CN112	Scania	1986
5293	NFO769	Scania K112TL	Van Hool Alizée 360	1988
5295	NPK130	Scania CN112	Scania	1988
5303	OWN344	Scania CN113CLB	Scania	1989
5304	OWX174	Scania CN113CLB	Scania	1989
5305	OBJ945	Volvo B10M-65	Säffle	1989
5306	OBG785	Volvo B10M-65	Säffle	1989
5307	ODY959	Scania K113TLB	Van Hool Alizée 360	1990

5308-5313

		Volvo B10M-60		Säffle		1990		
5308	OUS810	5310	OUF810	5311	OUW760	5312	OKD549	5313	OJR579
5309	OUG680							

5314	DTG092	Scania CN113CLB	Scania	1990
5316	DWX062	Scania CN113CLB	Scania	1990
5317	FHM099	Scania K113TLB	Van Hool Alizée 360	1991
5318	BZY140	Scania CN113CL	Scania	1991
5319	BWS190	Scania CN113CL	Scania	1991
5320	BZL210	Scania CN113CL	Scania	1991
5321	BYL480	Scania CN113CLB	Scania	1991
5322	AJS280	Volvo B10M-55	Säffle	1991
5323	AEL310	Volvo B10M-55	Säffle	1991
5324	CHZ480	Volvo B10M-60	Säffle	1991
5325	CJM140	Volvo B10M-60	Säffle	1991
5328	PEX200	Scania CN113ALB	Scania	1992
5329	PFF310	Scania CN113ALB	Scania	1992
5330	PFB130	Scania CN113ALB	Scania	1992
5331	PYO695	Volvo B10M-55	Säffle	1992
5332	PYW575	Volvo B10M-55	Säffle	1992

5338-5342

		Scania CN113CLL		Scania		1994		
5338	PSY058	5339	PTF088	5340	PSS018	5341	PTO368	5342	PTX328

5343	POR478	Volvo B10BLE-59	Carrus K204 City L	1993
5344	GWN223	Volvo B10M-70	Carrus Fifty	1995
5345	GWH113	Volvo B10M-70	Carrus Fifty	1995
5346	AMX035	Volvo B10M-70B	Carrus Fifty	1995
5347	AHP305	Volvo B10M-70	Carrus Fifty	1995
5348	JSD055	Volvo B10M-55	Säffle	1996
5350	JOH465	Volvo B10M-55	Säffle	1995
5351	JSA265	Volvo B10M-55	Säffle	1996
5370	LUE830	Volvo B10M-	Wiima	1984
5373	CZG180	Volvo B10M-	Wiima	1985
5374	MEU078	Volvo B10M-	Wiima	1986
5375	MWO319	Volvo B10M-	Wiima	1986
5376	MPX766	Volvo B10M-	Wiima	1987
5378	GEJ481	Volvo B10M-	Wiima	1987
5379	NPW716	Volvo B10M-	Wiima	1988
5380	NCY402	Volvo B10M-	Wiima	1988
5381	OJB392	Volvo B10M-	Wiima	1989

5382	OOK838	Volvo B10M-	Wiima	1990
5384	PSP683	Volvo B10M-	Wiima	1992
5385	PRW351	Volvo B10M-	Wiima	1992
5387	PWE279	Volvo B10M-	Carrus Fifty	1993
5388	JTP115	Volvo B10M-	Carrus Fifty	1995
6659	MZW292	Scania K113TLA	Van Hool Astrobel	1990
6660	LXZ432	Scania K113TLA	Van Hool Astrobel	1990
6663	LYY322	Scania K113TLA	Van Hool Astrobel	1990
7018	DJA805	Renault Master T35	Renault	1986
7660	AAO637	Vovo B58	Wiima	1980
7675	KOH193	Vovo B10M-70B	Wiima M302	1981

7676-7685   Volvo B10M-65   Wiima M302   1982

7676	BLO007	7680	AYT347	7681	HYO407	7682w	HEP337	7685w	KOW297

7685	KOW297	Volvo B10M-60	Wiima M302	1982
7688	EEJ298	Volvo B10M-60	Wiima M302	1982
7689	FPD400	Volvo B10M-65B	Wiima M401	1982
7703	FRL782	Volvo B10M-65	Wiima M353	1982
7704	HHO892	Volvo B10M-65	Wiima M353	1982
7705	GDC682	Volvo B10M-65	Wiima M353	1982
7706	FYF602	Volvo B10M-65	Wiima M353	1982
7709	FYS842	Volvo B10M-70B	Wiima M303	1982
7710	GJD642	Volvo B10M-70B	Wiima M303	1982
7717	GGP772	Volvo B10M-60	Wiima M401	1982
7721	LNE234	Volvo B10M-60	Wiima M452	1983

7722-7729   Volvo B10M-65   Wiima M303   1983

7722	LNA364	7724	LMP494	7725	LNK274	7728	LNL114	7729	LNJ414
7723	LNE164								

7731	LNB204	Volvo B10M-70B	Ajokki 5000E	1983
7734	LNM054	Volvo B10M-70B	Ajokki 5000E	1983
7735	LNK104	Volvo B10M-70B	Ajokki 5000E	1983
7742	DKP677	Volvo B10M-70B	Wiima M452	1985
7743	DMR937	Volvo B10M-70B	Wiima M452	1985
7744	DNT978	Volvo B10M-70B	Van Hool Alizée 210	1985
7745	DJE968	Volvo B10M-70B	Van Hool Alizée 210	1985
7747	DGH888	Volvo B10M-65	Van Hool Alizée 310	1985
7748	DSZ828	Volvo B10M-65	Van Hool Alizée 310	1985
7749	DKF578	Volvo B10M-65	Van Hool Alizée 310	1985
7751	LOD430	Volvo B10M-70B	Wiima M303	1985
7752	LJT190	Volvo B10M-70B	Wiima M303	1985
7753	LGW090	Volvo B10M-70B	Wiima M303	1985

7754-7764   Volvo B10M-70B   Wiima M452*   1985   7758/9 are model M303.

7754w	DCR951	7756	LFD775	7759	JSC865	7763	JXH665	7764	KTC965
7755	CYU871	7758	LEN855						

7765	ABS575	Volvo B10M-65	Wiima M452	1985
7766	ACC755	Volvo B10M-70B	Wiima M500 Finlandia	1986
7767	ACB505	Volvo B10M-70B	Wiima M500 Finlandia	1986

7768-7772   Volvo B10M-56B   Van Hool Alizée 360   1987

7768	MGE966	7769	MGC946	7770	MGJ836	7771	MFZ956	7772	MGX836

7773	MHD856	Volvo B10M-70B	Van Hool Alizée 360	1987

7776-7786   Volvo B10M-70B   Wiima M453   1987

7776	MJA726	7778	MHH966	7781	MJS606	7785	MJT856	7786	MJU936
7777	MHS566	7780	MJA656	7782	MJC746				

7787	MXG606	Volvo B10M-70B	Säffle	1987
7788	MWU716	Volvo B10M-70B	Säffle	1987
7789	FLK411	Volvo B10M-60	Wiima M452	1984
7790	NUH758	Volvo B10M-70B	Wiima M453	1988
7791	NUF668	Volvo B10M-70B	Wiima M453	1988
7792	NUK768	Volvo B10M-70B	Wiima M453	1988

7793	GEZ257	Volvo B10M-70B	Wiima M354	1989
7794	FZH217	Volvo B10M-70B	Wiima M354	1989
7795	FYT097	Volvo B10M-70B	Wiima M354	1989
7797	GSK047	Volvo B10M-70B	Delta Star 501	1989
7798	GXF487	Volvo B10M-70B	Delta Star 501	1989
7800	HCC227	Volvo B10M-70B	Delta Star 501	1989
7801	HKT197	Volvo B10M-70B	Delta Star 501	1989
7803	HBW447	Volvo B10M-58B	Delta Star 501	1989
7804	HTH167	Volvo B10M-58B	Delta Star 501	1989
7805	OPX351	Volvo B10M-70B	Wiima/Närk	1989
7806	NCP116	Volvo B10M-70B	Delta 9000 Superstar	1988
7809	OHT586	Volvo B10M-59	Säffle	1990
7810	OHY686	Volvo B10M-59	Säffle	1990
7811	OSP325	Volvo B10M-70B	Delta Star 501	1989

7812-7821 Volvo B10M-70B Van Hool Alizée 1990

7812	OEJ736	7814	OHM836	7816	OHN536	7818	OHP866	7820	OES566
7813	OHY756	7815	OJA736	7817w	OHR706	7819	OEF946	7821	OEM686

7822	OHW666	Volvo B10M-65	Van Hool Alizée 310	1990
7823	OHS886	Volvo B10M-65	Van Hool Alizée 310	1990
7824	OHM906	Volvo B10M-70B	Wiima M310	1990
7828	DTS195	Volvo B10M-70B	Säffle	1990
7829	DPW275	Volvo B10M-70B	Säffle	1990
7830	DTE325	Volvo B10M-70B	Säffle	1990

8001-8005 Mercedes-Benz O404 Mercedes-Benz 1997

8001	DTK762	8002	DTK812	8003	DTK822	8004	DTL622	8005	DTL562

8101-8116 Scania CR112 Scania 1982-83

8101	DKN711	8105	CYL821	8109	GJC537	8111	LHD244	8115	LHN154
8102	CZA801	8107	DUA786	8110	GJY747	8113	LHG344	8116	LJJ404
8104	CZW871								

8222	KPC755	Volvo B10M-60	Säffle	1981
8224	KPG555	Volvo B10M-60	Säffle	1981

8401-8406 Mercedes-Benz 0405N Mercedes-Benz 1991

8401	AMM353	8403	HMM355	8404	EMM356	8405	NMM356	8406	BKH263
8402	FMM354								

8701-8713 Renault Master T35 Renault 1990

8701	OBF674	8705	OWL570	8707	OGC549	8710	OCF671	8712	OBF678
8702	ORR679	8706	OFW839	8708	OFO889	8711	ORW919	8713	OCF670
8704	OSH819								

8717	PAO114	Ontario	Ontario	1989

SWEBUS FINLAND

Oy Swebus Finland Ab; Espoon Auto; Transbus

1	CBH205	Volvo B10M	Wiima K202	B44D	1993
2	CBH215	Volvo B10M	Wiima K202	B44D	1993
3	CBH226	Volvo B10M	Wiima K202	B44D	1993
4	FCC558	Volvo B10B	Carrus 204M	B44D	1996
5	FCC535	Volvo B10BLE	Carrus 204L	B43D	1996
6	JBA390	Volvo B10M	Wiima K202	B44D	1991
7	FCC527	Volvo B10BLE	Carrus 204L	B43D	1996
8	FCC588	Volvo B10BLE	Carrus 204L	B43D	1996
9	FCC557	Volvo B10BLE	Carrus 204L	B43D	1996
10	FCC602	Scania L113CLL	Carrus 204M	B43D	1996
11	IFO772	Volvo B10M	Wiima K202	B45D	1991
12	IFO854	Volvo B10M	Wiima K202	B45D	1991
13	IFO844	Volvo B10M	Wiima K202	B45D	1991
15	FCC610	Scania L113CLL	Carrus 204M	B43D	1996
18	FCC644	Volvo B10BLE	Carrus 204L	B43D	1996
19	FCC659	Volvo B10BLE	Carrus 204L	B43D	1996
10	FCC673	Volvo B10BLE	Carrus 204L	B43D	1996
21	FCC666	Scania L113CLL	Carrus 204M	B43D	1996
22	FCC689	Scania L113CLL	Carrus 204M	B43D	1996
23	YAM103	Volvo B10M	Wiima K202	B45D	1992
24	FCC704	Scania L113CLL	Carrus 204M	B43D	1996
25	YAM129	Volvo B10M	Wiima K202	B45D	1992
26	FCC734	Scania L113CLL	Carrus 204M	B43D	1996
27	YAL917	Volvo B10M	Wiima K202	B45D	1992
28	MKC730	Volvo B10M	Wiima K202	B45D	1990
29	FCC738	Scania L113CLL	Carrus 204M	B43D	1996
30	IFO857	Volvo B10M	Wiima K202	B45D	1991
31	IFO861	Volvo B10M	Wiima K202	B45D	1991
32	NBU409	Scania L113CLL	Carrus 204M	B43D	1996
33	NBU410	Scania L113CLL	Carrus 204M	B43D	1996
34	CBG522	Volvo B10M	Wiima K202	B44D	1993
35	CBG529	Volvo B10M	Wiima K202	B44D	1993
36	CBG530	Volvo B10M	Wiima K202	B44D	1993
37	CBG531	Volvo B10M	Wiima K202	B44D	1993
38	CBG619	Volvo B10M	Wiima K202	B44D	1993
39	CBG733	Volvo B10M	Wiima K202	B44D	1993
40	NBU421	Scania L113CLL	Carrus 204M	B43D	1996
41	CBG756	Volvo B10M	Wiima K202	B44D	1993
42	CBG754	Volvo B10M	Wiima K202	B44D	1993
43	NBU447	Scania L113CLL	Carrus 204M	B43D	1996
45	IFO904	Volvo B10M	Wiima K202	B45D	1991
48	JBM653	Volvo B10BLE	Carrus 204L	B40D	1995
49	JBM666	Volvo B10BLE	Carrus 204L	B40D	1995
50	ZCA850	Volvo B10M	Wiima K202	B45D	1988
51	JBM684	Volvo B10BLE	Carrus 204L	B40D	1995
52	JBM706	Volvo B10BLE	Carrus 204L	B40D	1995
53	ZCA853	Volvo B10M	Wiima K202	B45D	1988
54	ZCA854	Volvo B10M	Wiima K202	B45D	1988
55	ZCA855	Volvo B10M	Wiima K202	B45D	1988
56	ZCA856	Volvo B10M	Wiima K202	B45D	1988
57	CBH219	Volvo B10M	Wiima K202	B44D	1993
58	CBH238	Volvo B10M	Wiima K202	B44D	1993
59	OFV769	Volvo B10M	Wiima K202	B45D	1991
61	ZEA961	Volvo B10M	Wiima K202	B45D	1989
62	ZEA962	Volvo B10M	Wiima K202	B45D	1989
63	ZEA963	Volvo B10M	Wiima K202	B45D	1989
64	RFL285	Volvo B10M	Wiima K202	B43D	1991
65	RFL290	Volvo B10M	Wiima K202	B43D	1991
66	JBA630	Volvo B10M	Wiima K202	B43D	1991
67	BNT443	Volvo B10M	Wiima K202	B45D	1990
68	BNT482	Volvo B10M	Wiima K202	B45D	1990
69	BNT487	Volvo B10M	Wiima K202	B45D	1990
70	KGJ181	Volvo B10BLE	Carrus 204L	B40D	1995
71	RFL232	Volvo B10M	Wiima K202	B43D	1991
72	JBM728	Volvo B10BLE	Carrus 204L	B40D	1995

The latest arrivals with Swebus Norway are Volvo B10Bs, one of which is seen ready liveried for the Espoon Auto operation. *Swebus Norway*

73	RFL250	Volvo B10M	Wiima K202	B43D	1991
74	KGJ236	Volvo B10BLE	Carrus 204L	B40D	1995
75	KGJ199	Volvo B10BLE	Carrus 204L	B40D	1995
76	RFL213	Volvo B10M	Wiima K202	B43D	1991
78	KGJ254	Volvo B10BLE	Carrus 204L	B40D	1995
79	KGJ253	Volvo B10BLE	Carrus 204L	B40D	1995
80	KGJ297	Volvo B10BLE	Carrus 204L	B40D	1995
81	JBA451	Volvo B10M	Wiima K202	B45D	1991
82	JBA421	Volvo B10M	Wiima K202	B45D	1991
83	JBA435	Volvo B10M	Wiima K202	B45D	1991
84	KGJ296	Volvo B10BLE	Carrus 204L	B40D	1995
85	KGJ324	Volvo B10BLE	Carrus 204L	B40D	1995
86	JBA713	Volvo B10M	Wiima K202	B43D	1991
87	JBA710	Volvo B10M	Wiima K202	B43D	1991
88	JBA635	Volvo B10M	Wiima K202	B43D	1991
89	YAL969	Volvo B10M	Wiima K202	B45D	1992
90	YAL980	Volvo B10M	Wiima K202	B45D	1992
94	JBA862	Volvo B10M	Wiima K202	B44D	1991
95	JBA861	Volvo B10M	Wiima K202	B44D	1991
96	NBU355	Scania L113CLL	Carrus 204M	B43D	1996
97	BNA997	Volvo B10M	Wiima K202	B44D	1989
98	BNA998	Volvo B10M	Wiima K202	B44D	1989
99	BNA999	Volvo B10M	Wiima K202	B44D	1989
100	BNA900	Volvo B10M	Wiima K202	B44D	1989
105	XFM785	Volvo B10M	Wiima K202	B45D	1992
107	MKC637	Volvo B10M	Wiima K202	B45D	1990
108	KGJ337	Volvo B10BLE	Carrus 204L	B40D	1995
109	KGJ338	Volvo B10BLE	Carrus 204L	B40D	1995
110	NBU356	Scania L113CLL	Carrus 204M	B43D	1996
111	BNT530	Volvo B10M	Wiima K202	B45D	1990
112	BNT655	Volvo B10M	Wiima K202	B45D	1990
113	KGJ339	Volvo B10BLE	Carrus 204L	B40D	1995
114	BNT569	Volvo B10M	Wiima K202	B45D	1990
115	BNT632	Volvo B10M	Wiima K202	B45D	1990
116	NBU425	Scania N113CLL	Scania MAXcl	B35D	1996
117	KGJ353	Volvo B10BLE	Carrus 204L	B40D	1995
118	KGJ370	Volvo B10BLE	Carrus 204L	B40D	1995

119	KGJ377	Volvo B10BLE	Carrus 204L	B40D	1995
120	KGJ381	Volvo B10BLE	Carrus 204L	B40D	1995
121	KGJ390	Volvo B10BLE	Carrus 204L	B40D	1995
125	MKC658	Volvo B10M	Wiima K202	B45D	1990
126	NBU471	Scania L113CLL	Carrus 204M	B43D	1996
127	NBU424	Scania N113CLL	Scania MAXcl	B35D	1996
128	NBU465	Scania L113CLL	Carrus 204M	B43D	1996
129	NBU426	Scania N113CLL	Scania MAXcl	B35D	1996
131	NBU807	Volvo B10B-70	Säffle 2000	B45D	1996
133	NBU875	Volvo B10B-70	Säffle 2000	B45D	1996
135	NBU876	Volvo B10B-70	Säffle 2000	B45D	1996
136	AXU136	Volvo B10M	Wiima K202	B53F	1986
138	BBP138	Volvo B10M	Wiima K202	B53F	1989
139	BBP139	Volvo B10M	Wiima K202	B53F	1989
140	BNB140	Volvo B10M	Wiima K202	B45D	1989
141	BNB141	Volvo B10M	Wiima K202	B45D	1989
142	BNB142	Volvo B10M	Wiima K202	B45D	1989
143	XFM689	Volvo B10M	Wiima K202	B45D	1992
144	XFM856	Volvo B10M	Wiima K202	B45D	1992
145	XFM807	Volvo B10M	Wiima K202	B45D	1992
146	XFM767	Volvo B10M	Wiima K202	B45D	1992
147	NBU877	Volvo B10B-70	Säffle 2000	B45D	1996
148	BBP148	Volvo B10M	Wiima K202	B53F	1986
149	BBP149	Volvo B10M	Wiima K202	B53F	1986
150	NBU878	Volvo B10B-70	Säffle 2000	B45D	1996
151	BBP151	Volvo B10M	Wiima K202	B53F	1986
153	BBP153	Volvo B10M	Wiima K202	B53F	1986
155	NBU879	Volvo B10B-70	Säffle 2000	B45D	1996
158	NBU880	Volvo B10B-70	Säffle 2000	B45D	1996
160	NBU882	Volvo B10B-70	Säffle 2000	B45D	1996
161	NBU883	Volvo B10B-70	Säffle 2000	B45D	1996
162	NBU884	Volvo B10B-70	Säffle 2000	B45D	1996
163	NBU885	Volvo B10B-70	Säffle 2000	B45D	1996
164	NBU886	Volvo B10B-70	Säffle 2000	B45D	1996
166	NBU887	Volvo B10B-70	Säffle 2000	B45D	1996
200	NBU888	Volvo B10B-70	Säffle 2000	B45D	1996
201	BNT543	Volvo B10M	Wiima K202	B45D	1990
202	NBU889	Volvo B10B-70	Säffle 2000	B45D	1996
203	CBH303	Volvo B10M	Wiima K202	B44D	1993
204	CBH227	Volvo B10M	Wiima K202	B44D	1993
205	IFO742	Volvo B10M	Wiima K202	B45D	1991
206	MKC674	Volvo B10M	Wiima K202	B45D	1990
207	KGJ397	Volvo B10BLE	Carrus 204L	B40D	1995
208	BNT616	Volvo B10M	Wiima K202	B45D	1990
209	CBH258	Volvo B10M	Wiima K202	B44D	1993
210	BNT602	Volvo B10M	Wiima K202	B45D	1990
211	CBH330	Volvo B10M	Wiima K202	B44D	1993
212	MKC723	Volvo B10M	Wiima K202	B45D	1990
213	IFO755	Volvo B10M	Wiima K202	B45D	1991
214	CBH275	Volvo B10M	Wiima K202	B44D	1993
215	BFA519	Volvo B10M	Wiima K202	B45D	1990
216	KGJ402	Volvo B10BLE	Carrus 204L	B40D	1995
217	KGJ425	Volvo B10BLE	Carrus 204L	B40D	1995
218	KGJ437	Volvo B10BLE	Carrus 204L	B40D	1995
221	IFO756	Volvo B10M	Wiima K202	B45D	1991
222	JBA326	Volvo B10M	Wiima K202	B45D	1991
223	JBA354	Volvo B10M	Wiima K202	B45D	1991
226	YAL916	Volvo B10M	Wiima K202	B45D	1992
227	JBA372	Volvo B10M	Wiima K202	B45D	1991
228	XFM738	Volvo B10M	Wiima K202	B45D	1992
230	MKC766	Volvo B10M	Wiima K202	B45D	1990
231	XFM691	Volvo B10M	Wiima K202	B45D	1992
232	XFM712	Volvo B10M	Wiima K202	B45D	1992
237	NBU615	Volvo B10R-59	Säffle	B35D	1990
238	YAL902	Volvo B10M	Wiima K202	B45D	1992

Opposite:- **Oy Swebus Finland Ab have two operations in Finland, Espoon Auto and Transbus, both of which are represented here. The upper picture shows 127, NBU424, a Scania N113CLL with Scania Maxi bodywork fitted with full airconditioning and heating system. The lower picture shows Volvo 340, EGM933, a Volvo B10B with Carrus 204M bodywork. The Transbus fleet are numbered from 301 upwards, but the picture shows only the last two digits are displayed.** *Swebus Finland*

239	NBU611	Volvo B10R-59	Säffle	B35D	1990
240	NBU621	Volvo B10R-59	Säffle	B35D	1990
241	NBU624	Volvo B10R-59	Säffle	B35D	1990
242	CBG637	Volvo B10M	Wiima K202	B44D	1993
243	XFM723	Volvo B10M	Wiima K202	B45D	1992
244	NBU625	Volvo B10R-59	Säffle	B35D	1990
245	NBU617	Volvo B10R-59	Säffle	B35D	1990
246	NBU620	Volvo B10R-59	Säffle	B35D	1990
247	NBU616	Volvo B10R-59	Säffle	B35D	1990
250	IFO766	Volvo B10M	Wiima K202	B45D	1991
257	JBA890	Volvo B10M	Wiima K202	B45D	1991
258	UVJ658	Volvo B10M	Wiima M304	B47D	1986
259	UVJ659	Volvo B10M	Wiima M304	B47D	1986
260	AFA185	Volvo B10M	Wiima K202	B45D	1989
261	UVJ661	Volvo B10M	Wiima M304	B47D	1986
262	UVJ662	Volvo B10M	Wiima M304	B47D	1986
263	UVJ663	Volvo B10M	Wiima M304	B47D	1986
264	UVJ664	Volvo B10M	Wiima M304	B47D	1986
266	ZEA266	Volvo B10M	Wiima K202	B45D	1989
267	ZEA267	Volvo B10M	Wiima K202	B45D	1989
268	ZEA268	Volvo B10M	Wiima K202	B45D	1989
269	CBG662	Volvo B10M	Wiima K202	B44D	1993
271	YAL914	Volvo B10M	Wiima K202	B44D	1992
272	CBG681	Volvo B10M	Wiima K202	B44D	1993
273	YAM123	Volvo B10M	Wiima K202	B45D	1992
274	CBG700	Volvo B10M	Wiima K202	B44D	1993
275	CBG701	Volvo B10M	Wiima K202	B44D	1993
276	YAM114	Volvo B10M	Wiima K202	B45D	1992
277	XFM774	Volvo B10M	Wiima K202	B45D	1992
278	ZEA278	Volvo B10M	Wiima K202	B45D	1989
279	ZEA279	Volvo B10M	Wiima K202	B45D	1989
281	CBG721	Volvo B10M	Wiima K202	B44D	1993
282	CBG729	Volvo B10M	Wiima K202	B44D	1993
283	ZEA283	Volvo B10M	Wiima K202	B45D	1991
284	ZEA284	Volvo B10M	Wiima K202	B45D	1989
285	ZCS285	Volvo B10M	Wiima K202	B47D	1989
286	ZCS286	Volvo B10M	Wiima K202	B47D	1988
287	ZCS287	Volvo B10M	Wiima K202	B47D	1988
288	ZCS288	Volvo B10M	Wiima K202	B47D	1988
289	ZCS289	Volvo B10M	Wiima K202	B47D	1988
293	JBA880	Volvo B10M	Wiima K202	B45D	1991
296	XFM796	Volvo B10M	Wiima K202	B45D	1992
301	VGC897	Volkswagen Kombi	Volkswagen	M9	1995
302	NBU500	Volvo B10B-70	Carrus 204M	B46D	1996
303	JAT939	Scania K113T	Lahti 450 Eagle		1992
304	NBU493	Volvo B10B-70	Carrus 204M	B46D	1996
306	NBM491	Volvo B10B-70	Carrus 204M	B46D	1996
307	EFE617	Mercedes-Benz 1525L	Van Hool Alizée	DP45F	1996
308	NBM492	Volvo B10B-70	Carrus 204M	B46D	1990
309	EFE808	Mercedes-Benz 1525L	Van Hool Alizée	DP45F	1996
310	LGF866	Volvo B10B-70	Carrus Fifty	B48D	1994
311	LGF882	Volvo B10B-70	Carrus Fifty	B48D	1994
312	LGF885	Volvo B10B-70	Carrus Fifty	B48D	1994
313	SGE637	Volvo B10B-70	Carrus Fifty	B48D	1994
314	SGE740	Volvo B10B-70	Carrus Fifty	B48D	1994
315	SGE739	Volvo B10B-70	Carrus Fifty	B48D	1994
316	SGE699	Volvo B10B-70	Carrus Fifty	B48D	1994
317	SGE700	Volvo B10B-70	Carrus Fifty	B48D	1994
318	EGP219	Volvo B10B-70	Carrus 204M	B46D	1995
319	EGP220	Volvo B10B-70	Carrus 204M	B46D	1995
320	EGP239	Volvo B10B-70	Carrus 204M	B46D	1995
321	ZAB821	Volvo B10M	Wiima M304	B51D	1987
322	NBM487	Volvo B10B-70	Carrus 204M	B46D	1996
323	EFE123	Mercedes-Benz 1625L	Wiima M310	B45D	1990
324	IFO950	Volvo B10M	Wiima N202	AB65D	1991
325	YAH544	Scania L113CLB	Wiima M311	B45D	1992
327	EGP211	Volvo B10B-70	Carrus 204M	B46D	1995
328	EGP218	Volvo B10B-70	Carrus 204M	B46D	1995
330	EGP240	Volvo B10B-70	Carrus 204M	B46D	1995
331	EGP212	Volvo B10B-70	Carrus 204M	B46D	1995
332	CAA132	Volvo B10R-59	Wiima M310	B45D	1989
333	BFA982	Volvo B10R-59	Wiima M310	B45D	1989
334	UGM523	Volvo B10B-70	Carrus 204M	B46D	1996

335	BFA986	Volvo B10R-59	Wiima M310	B45D	1989
336	RGT837	Volvo B10B-70	Carrus 204M	B46D	1996
337	SJO120	Mercedes-Benz 1625L	Wiima M310	B45D	1990
339	EGP210	Volvo B10B-70	Carrus 204M	B46D	1995
340	EGM933	Volvo B10B-70	Carrus 204M	B46D	1995
341	RFH991	Volvo B10M-60	Van Hool Alizée	C49F	1991
342	RFH988	Volvo B10M-60	Van Hool Alizée	C49F	1991
343	EGM926	Volvo B10B-70	Carrus 204M	B46D	1995
344	UGM569	Volvo B10B-70	Carrus 204M	B46D	1996
345	EKA745	Volvo B10R-59	Wiima M310	DP57F	1988
346	UGM520	Volvo B10B-70	Carrus 204M	B46D	1996
#46	EBT746	Volvo B10R-59	Wiima M310	DP57F	1986
347	BFA251	Volvo B10R-59	Wiima M310	DP57F	1989
348	UGM570	Volvo B10B-70	Carrus 204M	B46D	1996
349	BFA256	Volvo B10R-59	Wiima M310	DP57F	1989
350	EEU115	Volvo B10R-59	Wiima M310	DP57F	1987
353	EEJ733	Volvo B10R-59	Wiima M310	DP57F	1987
354	EEJ724	Volvo B10R-59	Wiima M310	DP57F	1987
355	EET715	Volvo B10R-59	Wiima M310	DP57F	1986
357	NBU613	Volvo B10R-59	Säffle	B35D	1990
358	EBT758	Volvo B10R-59	Wiima M304	DP57F	1986
359	NBU623	Volvo B10R-59	Säffle	B35D	1990
360	EEU116	Volvo B10R-59	Wiima M304	DP57F	1987
362	EBT762	Volvo B10R-59	Wiima M310	DP57F	1986
366	UGM521	Volvo B10B-70	Carrus 204M	B46D	1996
369	UGM572	Volvo B10B-70	Carrus 204M	B46D	1996
370	EEU117	Volvo B10R-59	Wiima M310	DP57F	1987
371	UGM573	Volvo B10B-70	Carrus 204M	B46D	1996
372	UGM517	Volvo B10B-70	Carrus 204M	B46D	1996
373	EJV773	Volvo B10R-59	Wiima M310	DP57F	1988
374	UGM522	Volvo B10B-70	Carrus 204M	B46D	1996
375	EEU112	Volvo B10R-59	Wiima M304	DP57F	1987
376	EEU113	Volvo B10R-59	Wiima M304	DP57F	1987
377	EEU114	Volvo B10R-59	Wiima M304	DP57F	1987
379	EJV779	Volvo B10R-59	Wiima M310	DP57F	1988
380	EEU118	Volvo B10R-59	Wiima M304	DP57F	1987
381	EKA712	Volvo B10R-59	Wiima M310	DP57F	1988
382	EJV782	Volvo B10R-59	Wiima M310	DP57F	1988
383	EKA743	Volvo B10R-59	Wiima M310	DP57F	1988
385	BFA370	Volvo B10R-59	Wiima M310	DP57F	1988
389	EBT739	Volvo B10R-59	Wiima M304	DP57F	1986
390	EEU119	Volvo B10R-59	Wiima M304	DP57F	1987
391	RFH529	Volvo B10R-59	Wiima M310	C55F	1991
392	RFH533	Volvo B10R-59	Wiima M310	C55F	1991
393	BFA321	Volvo B10R-59	Wiima M310	DP57F	1989
394	BFA340	Volvo B10R-59	Wiima M310	DP57F	1989
395	BFA913	Volvo B10R-59	Wiima M310	DP57F	1990
396	UGM571	Volvo B10B-70	Carrus 204M	B46D	1996
397	RFH495	Volvo B10R-59	Wiima M310	DP55F	1991
398	RFH488	Volvo B10R-59	Wiima M310	DP55F	1991
399	RFH711	Volvo B10R-59	Wiima M310	DP55F	1991

Carrus Fifty bodywork is fitted to Transbus 10 - 310, LGF866, in the main Swebus Finland fleet. The vehicle carries a fawn, yellow and black livery.
Swebus Finland

UK Vehicle Index

Reg	Operator	Reg	Operator	Reg	Operator	Reg	Operator
13CLT	Western	A8GGT	Midland Red	A308RSU	Western	A729ANH	United Counties
109DRM	Cumberland	A13RBL	Red & White	A314XWG	East Midland	A730LNC	Manchester
126ASV	Bluebird Buses	A14RBL	Red & White	A315XWG	East Midland	A743NNA	Manchester
127ASV	Bluebird Buses	A15RBL	Red & White	A316XWG	East Midland	A745NNA	Manchester
128ASV	Bluebird Buses	A17RBL	Red & White	A317XWG	East Midland	A747NNA	Manchester
147YFM	Bluebird Buses	A20RBL	Red & White	A318XWG	East Midland	A749NNA	Manchester
230HUE	Midland Red	A21HNC	Manchester	A319YWJ	East Midland	A751NNA	Manchester
283URB	Western	A22HNC	Manchester	A320YWJ	East Midland	A757NNA	Manchester
295UB	Western	A23HNC	Manchester	A321YWJ	East Midland	A761NNA	Manchester
331HWD	Midland Red	A24HNC	Manchester	A322AKU	East Midland	A762NNA	Manchester
400DCD	Stagecoach South	A25HNC	Manchester	A323AKU	East Midland	A764NNA	Manchester
401DCD	Stagecoach South	A26ORJ	Manchester	A324AKU	East Midland	A823SUL	Stagecoach South
402DCD	Stagecoach South	A27ORJ	Manchester	A325AKU	East Midland	A824SUL	Western
403DCD	Stagecoach South	A28ORJ	Manchester	A469TUV	Circle Line	A825SUL	Fife Scottish
404DCD	Stagecoach South	A29ORJ	Manchester	A523YSD	Western	A826SUL	Transit
405DCD	Stagecoach South	A30ORJ	Manchester	A541HAC	Red & White	A827SUL	Transit
406DCD	Stagecoach South	A31ORJ	Manchester	A542HAC	Midland Red	A828SUL	Selkent
407DCD	Stagecoach South	A32ORJ	Manchester	A543HAC	Midland Red	A829SUL	Selkent
408DCD	Stagecoach South	A33ORJ	Manchester	A544HAC	Midland Red	A830SUL	Selkent
409DCD	Stagecoach South	A39XHE	East Midland	A545HAC	Midland Red	A832SUL	Fife Scottish
410DCD	Stagecoach South	A41XHE	East Midland	A546HAC	Midland Red	A833SUL	Western
411DCD	Stagecoach South	A42XHE	East Midland	A547HAC	Midland Red	A834SUL	Selkent
412DCD	Stagecoach South	A44FRS	Bluebird Buses	A548HAC	Red & White	A836SUL	Selkent
413DCD	Stagecoach South	A44XHE	East Midland	A549HAC	Red & White	A837SUL	Selkent
414DCD	Stagecoach South	A45FRS	Bluebird Buses	A561KWY	Cambus	A838SUL	Selkent
415DCD	Stagecoach South	A46FRS	Bluebird Buses	A581HDB	Manchester	A840SUL	Transit
416DCD	Stagecoach South	A47FRS	Bluebird Buses	A582HDB	Manchester	A841SUL	Selkent
417DCD	Stagecoach South	A65THX	Selkent	A583HDB	Manchester	A842SUL	Selkent
418DCD	Stagecoach South	A66THX	Fife Scottish	A584HDB	Manchester	A843SUL	Selkent
419DCD	Stagecoach South	A67THX	Selkent	A585HDB	Manchester	A845SUL	Selkent
420DCD	Stagecoach South	A71GEE	East Midland	A603THV	Selkent	A846SUL	Transit
420GAC	Midland Red	A72GEE	East Midland	A607THV	Fife Scottish	A847SUL	Selkent
421DCD	Stagecoach South	A73GEE	East Midland	A613THV	Fife Scottish	A848SUL	Selkent
422DCD	Stagecoach South	A74GEE	East Midland	A622THV	Transit	A849SUL	Transit
423DCD	Stagecoach South	A75NAC	Midland Red	A625THV	Selkent	A850SUL	Selkent
424DCD	Stagecoach South	A76NAC	Midland Red	A626THV	Transit	A854SUL	Selkent
439UG	Western	A76THX	Selkent	A627THV	Selkent	A855SUL	East London
461CLT	East London	A77THX	Western	A628THV	Selkent	A856SUL	Selkent
467WYA	Circle Line	A102DAO	Cumberland	A629THV	Selkent	A857SUL	Selkent
472YMF	Stagecoach South	A116ESA	Bluebird Buses	A630THV	Selkent	A858SUL	Fife Scottish
485CLT	East London	A117ESA	Bluebird Buses	A631THV	Selkent	A859SUL	Selkent
490CLT	Bluebird Buses	A118ESA	Bluebird Buses	A632THV	Selkent	A866SUL	Selkent
491GAC	Midland Red	A121GSA	Bluebird Buses	A634THV	Selkent	A867SUL	Fife Scottish
495FFJ	Western	A122GSA	Bluebird Buses	A635THV	Selkent	A868SUL	Selkent
511OHU	Cheltenham & Glos	A123GSA	Bluebird Buses	A636THV	Selkent	A873SUL	Fife Scottish
527CLT	East London	A124GSA	Bluebird Buses	A645THV	Selkent	A874SUL	East London
630DYE	East London	A125GSA	Bluebird Buses	A648THV	Selkent	A876SUL	Western
647DYE	United Counties	A126GSA	Bluebird Buses	A650THV	Fife Scottish	A877SUL	Selkent
685DYE	United Counties	A127GSA	Bluebird Buses	A652THV	Selkent	A880SUL	Selkent
703DYE	Western	A138MRN	Cumberland	A657HNB	Manchester	A881SUL	Selkent
837XHW	Transit	A142MRN	Ribble	A660HNB	Manchester	A882SUL	Selkent
866NHT	Bluebird Buses	A143MRN	Ribble	A663WSU	Bluebird Buses	A883SUL	Selkent
896HOD	Western	A145OFR	Ribble	A668HNB	Manchester	A885SUL	Selkent
927GTA	Bluebird Buses	A156OFR	Ribble	A671HNB	Manchester	A902SYE	Fife Scottish
1412NE	Bluebird Buses	A157OFR	Ribble	A678HNB	Manchester	A905SYE	Transit
3063VC	Oxford	A158OFR	Ribble	A679HNB	Manchester	A905XYE	Red & White
3273AC	Midland Red	A159OFR	Ribble	A681KDV	Cambus	A918SYE	Western
4828VC	Midland Red	A208EHN	Transit	A683HNB	Manchester	A921SYE	Fife Scottish
552OHU	Midland Red	A209EHN	Transit	A683KDV	Cambus	A922SYE	Fife Scottish
5796MX	Western	A211EHN	Transit	A690HNB	Manchester	A925SYE	Selkent
6253VC	Midland Red	A213FVN	Transit	A693HNB	Manchester	A926SYE	Selkent
6804VC	Circle Line	A214MCK	Circle Line	A705LNC	Manchester	A935SYE	Fife Scottish
9258VC	Oxford	A227MDD	Red & White	A725LNC	Manchester	A940XGG	Bluebird Buses
9492SC	Bluebird Buses	A243YGF	East Midland	A726LNC	Manchester	A941XGG	Bluebird Buses
9737VC	Midland Red	A306YSJ	Western	A728ANH	United Counties	A942XGG	Bluebird Buses

Reg	Operator	Reg	Operator	Reg	Operator
A944SYE	Fife Scottish	ANA160Y	Manchester	AYJ102T	Stagecoach South	B106WUV	Bluebird Buses
A945SYE	Fife Scottish	ANA162Y	Manchester	AYJ107T	Stagecoach South	B106WUV	Selkent
A949SYE	East London	ANA163Y	Manchester	B21TVU	Manchester	B107UAT	Transit
A950SYE	Selkent	ANA164Y	Manchester	B22TVU	Manchester	B108CCS	Fife Scottish
A951SYE	Selkent	ANA165Y	Manchester	B23TVU	Manchester	B108UAT	Transit
A953SYE	East London	ANA170Y	Manchester	B24CGA	Western	B108WUV	Selkent
A960SYE	East London	ANA173Y	Manchester	B24TVU	Manchester	B109UAT	Transit
A961SYE	Selkent	ANA179Y	Manchester	B25TVU	Manchester	B110SJA	Manchester
A965SYE	East London	ANA180Y	Manchester	B26TVU	Manchester	B110UAT	Transit
A967YSX	Fife Scottish	ANA190Y	Manchester	B27PAJ	Transit	B110WUV	Bluebird Buses
A968YSX	Fife Scottish	ANA211T	Western	B27TVU	Manchester	B112WUV	Selkent
A969YSX	Fife Scottish	ANA639Y	Manchester	B28PAJ	Transit	B113WUV	Selkent
A970YSX	Fife Scottish	ARN888Y	Cumberland	B28TVU	Manchester	B114SJA	Manchester
A971SYE	East London	ARN889Y	Ribble	B29PAJ	Transit	B114WUV	Bluebird Buses
A971YSX	Fife Scottish	ARN890Y	Ribble	B29TVU	Manchester	B115WUV	Selkent
A972YSX	Fife Scottish	ARN892Y	Cheltenham & Glos	B30PAJ	Transit	B116WUV	Selkent
A973YSX	Fife Scottish	ARP601X	United Counties	B30TVU	Manchester	B117TVU	Manchester
A974YSX	Fife Scottish	ARP602X	United Counties	B31PAJ	Transit	B117WUV	Selkent
A975OST	Cumberland	ARP604X	United Counties	B32PAJ	Transit	B118TVU	Manchester
A976SYE	Selkent	ARP605X	United Counties	B34PJA	Manchester	B118WUV	Selkent
A978OST	Ribble	ARP606X	United Counties	B35PJA	Manchester	B119TVU	Manchester
A978SYE	Selkent	ARP607X	United Counties	B36PJA	Manchester	B119WUV	Fife Scottish
A979OST	Ribble	ARP608X	United Counties	B39PJA	Manchester	B121TVU	Manchester
A988SYE	Selkent	ARP609X	United Counties	B43MAO	Cumberland	B121WUV	Stagecoach South
A996SYE	East London	ARP610X	United Counties	B49PJA	Manchester	B122TVU	Manchester
A999SYE	Selkent	ARP611X	United Counties	B52DWE	East Midland	B122WUV	Selkent
AAE644V	Cheltenham & Glos	ASA23T	Western	B53DWJ	East Midland	B124TVU	Manchester
AAE648V	Cheltenham & Glos	ASA27T	Western	B53PJA	Manchester	B124WUV	Stagecoach South
AAE649V	Cheltenham & Glos	ASJ206T	Western	B54DWJ	East Midland	B125TVU	Manchester
AAE650V	Cheltenham & Glos	ASJ207T	Western	B55PJA	Manchester	B125WUV	Stagecoach South
AAE651V	Cheltenham & Glos	AVK134V	Busways	B56PJA	Manchester	B126WNB	Manchester
AAE659V	Cheltenham & Glos	AVK135V	Busways	B57PJA	Manchester	B132WNB	Manchester
AAE660V	Cheltenham & Glos	AVK136V	Busways	B58PJA	Manchester	B133WNB	Manchester
AAE665V	Cheltenham & Glos	AVK138V	Busways	B60PJA	Manchester	B135WNB	Manchester
AAP647T	Stagecoach South	AVK139V	Busways	B60WKH	Transit	B137WNB	Manchester
AAP671T	Stagecoach South	AVK140V	Midland Red	B65PJA	Manchester	B138WNB	Manchester
AAX465A	Red & White	AVK141V	Busways	B67PJA	Manchester	B139WNB	Manchester
AAX488A	Red & White	AVK142V	Transit	B69PJA	Manchester	B143WNB	Manchester
AAX489A	Red & White	AVK143V	Midland Red	B70PJA	Manchester	B145WNB	Manchester
AAX516A	Red & White	AVK145V	Midland Red	B72PJA	Manchester	B146XNA	Manchester
AAX538A	Red & White	AVK146V	Busways	B74PJA	Manchester	B147XNA	Manchester
AAX544A	Red & White	AVK147V	Transit	B77PJA	Manchester	B149XNA	Manchester
AAX575A	Red & White	AVK148V	Transit	B79WUV	Selkent	B150DHL	East Midland
AAX589A	Bluebird Buses	AVK149V	Busways	B80PJA	Manchester	B150XNA	Manchester
AAX600A	Bluebird Buses	AVK150V	Busways	B81WUV	Selkent	B151DHL	East Midland
AAX601A	Bluebird Buses	AVK154V	Busways	B82PJA	Manchester	B151WRN	Cumberland
AAX631A	Bluebird Buses	AVK156V	Busways	B83WUV	Selkent	B152DHL	East Midland
ABV669A	Fife Scottish	AVK158V	Busways	B84PJA	Manchester	B152TRN	Ribble
AET181T	Midland Red	AVK159V	Busways	B84WUV	Fife Scottish	B153DHL	East Midland
AET185T	Red & White	AVK160V	Busways	B86SJA	Manchester	B153WRN	Cumberland
AET187T	Stagecoach South	AVK161V	Busways	B87SJA	Manchester	B153XNA	Manchester
AFJ738T	Oxford	AVK163V	Red & White	B88SJA	Manchester	B154DHL	East Midland
AFM1W	Ribble	AVK166V	Red & White	B89SJA	Manchester	B154WRN	Cumberland
AKG162A	Bluebird Buses	AVK167V	Midland Red	B89WUV	Selkent	B154XNA	Manchester
AKG197A	Devon	AVK168V	Midland Red	B91SJA	Manchester	B155DHL	East Midland
AKG214A	Devon	AVK169V	Midland Red	B91WUV	Selkent	B155XNA	Manchester
AKV137V	Circle Line	AVK170V	Busways	B92WUV	Selkent	B158WRN	Bluebird Buses
ALD968B	Bluebird Buses	AVK171V	Busways	B93WUV	Bluebird Buses	B162WRN	Cumberland
ANA1Y	Manchester	AVK172V	Midland Red	B94SJA	Manchester	B177FFS	Fife Scottish
ANA2Y	Manchester	AVK173V	Red & White	B95SJA	Manchester	B178FFS	Fife Scottish
ANA3Y	Manchester	AVK174V	Midland Red	B96WUV	Selkent	B179FFS	Fife Scottish
ANA4Y	Manchester	AVK180V	Busways	B97WUV	Fife Scottish	B180FFS	Fife Scottish
ANA6Y	Manchester	AVK181V	Midland Red	B99WUV	Selkent	B181FFS	Fife Scottish
ANA7Y	Manchester	AVK183V	Busways	B100WUV	Bluebird Buses	B182FFS	Fife Scottish
ANA8Y	Manchester	AYJ89T	Stagecoach South	B101WUV	Selkent	B183FFS	Fife Scottish
ANA9Y	Manchester	AYJ91T	Stagecoach South	B103HAO	Cumberland	B184FFS	Fife Scottish
ANA10Y	Manchester	AYJ92T	Stagecoach South	B103WUV	Selkent	B185FFS	Fife Scottish
ANA153Y	Manchester	AYJ95T	Stagecoach South	B105HAO	Cumberland	B186FFS	Fife Scottish
ANA154Y	Manchester	AYJ97T	Stagecoach South	B106HAO	Cumberland	B214OAJ	Transit
ANA158Y	Manchester	AYJ100T	Stagecoach South	B106UAT	Transit	B215OAJ	Transit

B216OAJ	Transit	BHY499V	Red & White	C87CHM	Selkent	C191YBA	Manchester
B217OAJ	Transit	BHY996V	Cheltenham & Glos	C92CHM	Selkent	C193YBA	Manchester
B218OAJ	Transit	BHY997V	Cheltenham & Glos	C94CHM	Selkent	C195YBA	Manchester
B348LSO	Bluebird Buses	BHY998V	Cheltenham & Glos	C97CHM	Selkent	C196YBA	Manchester
B349LSO	Bluebird Buses	BIW4977	Midland Red	C98CHM	Selkent	C197YBA	Manchester
B350LSO	Bluebird Buses	BJG671V	Stagecoach South	C100HSJ	Transit	C198YBA	Manchester
B351LSO	Bluebird Buses	BJG672V	Stagecoach South	C103CHM	Selkent	C199YBA	Manchester
B352LSO	Bluebird Buses	BJG673V	Stagecoach South	C104CHM	Selkent	C205CBU	Manchester
B353LSO	Bluebird Buses	BJG674V	Stagecoach South	C105CHM	Selkent	C207CBU	Manchester
B354LSO	Bluebird Buses	BJG675V	Stagecoach South	C105KDS	Western	C208CBU	Manchester
B355LSO	Bluebird Buses	BJV103L	East Midland	C106CHM	Selkent	C210CBU	Manchester
B356LSO	Bluebird Buses	BKE849T	Stagecoach South	C106KDS	Western	C212CBU	Manchester
B357LSO	Bluebird Buses	BKE859T	Stagecoach South	C107CHM	Selkent	C213CBU	Manchester
B358LSO	Bluebird Buses	BNC936T	Midland Red	C108CHM	Selkent	C214CBU	Manchester
B359LSO	Bluebird Buses	BOU6V	Cheltenham & Glos	C109CHM	Selkent	C215CBU	Manchester
B360LSO	Bluebird Buses	BPT903S	Red & White	C110CHM	Selkent	C216CBU	Manchester
B625DWF	East Midland	BPY403T	Transit	C111CAT	Transit	C219WAJ	Transit
B626DWF	East Midland	BSJ895T	Western	C111CHM	Selkent	C220WAJ	Transit
B627DWF	East Midland	BSJ896T	Western	C111JCS	Bluebird Buses	C221CBU	Manchester
B628DWF	East Midland	BSJ917T	Western	C112CAT	Transit	C221WAJ	Transit
B629DWF	East Midland	BSJ930T	Western	C112CHM	Selkent	C222WAJ	Transit
B630DWF	East Midland	BSJ931T	Western	C112GSJ	Western	C224CBU	Manchester
B631DWF	East Midland	BSK756	Bluebird Buses	C113CAT	Transit	C226ENE	Manchester
B632DWF	East Midland	BTX332J	Red & White	C114CHM	Selkent	C230ENE	Manchester
B633DWF	East Midland	BUH211V	Devon	C115CHM	Selkent	C234ENE	Manchester
B866JVK	Busways	BUH232V	Red & White	C116CHM	Selkent	C236EVU	Manchester
B891UAS	Ribble	BUH239V	Ribble	C117CHM	Selkent	C255FRJ	Manchester
B892UAS	Cumberland	BUH240V	Ribble	C118CHM	Selkent	C310ENA	Manchester
B893UAS	Cumberland	BUT24Y	Transit	C119CHM	Selkent	C326HWJ	East Midland
B894UAS	Ribble	BVP771V	Midland Red	C120CHM	Selkent	C327HWJ	East Midland
B895UAS	Cumberland	BVP772V	Midland Red	C120PNV	United Counties	C328HWJ	East Midland
B896UAS	Ribble	BVP808V	Midland Red	C121CHM	Selkent	C329HWJ	East Midland
B897UAS	Ribble	BVP816V	Midland Red	C121PNV	United Counties	C330HWJ	East Midland
B898UAS	Ribble	BVP817V	Midland Red	C122CAT	Transit	C331HWJ	East Midland
B899UAS	Cumberland	BVP818V	Midland Red	C122CHM	Selkent	C332HWJ	East Midland
B900WRN	Cumberland	BYJ919Y	Western	C122PNV	United Counties	C333HWJ	East Midland
B901TVR	Manchester	BYW397V	Red & White	C123CAT	Transit	C334HWJ	East Midland
B902TVR	Manchester	C23CHM	Selkent	C124CAT	Transit	C335HWJ	East Midland
B903TVR	Manchester	C28CHM	Selkent	C125CAT	Transit	C336HWJ	East Midland
B904TVR	Manchester	C29CHM	Selkent	C128CAT	Transit	C336SFL	Cambus
B905TVR	Manchester	C30CHM	Selkent	C129CAT	Transit	C382SAO	Cumberland
B906TVR	Manchester	C42CHM	Selkent	C131CAT	Transit	C383SAO	Cumberland
B907TVR	Manchester	C43CHM	Selkent	C156YBA	Manchester	C461SSO	Bluebird Buses
B908TVR	Manchester	C44CHM	Selkent	C158YBA	Manchester	C462SSO	Bluebird Buses
B909TVR	Manchester	C45CHM	Selkent	C164YBA	Manchester	C463SSO	Bluebird Buses
B910ODU	Midland Red	C51CHM	Selkent	C165YBA	Manchester	C466SSO	Bluebird Buses
B910TVR	Manchester	C53CHM	Selkent	C166YBA	Manchester	C467SSO	Bluebird Buses
B911ODU	Midland Red	C54CHM	Selkent	C167YBA	Manchester	C468SSO	Bluebird Buses
B911TVR	Manchester	C55CHM	Selkent	C169YBA	Manchester	C469SSO	Bluebird Buses
B912ODU	Midland Red	C57CHM	Selkent	C170ECK	Cumberland	C470SSO	Bluebird Buses
B912TVR	Manchester	C60CHM	Selkent	C170YBA	Manchester	C544RAO	Transit
B913TVR	Manchester	C61CHM	Selkent	C171ECK	Ribble	C591SHC	Western
B914TVR	Manchester	C62CHM	Selkent	C172ECK	Ribble	C601LFT	Busways
B915TVR	Manchester	C64CHM	Selkent	C172YBA	Manchester	C602LFT	Busways
B916TVR	Manchester	C67CHM	Selkent	C173ECK	Ribble	C603LFT	Busways
B917TVR	Manchester	C68CHM	Selkent	C173YBA	Manchester	C604LFT	Busways
B918TVR	Manchester	C69CHM	Selkent	C174ECK	Cumberland	C605LFT	Busways
B919TVR	Manchester	C70CHM	Selkent	C174YBA	Manchester	C606LFT	Busways
B920TVR	Manchester	C71CHM	Selkent	C175ECK	Cumberland	C608LFT	Busways
B960ODU	Midland Red	C72CHM	Selkent	C175YBA	Manchester	C609LFT	Busways
B961ODU	Midland Red	C73CHM	Selkent	C176ECK	Cumberland	C610LFT	Busways
B973OSB	Red & White	C74CHM	Selkent	C176YBA	Manchester	C611LFT	Busways
BAU179T	United Counties	C75CHM	Selkent	C177ECK	Cumberland	C612LFT	Busways
BCS865T	Western	C76CHM	Selkent	C178ECK	Ribble	C613LFT	Busways
BCS869T	Western	C77CHM	Selkent	C178YBA	Manchester	C614LFT	Busways
BCS870T	Western	C80CHM	Selkent	C179ECK	Cumberland	C615LFT	Busways
BCS871T	Circle Line	C81CHM	Selkent	C179YBA	Manchester	C616LFT	Busways
BCW827V	Stagecoach South	C82CHM	Selkent	C181YBA	Manchester	C617LFT	Busways
BFW136W	East Midland	C83CHM	Selkent	C184YBA	Manchester	C617SFH	Circle Line
BHO441V	East Midland	C86CHM	Selkent	C185YBA	Manchester	C618LFT	Busways

The 1998 Stagecoach Bus Handbook

C619LFT	Busways	C802USG	Fife Scottish	CUL130V	Selkent	D130FYM	Selkent
C620LFT	Busways	C803USG	Fife Scottish	CUL137V	Selkent	D131FYM	Selkent
C621LFT	Busways	C804USG	Fife Scottish	CUL140V	Selkent	D131PTT	Devon
C621SFH	Circle Line	C805USG	Fife Scottish	CUL142V	Selkent	D131UGB	Western
C622LFT	Busways	C806USG	Fife Scottish	CUL163V	East London	D132FYM	Selkent
C623LFT	Busways	C807BYY	Selkent	CUL168V	Stagecoach South	D132PTT	Oxford
C624LFT	Busways	C807USG	Fife Scottish	CUL169V	Stagecoach South	D133FYM	Selkent
C625LFT	Busways	C809BYY	Selkent	CUL175V	Selkent	D134FYM	Selkent
C626LFT	Busways	C810BYY	Selkent	CUL179V	Western	D134PTT	Devon
C627LFT	Busways	C811BYY	Selkent	CUL180V	Stagecoach South	D136FYM	Selkent
C628LFT	Busways	C812BYY	Selkent	CUL189V	Western	D137FYM	Selkent
C629LFT	Busways	C815BYY	Selkent	CUL190V	Stagecoach South	D137PTT	Oxford
C630LFT	Busways	C818BYY	Selkent	CUL193V	Selkent	D141FYM	Selkent
C631LFT	Busways	C819BYY	Selkent	CUL197V	Western	D142FYM	Selkent
C632LFT	Busways	C962XVC	Midland Red	CUL198V	Stagecoach South	D144FYM	Selkent
C633LFT	Busways	C963XVC	Midland Red	CUL208V	Western	D145FYM	Selkent
C634LFT	Busways	C964XVC	Midland Red	CUL209V	Western	D164VRP	Red & White
C635LFT	Busways	CBV2S	Cumberland	CUL214V	Selkent	D183VRP	Red & White
C636LFT	Busways	CBV6S	Red & White	CUL215V	Stagecoach South	D211VEV	Stagecoach South
C637LFT	Busways	CBV16S	Midland Red	CUL222V	Selkent	D230UHC	Western
C638LFT	Busways	CBV21S	Ribble	CUL223V	Selkent	D260JVR	Manchester
C639LFT	Busways	CD7045	Stagecoach South	CUL224V	Selkent	D268JVR	Manchester
C640LFT	Busways	CEO720W	Ribble	CUL225V	Stagecoach South	D269JVR	Manchester
C641LFT	Busways	CEO721W	Cumberland	CUV192C	United Counties	D272JVR	Manchester
C642LFT	Busways	CJH117V	Stagecoach South	CUV272C	East London	D277FAS	Fife Scottish
C643LFT	Busways	CJH119V	Stagecoach South	CUV286C	East London	D277JVR	Manchester
C644LFT	Busways	CJH120V	Stagecoach South	CUV300C	East London	D278FAS	Fife Scottish
C645LFT	Busways	CJH142V	Stagecoach South	CUV303C	East London	D279FAS	Fife Scottish
C646LFT	Busways	CJH145V	Stagecoach South	CUV311C	East London	D298YTY	Busways
C647LFT	Busways	CJJ677W	Stagecoach South	CWR525Y	Ribble	D305YTY	Busways
C648LFT	Busways	CJJ679W	Stagecoach South	CWR526Y	Ribble	D322MNC	Bluebird Buses
C649LFT	Busways	CPO100W	Stagecoach South	CWX669T	Ribble	D367JJD	Selkent
C650LFT	Busways	CPO98W	Stagecoach South	CYJ492Y	Red & White	D380XRS	Cumberland
C651LFT	Busways	CRS60T	Bluebird Buses	CYJ493Y	Red & White	D381XRS	Cumberland
C651XDF	Cheltenham & Glos	CRS61T	Bluebird Buses	D35UAO	Manchester	D383XRS	United Counties
C652LFT	Busways	CRS62T	Bluebird Buses	D36UAO	Cumberland	D384XAO	Cumberland
C653LFT	Busways	CRS63T	Bluebird Buses	D41UAO	Western	D385XRS	Bluebird Buses
C654LFT	Busways	CRS68T	Bluebird Buses	D44UAO	Cumberland	D386XRS	Bluebird Buses
C655LFT	Busways	CRS69T	Bluebird Buses	D45UAO	Cumberland	D387XRS	Bluebird Buses
C656LFT	Busways	CRS70T	Bluebird Buses	D94EKV	Western	D388XRS	Bluebird Buses
C657LFT	Busways	CRS71T	Bluebird Buses	D103PTT	Oxford	D389XRS	Bluebird Buses
C658LFT	Busways	CRS73T	Bluebird Buses	D109NDW	Red & White	D401TFT	Busways
C659LFT	Busways	CRS74T	Bluebird Buses	D109NUS	Western	D402TFT	Busways
C659XDF	Cheltenham & Glos	CSF159W	Fife Scottish	D110NUS	Western	D403TFT	Transit
C660LFT	Busways	CSF160W	Fife Scottish	D110PTT	Devon	D404TFT	Devon
C661LFT	Busways	CSF161W	Fife Scottish	D111NUS	Western	D405TFT	Devon
C662LFT	Busways	CSF162W	Fife Scottish	D111PTT	Devon	D407TFT	Devon
C663LFT	Busways	CSF163W	Western	D112PTT	Devon	D408TFT	Devon
C664LFT	Busways	CSF164W	Fife Scottish	D113PTT	Devon	D409TFT	Devon
C665LFT	Busways	CSF165W	Fife Scottish	D114NUS	Western	D411TFT	Transit
C693VAD	Circle Line	CSF166W	Fife Scottish	D114PTT	Devon	D412TFT	Devon
C694VAD	Circle Line	CSF167W	Fife Scottish	D115NUS	Western	D413TFT	Devon
C696VAD	Circle Line	CSF168W	Fife Scottish	D116NUS	Western	D414TFT	Devon
C738CUC	Circle Line	CSF169W	Fife Scottish	D116PTT	Devon	D415TFT	Busways
C787USG	Fife Scottish	CSO386Y	Western	D117NUS	Western	D416TFT	Devon
C788USG	Fife Scottish	CSU920	Bluebird Buses	D117PTT	Devon	D417TFT	Devon
C789USG	Fife Scottish	CSU921	Bluebird Buses	D122NUS	Western	D418TFT	Devon
C790USG	Fife Scottish	CSU922	Bluebird Buses	D122PTT	Oxford	D419TFT	Busways
C791USG	Fife Scottish	CSU923	Bluebird Buses	D123FYM	Selkent	D420TFT	Devon
C792USG	Fife Scottish	CSU978	Stagecoach South	D123NUS	Western	D436RYS	Bluebird Buses
C793USG	Fife Scottish	CSU992	Stagecoach South	D124FYM	Selkent	D437XRS	Bluebird Buses
C794USG	Fife Scottish	CSV219	Midland Red	D124NUS	Western	D438XRS	Bluebird Buses
C795USG	Fife Scottish	CUB72Y	Western	D125FYM	Selkent	D512CSF	Fife Scottish
C796USG	Fife Scottish	CUB73Y	Western	D125PTT	Devon	D516DSX	Fife Scottish
C797USG	Fife Scottish	CUL79V	Stagecoach South	D126FYM	Selkent	D517DSX	Fife Scottish
C798USG	Fife Scottish	CUL80V	East London	D127FYM	Selkent	D518DSX	Fife Scottish
C799USG	Fife Scottish	CUL86V	Selkent	D128FYM	Selkent	D519DSX	Fife Scottish
C800HCS	Western	CUL98V	Selkent	D128NUS	Western	D520DSX	Fife Scottish
C800USG	Fife Scottish	CUL114V	Selkent	D129FYM	Selkent	D521DSX	Fife Scottish
C801USG	Fife Scottish	CUL120V	Selkent	D129NUS	Western	D522DSX	Fife Scottish

Reg	Operator	Reg	Operator	Reg	Operator	Reg	Operator
D523DSX	Fife Scottish	DSV943	Cumberland	E138SAT	Transit	E500LFL	Cambus
D523KSE	Bluebird Buses	DWF22V	East Midland	E139SAT	Transit	E501LFL	Cambus
D524DSX	Fife Scottish	DWF23V	East Midland	E140SAT	Transit	E502LFL	Cambus
D528RCK	Cumberland	DWF24V	East Midland	E141SAT	Transit	E510PVV	Cumberland
D529RCK	Cumberland	DWF26V	East Midland	E142BKH	Transit	E511PVV	Cumberland
D533RCK	Cumberland	DWF188V	Bluebird Buses	E143BKH	Transit	E512PVV	Cumberland
D559RCK	Cumberland	DWF190V	Bluebird Buses	E144BKH	Transit	E635BVK	Busways
D560RCK	Cumberland	DWF191V	Bluebird Buses	E145BKH	Transit	E637BVK	Busways
D604HTC	Circle Line	DWF193V	Bluebird Buses	E146BKH	Transit	E638YUS	Western
D605HTC	Circle Line	E47CHH	Cumberland	E147BKH	Transit	E643DCK	Western
D606HTC	Circle Line	E47HFE	East Midland	E148BKH	Transit	E644KYW	Circle Line
D614ASG	Fife Scottish	E48CHH	Cumberland	E149BKH	Transit	E645KYW	Western
D615ASG	Fife Scottish	E48HFE	East Midland	E150BKH	Transit	E646DCK	Western
D639NOD	Devon	E49CHH	Cumberland	E151BKH	Transit	E663JAD	Circle Line
D647NOD	Devon	E49HFE	East Midland	E155CGJ	East London	E665JAD	Circle Line
D648NOD	Devon	E50CHH	Cumberland	E200BDV	Devon	E667JAD	Circle Line
D649NOD	Devon	E50HFE	East Midland	E205BDV	Devon	E676KDG	Circle Line
D650NOD	Devon	E51HFE	East Midland	E209BDV	Devon	E709MFV	Transit
D654NOD	Devon	E56HFE	East Midland	E210BDV	Devon	E712LYU	East London
D656NOD	Devon	E57HFE	East Midland	E211BDV	Devon	E713LYU	Bluebird Buses
D713CSC	Fife Scottish	E58HFE	East Midland	E216BDV	Devon	E714LYU	Bluebird Buses
D744BRS	Bluebird Buses	E60WDT	East Midland	E305BWL	Oxford	E721BVO	East Midland
D777NDV	Devon	E61JFV	Ribble	E306BWL	Oxford	E746SKR	Stagecoach South
D778NDV	Devon	E61WDT	East Midland	E308HPU	Red & White	E747SKR	Stagecoach South
D779NDV	Devon	E62JFV	Ribble	E309BWL	Oxford	E748SKR	Stagecoach South
D780NDV	Devon	E62WDT	Red & White	E309HPU	Red & White	E749SKR	Stagecoach South
D781NDV	Devon	E63JFV	Ribble	E315NWK	Midland Red	E750SKR	Stagecoach South
D784NDV	Devon	E63WDT	Red & White	E316HLO	Red & White	E751SKR	Stagecoach South
D785NDV	Devon	E64JFV	Ribble	E364YGB	Bluebird Buses	E752SKR	Stagecoach South
D786NDV	Devon	E65JFV	Ribble	E421AFT	Busways	E753SKR	Stagecoach South
D787NDV	Devon	E66JFV	Ribble	E422AFT	Busways	E754UKR	Stagecoach South
D789NDV	Oxford	E76RCS	Western	E423AFT	Busways	E755UKR	Stagecoach South
D792NDV	Devon	E77RCS	Western	E424AFT	Busways	E800WDV	Devon
D796NDV	Devon	E84HRN	Ribble	E425AFT	Busways	E802WDV	Devon
D797NDV	Devon	E85HRN	Ribble	E426AFT	Busways	E806WDV	Devon
D798NDV	Devon	E86HRN	Ribble	E427AFT	Busways	E810WDV	Devon
D799NDV	Devon	E87HRN	Ribble	E428AFT	Busways	E815WDV	Devon
D918KPT	Busways	E87KGV	Red & White	E429AFT	Busways	E816WDV	Devon
DAK201V	Red & White	E88HRN	Ribble	E430AFT	Busways	E822WDV	Devon
DBV24W	Cumberland	E89HRN	Ribble	E431AFT	Busways	E825ATT	Devon
DBV25W	Stagecoach South	E90JHG	Ribble	E432AFT	Busways	E827ATT	Devon
DBV26W	Red & White	E90YWB	East Midland	E433AFT	Busways	E829ATT	Oxford
DBV30W	Ribble	E91LBV	Ribble	E433YHL	Midland Red	E830ATT	Devon
DBV32W	Cumberland	E91YWB	East Midland	E434AFT	Busways	E842KAS	Bluebird Buses
DBV38W	Ribble	E92LHG	Ribble	E435AFT	Busways	E864RCS	Western
DBV39W	Ribble	E92YWB	East Midland	E436AFT	Devon	E865RCS	Western
DBV40W	Ribble	E93LHG	Ribble	E437AFT	Busways	E866RCS	Western
DBV41W	Ribble	E93YWB	East Midland	E438AFT	Devon	E867RCS	Western
DBV42W	Ribble	E94LHG	Ribble	E439AFT	Devon	E880DRA	East Midland
DBV43W	Ribble	E94YWB	East Midland	E440AFT	Busways	E901KYR	Busways
DBV100W	Cumberland	E95YWB	East Midland	E441AFT	Devon	E905KYR	Busways
DBV131Y	Ribble	E96YWB	East Midland	E442AFT	Busways	E906KYR	Busways
DBV132Y	Ribble	E97YWB	East Midland	E443AFT	Busways	E907KYR	Busways
DBV134Y	Cumberland	E98YWB	East Midland	E445AFT	Busways	E908KYR	Busways
DBV137Y	Ribble	E101JFV	Ribble	E446AFT	Devon	E909KSG	Fife Scottish
DBV829W	Ribble	E102JFV	Ribble	E447AFT	Busways	E909KYR	Busways
DBV831W	Ribble	E113RBO	Red & White	E448AFT	Devon	E910KSG	Fife Scottish
DBV832W	Ribble	E114SDW	Red & White	E449AFT	Busways	E910KYR	Busways
DBV834W	Western	E115SDW	Red & White	E450AFT	Busways	E911KYR	Busways
DBV835W	Ribble	E130ORP	United Counties	E451AFT	Busways	E912KYR	Busways
DBV839W	Ribble	E131ORP	United Counties	E452AFT	Busways	E914KYR	Busways
DBV841W	Ribble	E132ORP	United Counties	E453AFT	Busways	E915KYR	Busways
DDW433V	Devon	E132SAT	Transit	E454AFT	Busways	E917KYR	Busways
DDW434V	Red & White	E133ORP	United Counties	E455AFT	Busways	E918KYR	Busways
DDZ8844	Bluebird Buses	E133SAT	Transit	E456AFT	Busways	E919KYR	Busways
DGS625	Bluebird Buses	E134ORP	United Counties	E457AFT	Busways	E920KYR	Busways
DHW350W	Circle Line	E134SAT	Transit	E458AFT	Busways	E921KYR	Busways
DHW352W	Circle Line	E135SAT	Transit	E459AFT	Busways	E922KYR	Busways
DMS20V	Red & White	E136SAT	Transit	E460AFT	Transit	E923KYR	Busways
DMS22V	Red & White	E137SAT	Transit	E499TSJ	Western	E924KYR	Busways

Reg	Operator	Reg	Operator	Reg	Operator	Reg	Operator
E925KYR	Busways	ESU435	Western	F112YWO	Red & White	F300DRJ	Manchester
E927KYR	Busways	ESU913	Manchester	F113HVK	Busways	F301DRJ	Manchester
E927PBE	East Midland	ESU920	Manchester	F114HVK	Busways	F301MYJ	Stagecoach South
E928PBE	East Midland	ETC310W	Manchester	F114YWO	Red & White	F302MYJ	Stagecoach South
E929PBE	East Midland	EWE202V	Bluebird Buses	F115HVK	Busways	F303MYJ	Stagecoach South
E930PBE	East Midland	EWE203V	East Midland	F116HVK	Busways	F304DRJ	Manchester
E947BHS	Bluebird Buses	EWE205V	Bluebird Buses	F117HVK	Busways	F304MYJ	Stagecoach South
EAP973V	Stagecoach South	EWE206V	East Midland	F118HVK	Busways	F305MYJ	Stagecoach South
EAP984V	Stagecoach South	EWR656Y	Red & White	F118YVP	Circle Line	F306MYJ	Stagecoach South
EAP985V	Stagecoach South	EWS740W	Circle Line	F119HVK	Busways	F307MYJ	Stagecoach South
EAP986V	Stagecoach South	EWS743W	Cheltenham & Glos	F119YVP	Western	F308MYJ	Stagecoach South
EAP987V	Stagecoach South	EWS746W	Cheltenham & Glos	F120HVK	Busways	F309MYJ	Stagecoach South
EAP988V	Stagecoach South	EWS748W	Cheltenham & Glos	F121HVK	Busways	F310MYJ	Fife Scottish
EAP990V	Stagecoach South	EWS751W	Cheltenham & Glos	F122HVK	Busways	F311DET	Cheltenham & Glos
EAP991V	Stagecoach South	EWY74Y	Western	F123HVK	Busways	F311EJO	Oxford
EAP992V	Stagecoach South	EWY75Y	Western	F124HVK	Busways	F311MYJ	Fife Scottish
EAP996V	Bluebird Buses	EWY76Y	Western	F125HVK	Busways	F312EJO	Oxford
ECS877V	Circle Line	EYE229V	Stagecoach South	F125YVP	Red & White	F312MYJ	Fife Scottish
ECS878V	Western	EYE230V	Selkent	F128YVP	Western	F314EJO	Oxford
ECS879V	Western	EYE233V	Stagecoach South	F135SPX	Cumberland	F316EJO	Oxford
ECS880V	Western	EYE236V	Western	F135URP	United Counties	F317EJO	Oxford
ECS882V	Western	EYE237V	Stagecoach South	F136SPX	Cumberland	F318EJO	Oxford
EDS50A	Bluebird Buses	EYE240V	Stagecoach South	F137SPX	Cumberland	F319EJO	Oxford
EFU935Y	East Midland	EYE244V	Stagecoach South	F149XCS	Western	F320EJO	Oxford
EJR104W	Busways	EYE246V	Western	F152HAT	Transit	F321EJO	Oxford
EJR105W	Busways	EYE248V	Western	F153HAT	Transit	F322EJO	Oxford
EJR106W	Midland Red	EYE250V	Stagecoach South	F154HAT	Transit	F323EJO	Oxford
EJR107W	Busways	F32CWY	East London	F155HAT	Transit	F324EJO	Oxford
EJR108W	Busways	F41XCS	Western	F156FWY	East London	F334JHS	Western
EJR109W	Busways	F50CWY	East London	F156HAT	Transit	F392DHL	Red & White
EJR110W	Busways	F55RFS	Circle Line	F157HAT	Transit	F394DHL	Selkent
EJR111W	Busways	F56RFS	Circle Line	F160FWY	East London	F402KOD	Oxford
EJR112W	Busways	F57RFS	Circle Line	F164XCS	Bluebird Buses	F403KOD	Oxford
EJR113W	Circle Line	F58RFS	Circle Line	F165FWY	East London	F404KOD	Devon
EJR114W	Busways	F60RFS	Circle Line	F166FWY	East London	F405KOD	Devon
EJR115W	Busways	F65RFS	Western	F167SMT	Cambus	F406KOD	Devon
EJR117W	Busways	F71LAL	Midland Red	F168SMT	Cambus	F407KOD	Devon
EJR118W	Busways	F74DCW	Red & White	F169FWY	Bluebird Buses	F408KOD	Devon
EJR119W	Busways	F75TFU	East Midland	F170FWY	East London	F409KOD	Oxford
EJR122W	Busways	F76TFU	East Midland	F171FWY	East London	F410KOD	Devon
EJR123W	Busways	F77HAU	Bluebird Buses	F171SMT	Cambus	F411KOD	Devon
EJV31Y	East Midland	F77TFU	East Midland	F172FWY	East London	F412KOD	Devon
EJV32Y	East Midland	F78TFU	East Midland	F173FWY	East London	F413KOD	Devon
EJV33Y	East Midland	F85XCS	Western	F174FWY	East London	F424GGB	Bluebird Buses
EJV34Y	East Midland	F101HVK	Busways	F175FWY	East London	F506NJE	Cambus
EKW614V	East Midland	F102HVK	Busways	F176FWY	East London	F507NJE	Cambus
EKW615V	East Midland	F103HVK	Busways	F177FWY	Bluebird Buses	F508NJE	Cambus
EKW616V	East Midland	F103XCW	Ribble	F178FWY	East London	F509NJE	Cambus
EKY21V	East Midland	F104HVK	Busways	F179FWY	East London	F510NJE	Cambus
EKY22V	East Midland	F104XCW	Ribble	F180FWY	East London	F511NJE	Cambus
EKY23V	East Midland	F105HVK	Busways	F197ASD	Western	F512NJE	Cambus
EKY24V	East Midland	F105XCW	Ribble	F201FHH	Cumberland	F513NJE	Cambus
EKY25V	East Midland	F105YWO	Red & White	F202FHH	Cumberland	F514NJE	Cambus
EKY27V	East Midland	F106HVK	Busways	F243OFP	Red & White	F515NJE	Cambus
EKY28V	East Midland	F106XCW	Ribble	F251JRM	Transit	F516NJE	Cambus
EKY29V	East Midland	F106YWO	Red & White	F252JRM	Transit	F517NJE	Cambus
ENJ909V	Stagecoach South	F107HVK	Busways	F253KAO	Transit	F524WSJ	Western
ENJ910V	Stagecoach South	F107NRT	United Counties	F262WSD	Red & White	F601MSL	Stagecoach South
ENJ911V	Stagecoach South	F107XCW	Ribble	F277WAF	Bluebird Buses	F601UVN	Transit
ENJ912V	Stagecoach South	F108HVK	Busways	F282DRJ	Manchester	F602MSL	Stagecoach South
ENJ914V	Stagecoach South	F108XCW	Ribble	F283DRJ	Manchester	F602UVN	Transit
ENJ915V	Stagecoach South	F109HVK	Busways	F285DRJ	Manchester	F603MSL	Stagecoach South
ENJ916V	Stagecoach South	F109XCW	Ribble	F286KGK	Fife Scottish	F603UVN	Transit
ENJ917V	Stagecoach South	F110HVK	Busways	F289DRJ	Manchester	F604MSL	Stagecoach South
ENJ918V	Stagecoach South	F110NES	United Counties	F291DRJ	Manchester	F604UVN	Transit
ERV115W	Stagecoach South	F110XCW	Ribble	F294DRJ	Manchester	F605MSL	Stagecoach South
ERV116W	Stagecoach South	F111HVK	Busways	F295DRJ	Manchester	F605UVN	Transit
ERV117W	Stagecoach South	F111XCW	Ribble	F296DRJ	Manchester	F606MSL	Stagecoach South
ERV118W	Stagecoach South	F112HVK	Busways	F297DRJ	Manchester	F606UVN	Transit
ESU263	Busways	F112XCW	Ribble	F298DRJ	Manchester	F607UVN	Transit

Reg	Operator	Reg	Operator	Reg	Operator	Reg	Operator
F608UVN	Transit	F742FDV	Devon	F920JRG	Busways	G98PCK	Ribble
F609UVN	Transit	F743FDV	Devon	F947NER	Manchester	G101AAD	Cheltenham & Glos
F609XMS	Devon	F744FDV	Devon	F948NER	Manchester	G102AAD	Cheltenham & Glos
F610UVN	Transit	F745FDV	Devon	F958HTO	Devon	G103AAD	Cheltenham & Glos
F614XMS	Devon	F746FDV	Oxford	FAO419V	United Counties	G104AAD	Cheltenham & Glos
F615XMS	Devon	F748FDV	Devon	FAO420V	Cumberland	G105AAD	Cheltenham & Glos
F616XMS	Devon	F750FDV	Devon	FAO421V	Cumberland	G105KUB	East London
F617XMS	Devon	F755FDV	Devon	FAO422V	Cumberland	G106KUB	East London
F619XMS	Devon	F756FDV	Devon	FAO423V	Cumberland	G107KUB	East London
F620MSL	United Counties	F757FDV	Devon	FAO424V	Cumberland	G108CEH	Busways
F620XMS	Devon	F758FDV	Devon	FAO425V	Cumberland	G113SKX	Busways
F621MSL	United Counties	F759FDV	Devon	FAO426V	Cumberland	G115OGA	Midland Red
F621XMS	Transit	F760FDV	Devon	FAO427V	Cumberland	G119KUB	East London
F622MSL	United Counties	F761EKM	Stagecoach South	FAO428V	Cumberland	G178PAO	Cumberland
F623MSL	United Counties	F762EKM	Stagecoach South	FAO429V	Bluebird Buses	G179PAO	Ribble
F624MSL	United Counties	F762FDV	Devon	FBR53D	Busways	G180JHG	Cumberland
F624XMS	Transit	F763EKM	Stagecoach South	FDV784V	Ribble	G180PAO	Ribble
F625MSL	United Counties	F763FDV	Devon	FDV799V	Cumberland	G181JHG	Cumberland
F625XMS	Transit	F764EKM	Stagecoach South	FDV810V	Bluebird Buses	G181PAO	Ribble
F626MSL	United Counties	F764FDV	Oxford	FDV812V	United Counties	G182JHG	Cumberland
F627MSL	United Counties	F765EKM	Stagecoach South	FDV813V	Ribble	G182PAO	Ribble
F628MSL	United Counties	F765FDV	Oxford	FDV816V	Bluebird Buses	G183JHG	Cumberland
F629MSL	United Counties	F766EKM	Stagecoach South	FDV817V	Ribble	G183PAO	Ribble
F629XMS	Transit	F766FDV	Oxford	FDV818V	Stagecoach South	G184JHG	Cumberland
F630MSL	United Counties	F767EKM	Stagecoach South	FDV819V	Bluebird Buses	G184PAO	Ribble
F630XMS	Devon	F767FDV	Oxford	FDV829V	Stagecoach South	G185JHG	Cumberland
F631MSL	United Counties	F768FDV	Oxford	FDV830V	Stagecoach South	G185PAO	Ribble
F631XMS	Devon	F769FDV	Oxford	FDV831V	Stagecoach South	G186JHG	Cumberland
F632MSL	United Counties	F770FDV	Oxford	FDV832V	United Counties	G186PAO	Ribble
F633MSL	United Counties	F771EKM	Stagecoach South	FDV833V	Ribble	G187JHG	Ribble
F634MSP	United Counties	F772EKM	Stagecoach South	FDV835V	United Counties	G187PAO	Ribble
F635YRP	United Counties	F772FDV	Devon	FDV839V	Stagecoach South	G188JHG	Ribble
F636YRP	United Counties	F773EKM	Stagecoach South	FDV840V	Bluebird Buses	G188PAO	Ribble
F637YRP	United Counties	F774EKM	Stagecoach South	FES831W	Bluebird Buses	G189JHG	Cumberland
F638YRP	United Counties	F775EKM	Stagecoach South	FPR62V	Stagecoach South	G189PAO	Ribble
F641XMS	Devon	F776FDV	Oxford	FRP912T	United Counties	G190PAO	Ribble
F651RBP	Stagecoach South	F781KKP	Stagecoach South	FSD687V	Western	G191PAO	Ribble
F660PWK	Midland Red	F782KKP	Stagecoach South	FSL61W	Transit	G192PAO	Cumberland
F661PWK	Midland Red	F803FAO	Cumberland	FSL62W	Transit	G193PAO	Bluebird Buses
F677PDF	Cheltenham & Glos	F804FAO	Cumberland	FSU737	Western	G194PAO	Bluebird Buses
F701BAT	Transit	F805FAO	Cumberland	FSU739	Western	G195PAO	Bluebird Buses
F702BAT	Transit	F806FAO	Cumberland	FUH33V	Ribble	G196PAO	Bluebird Buses
F703BAT	Transit	F807FAO	Cumberland	FVR294V	Ribble	G197PAO	Bluebird Buses
F704BAT	Transit	F808FAO	Cumberland	FWH461Y	Manchester	G198PAO	Bluebird Buses
F705BAT	Transit	F809FAO	Cumberland	FWH462Y	Manchester	G199PAO	Bluebird Buses
F706CAG	Transit	F810FAO	Cumberland	FYX824W	Midland Red	G200PAO	Bluebird Buses
F714FDV	Devon	F811FAO	Cumberland	G26XBK	Circle Line	G201PAO	Bluebird Buses
F715FDV	Devon	F862FWB	Bluebird Buses	G28TGW	Devon	G202PAO	Bluebird Buses
F716FDV	Devon	F871UAC	Circle Line	G30TGW	Devon	G203PAO	Bluebird Buses
F717FDV	Devon	F901JRG	Busways	G31TGW	Selkent	G210SSL	Stagecoach South
F718FDV	Devon	F902JRG	Busways	G32TGW	Selkent	G211SSL	Stagecoach South
F719FDV	Devon	F903JRG	Busways	G34TGW	Devon	G212SSL	Stagecoach South
F720FDV	Devon	F904JRG	Busways	G35TGW	Devon	G213SSL	Stagecoach South
F722FDV	Devon	F905JRG	Busways	G36TGW	Devon	G214SSL	Stagecoach South
F723FDV	Devon	F906JRG	Busways	G37TGW	Devon	G251TSL	Western
F724FDV	Oxford	F907JRG	Busways	G38TGW	Selkent	G252TSL	Western
F726FDV	Devon	F908JRG	Busways	G39TGW	Selkent	G253TSL	Western
F728FDV	Devon	F909JRG	Busways	G40TGW	Red & White	G254TSL	Western
F729FDV	Devon	F910JRG	Busways	G67PFR	Ribble	G255TSL	Western
F730FDV	Devon	F911JRG	Busways	G68PFR	Ribble	G256TSL	Bluebird Buses
F731FDV	Devon	F912JRG	Busways	G71APO	Stagecoach South	G257TSL	Bluebird Buses
F732FDV	Devon	F912YWY	East London	G72APO	Western	G258TSL	Bluebird Buses
F733FDV	Devon	F913JRG	Busways	G73APO	Stagecoach South	G259TSL	Bluebird Buses
F734FDV	Oxford	F913YWY	East London	G79VFW	East Midland	G260TSL	Bluebird Buses
F735FDV	Devon	F914JRG	Busways	G80VFW	East Midland	G261TSL	Bluebird Buses
F736FDV	Devon	F915JRG	Busways	G81VFW	East Midland	G262TSL	Bluebird Buses
F737FDV	Devon	F916JRG	Busways	G86KUB	Bluebird Buses	G263TSL	Cumberland
F738FDV	Devon	F917JRG	Busways	G91KUB	East London	G264TSL	Cumberland
F740FDV	Devon	F918JRG	Busways	G96MRN	Ribble	G265TSL	Cumberland
F741FDV	Devon	F919JRG	Busways	G97MRN	Ribble	G266TSL	Cumberland

Leyland Lynx now operate from eight of the British Stagecoach fleets though only small numbers are based at East Midland, Midland Red and Western Buses; the latter gained the type from AA Buses. Pictured in Leamington, with G & G Travel lettering, is Midland Red F660PWK, one of only two in that fleet.

G267TSL	Cumberland	G301WHP	Midland Red	G611CEF	Transit	G706TCD	Stagecoach South
G268TSL	Cumberland	G302WHP	Midland Red	G612CEF	Transit	G707TCD	Stagecoach South
G269TSL	Cumberland	G303WHP	Midland Red	G613CEF	Transit	G708TCD	Stagecoach South
G270TSL	Bluebird Buses	G337KKW	Fife Scottish	G614CEF	Transit	G709TCD	Stagecoach South
G271TSL	Bluebird Buses	G338KKW	Fife Scottish	G615CEF	Transit	G710TCD	Stagecoach South
G272TSL	Bluebird Buses	G339KKW	East Midland	G616CEF	Transit	G767CDU	Ribble
G273TSL	Bluebird Buses	G340KKW	East Midland	G617CEF	Transit	G801JRH	Transit
G274TSL	Bluebird Buses	G341KKW	East Midland	G618CEF	Transit	G802JRH	Transit
G275TSL	Bluebird Buses	G342KKW	East Midland	G619CEF	Transit	G803JRH	Transit
G276TSL	Bluebird Buses	G343KKW	East Midland	G620CEF	Transit	G804JRH	Transit
G277TSL	Bluebird Buses	G461SGB	Western	G639EVV	United Counties	G805JRH	Transit
G278TSL	Bluebird Buses	G505XLO	Red & White	G640EVV	United Counties	G806JRH	Transit
G279TSL	Bluebird Buses	G520LWU	Cumberland	G641EVV	United Counties	G807LAG	Transit
G280TSL	Fife Scottish	G530LWU	Western	G642EVV	United Counties	G807RTS	Stagecoach South
G281TSL	Fife Scottish	G531LWU	Western	G643EVV	United Counties	G808LAG	Transit
G282TSL	Bluebird Buses	G532LWU	Western	G644EVV	United Counties	G808RTS	Stagecoach South
G283TSL	Bluebird Buses	G535LWU	Western	G645EVV	United Counties	G809RTS	Stagecoach South
G284TSL	Bluebird Buses	G546LWU	Cheltenham & Glos	G646DBG	Stagecoach South	G820KWF	East Midland
G285TSL	Bluebird Buses	G547LWU	Circle Line	G646EVV	United Counties	G821KWF	East Midland
G286TSL	Bluebird Buses	G565PHH	Cumberland	G647EVV	United Counties	G822KWF	East Midland
G287TSL	Bluebird Buses	G566PHH	Cumberland	G648EVV	United Counties	G823KWF	East Midland
G288TSL	Bluebird Buses	G567PHH	Cumberland	G649EVV	United Counties	G824KWF	East Midland
G289TSL	Bluebird Buses	G568PRM	Ribble	G679AAD	Cheltenham & Glos	G825KWF	East Midland
G290TSL	Bluebird Buses	G569PRM	Ribble	G680AAD	Cheltenham & Glos	G825VGA	Western
G291TSL	Bluebird Buses	G570PRM	Ribble	G681AAD	Cheltenham & Glos	G826KWF	East Midland
G292TSL	Bluebird Buses	G571PRM	Ribble	G682AAD	Cheltenham & Glos	G827KWF	East Midland
G293TSL	Cumberland	G572PRM	Ribble	G683AAD	Cheltenham & Glos	G831UDV	Oxford
G294TSL	Cumberland	G573PRM	Ribble	G684KNW	East London	G832UDV	Oxford
G295TSL	Cumberland	G574FSD	Western	G689KNW	Red & White	G833UDV	Oxford
G296TSL	Cumberland	G574PRM	Ribble	G701TCD	Stagecoach South	G834UDV	Oxford
G297TSL	Cumberland	G575PRM	Ribble	G702TCD	Stagecoach South	G835UDV	Oxford
G298TSL	Cumberland	G576PRM	Ribble	G703TCD	Stagecoach South	G836UDV	Oxford
G299TSL	Cumberland	G577PRM	Ribble	G704TCD	Stagecoach South	G837UDV	Oxford
G300TSL	Cumberland	G578PRM	Ribble	G705TCD	Stagecoach South	G838UDV	Oxford

G839UDV	Oxford	GHV102N	Western	H102HDV	Bluebird Buses	H401MRW	Midland Red
G840UDV	Oxford	GHV948N	Western	H103HDV	Bluebird Buses	H402DEG	East Midland
G841UDV	Oxford	GLJ490N	Manchester	H104HDV	Oxford	H402KPY	Stagecoach South
G842UDV	Oxford	GMB654T	Western	H105HDV	Bluebird Buses	H402MRW	Midland Red
G843UDV	Oxford	GMS285S	Western	H106HDV	Western	H403MRW	Midland Red
G912KWF	Devon	GMS292S	Western	H107HDV	Western	H404MRW	Midland Red
G919KWF	Devon	GNF6V	Cheltenham & Glos	H108HDV	Bluebird Buses	H405MRW	Midland Red
G920KWF	Devon	GNF8V	Cheltenham & Glos	H109HDV	Oxford	H406MRW	Midland Red
G921TCU	Busways	GNF9V	Cheltenham & Glos	H110HDV	Bluebird Buses	H407GAV	Cambus
G922TCU	Busways	GNF10V	Cheltenham & Glos	H112SAO	Cumberland	H421BNL	Busways
G923TCU	Busways	GNF11V	Cheltenham & Glos	H113ABV	Ribble	H422BNL	Busways
G924KWF	Devon	GOL426N	Midland Red	H113SAO	Cumberland	H423BNL	Busways
G924TCU	Busways	GPJ894N	Stagecoach South	H114ABV	Ribble	H424BNL	Busways
G925TCU	Busways	GRM625V	Cumberland	H114SAO	Cumberland	H425BNL	Busways
G926TCU	Busways	GRS343E	Bluebird Buses	H115ABV	Ribble	H426BNL	Busways
G947TDV	Oxford	GSO1V	Bluebird Buses	H115SAO	Cumberland	H427BNL	Busways
G948TDV	Oxford	GSO2V	United Counties	H116SAO	Cumberland	H428BNL	Busways
G949TDV	Oxford	GSO6V	United Counties	H117SAO	Cumberland	H428EFT	Busways
G950TDV	Oxford	GSO7V	United Counties	H118SAO	Cumberland	H429BNL	Busways
G951TDV	Oxford	GSO8V	East Midland	H119SAO	Cumberland	H429EFT	Busways
G952TDV	Oxford	GSO77V	Western	H126ACU	Busways	H430BNL	Busways
G954TDV	Oxford	GSO82V	Western	H127ACU	Busways	H430EFT	Busways
G974ARV	Stagecoach South	GSO83V	Western	H131GVM	Manchester	H431EFT	Busways
G975ARV	Stagecoach South	GSO84V	Western	H132GVM	Manchester	H432EFT	Busways
G976ARV	Western	GSO89V	Bluebird Buses	H133GVM	Manchester	H433EFT	Busways
G977ARV	Stagecoach South	GSO90V	Bluebird Buses	H134GVM	Manchester	H434EFT	Busways
G978ARV	Stagecoach South	GSO91V	Bluebird Buses	H135GVM	Manchester	H435EFT	Busways
GAJ129V	Transit	GSO92V	Bluebird Buses	H136GVM	Manchester	H436EFT	Busways
GAJ130V	Transit	GSO93V	Bluebird Buses	H137GVM	Manchester	H437EFT	Busways
GAJ131V	Transit	GSO94V	Bluebird Buses	H138GVM	Manchester	H455WGG	Western
GAJ132V	Transit	GSO95V	Bluebird Buses	H139GVM	Manchester	H463GVM	Manchester
GAJ133V	Transit	GSU341	Fife Scottish	H140GVM	Manchester	H464GVM	Manchester
GAJ134V	Transit	GSU342	Fife Scottish	H142UUA	Selkent	H465GVM	Manchester
GAJ135V	Transit	GSU343	Fife Scottish	H143UUA	Selkent	H466GVM	Manchester
GAJ136V	Transit	GSU344	Fife Scottish	H144UUA	East London	H466WGG	Western
GAZ4381	Cambus	GSU859T	Manchester	H145UUA	Selkent	H467GVM	Manchester
GAZ4382	Cambus	GTX738W	Red & White	H147UUA	Selkent	H473CEG	Cambus
GBU17V	Manchester	GTX743W	Red & White	H148UUA	East London	H474CEG	Cambus
GBU20V	Manchester	GTX748W	Red & White	H149UUA	Selkent	H475CEG	Cambus
GBU22V	Manchester	GTX750W	Red & White	H150UUA	East London	H482BEE	East Midland
GBU24V	Manchester	GTX753W	Red & White	H151UUA	Selkent	H483BEE	East Midland
GBU27V	Manchester	GTX754W	Midland Red	H152UUA	Selkent	H484BEE	East Midland
GBU28V	Manchester	GWE617V	East Midland	H153UUA	Selkent	H485BEE	East Midland
GBU29V	Manchester	GWE618V	East Midland	H154UUA	Selkent	H509AGC	Fife Scottish
GBV101N	Ribble	GWE619V	East Midland	H159EJU	Red & White	H556TUG	Red & White
GBV110N	Ribble	GYE252W	Western	H160WWT	East London	H564WWR	Selkent
GCS33V	Western	GYE254W	Western	H162WWT	East London	H617ACK	Ribble
GCS37V	Western	GYE260W	Selkent	H169WWT	Selkent	H618ACK	Ribble
GCS38V	Western	GYE261W	East London	H170WWT	East London	H619ACK	Ribble
GCS41V	Western	GYE262W	Selkent	H171WWT	East London	H620ACK	Ribble
GCS45V	Western	GYE263W	Selkent	H174WWT	East London	H621ACK	Ribble
GCS47V	Western	GYE264W	East London	H176WWT	East London	H622ACK	Ribble
GCS48V	Western	GYE266W	East London	H180GTA	Western	H623ACK	Ribble
GCS49V	Western	GYE267W	Selkent	H181GTA	Bluebird Buses	H639UWR	Oxford
GCS51V	Western	GYE268W	East London	H191WFR	Cumberland	H640UWR	Oxford
GCS53V	Western	GYE272W	East London	H192WFR	Cumberland	H641UWR	Oxford
GCS57V	Western	GYE273W	Western	H193WFR	Ribble	H642UWR	Cambus
GCS58V	Western	GYE281W	Western	H194WFR	Cumberland	H643UWR	Cambus
GCS60V	Western	GYJ919V	Stagecoach South	H195WFR	Ribble	H649UWR	Cambus
GCS61V	Western	GYJ920V	Stagecoach South	H196WFR	Ribble	H650UWR	Oxford
GCS62V	Western	GYJ921V	Stagecoach South	H197WFR	Ribble	H652UWR	Cambus
GCS65V	Western	GYJ922V	Stagecoach South	H257THL	East Midland	H653UWR	Cambus
GCS69V	Western	H36YCW	Ribble	H301PAX	Red & White	H654UWR	East London
GFN546N	Stagecoach South	H37YCW	Ribble	H344SWA	East Midland	H654VVV	United Counties
GFR101W	Ribble	H38YCW	Ribble	H345SWA	East Midland	H655UWR	East London
GGM71W	Red & White	H39YCW	Ribble	H346SWA	East Midland	H657UWR	East London
GGM80W	Stagecoach South	H71XKH	Transit	H347SWA	East Midland	H667BNL	Busways
GGM81W	Stagecoach South	H78CFV	Ribble	H348SWA	East Midland	H668BNL	Busways
GHB146N	Red & White	H79CFV	Ribble	H370PNY	Devon	H669BNL	Busways
GHB148N	Red & White	H101HDV	Bluebird Buses	H401DMJ	Transit	H670BNL	Busways

Ten Leyland Swift buses are included in the British operation fleets, three with Red & White and seven with Ribble. One of the latter, 297, H37YCW is seen on Hyndburn Circular service 6 at Accrington bus station. As we go to press we learn that the type is to be used at Ribble's Bolton depot, displacing minibuses. *Nick Coleman*

H671BNL	Busways	H814WKH	Transit	HDZ2609	Transit	HTY139W	Midland Red
H672BNL	Busways	H815CBP	Stagecoach South	HDZ2610	Transit	HUD475S	Midland Red
H673BNL	Busways	H815WKH	Transit	HDZ2611	Transit	HUD479S	Midland Red
H674BNL	Busways	H816CBP	Stagecoach South	HDZ2612	Transit	HUD480S	Midland Red
H675BNL	Busways	H816WKH	Transit	HDZ2613	Transit	HUF451X	Stagecoach South
H676BNL	Busways	H817CBP	Stagecoach South	HDZ2614	Circle Line	HUF579X	Stagecoach South
H679BTP	Stagecoach South	H818CBP	Stagecoach South	HDZ2615	Transit	HUF592X	Stagecoach South
H680BTP	Stagecoach South	H819CBP	Stagecoach South	HDZ2616	Transit	HUF593X	Stagecoach South
H721CNC	Manchester	H882LOX	Fife Scottish	HDZ8683	Transit	HUF603X	Stagecoach South
H724CNC	Manchester	H883LOX	Fife Scottish	HEU122N	Circle Line	HUF604X	Stagecoach South
H726CNC	Manchester	H885LOX	Fife Scottish	HFG923V	Stagecoach South	HUF625X	Stagecoach South
H727FNC	Manchester	H889NFS	Devon	HFM561D	Bluebird Buses	HUF626X	Stagecoach South
H728FNC	Manchester	H912XGA	Midland Red	HGM335E	Bluebird Buses	HUF639X	Stagecoach South
H784GTA	Bluebird Buses	H985FTT	Bluebird Buses	HHH370V	Ribble	HVS937	United Counties
H785GTA	Bluebird Buses	H986FTT	Western	HHH372V	Western	HWG207W	Bluebird Buses
H786GTA	Bluebird Buses	H987FTT	Western	HHH373V	Cumberland	HWJ620W	East Midland
H789GTA	Western	H988FTT	Oxford	HIL6075	Cheltenham & Glos	HWJ621W	East Midland
H790GTA	Oxford	H989FTT	Bluebird Buses	HIL8410	Red & White	IIL1321	Transit
H801BKK	Stagecoach South	HAH237V	Circle Line	HJT45N	Red & White	IIL3503	Stagecoach South
H802BKK	Stagecoach South	HBD914T	United Counties	HKE690L	Stagecoach South	IIL3504	Fife Scottish
H803BKK	Stagecoach South	HBD915T	United Counties	HNE252V	Bluebird Buses	IIL3505	Stagecoach South
H804BKK	Stagecoach South	HBD916T	United Counties	HNE253V	Cumberland	IIL3506	Fife Scottish
H805BKK	Stagecoach South	HBD917T	Cheltenham & Glos	HNE254V	Bluebird Buses	IIL3507	Western
H806BKK	Stagecoach South	HDS566H	Western	HPK503N	Stagecoach South	J24MCW	Ribble
H807BKK	Stagecoach South	HDV639E	Bluebird Buses	HPK505N	Stagecoach South	J25MCW	Ribble
H808BKK	Stagecoach South	HDZ2601	Transit	HPY423V	Transit	J41GGB	Red & White
H809BKK	Stagecoach South	HDZ2602	Circle Line	HSB698Y	Western	J42GGB	Red & White
H809WKH	Transit	HDZ2603	Transit	HSK760	Bluebird Buses	J91DJV	East Midland
H810BKK	Stagecoach South	HDZ2604	Transit	HSR136W	Bluebird Buses	J92DJV	East Midland
H810WKH	Transit	HDZ2605	Transit	HSV194	East Midland	J93DJV	East Midland
H811WKH	Transit	HDZ2606	Transit	HSV195	East Midland	J94DJV	East Midland
H812WKH	Transit	HDZ2607	Transit	HSV196	East Midland	J101WSC	Ribble
H813WKH	Transit	HDZ2608	Circle Line	HTG354N	Red & White	J102WSC	Ribble

Reg	Operator	Reg	Operator	Reg	Operator	Reg	Operator
J103WSC	Ribble	J228JJR	Transit	J501GCD	Stagecoach South	J702CWT	Midland Red
J104WSC	Ribble	J230XKY	East London	J502FPS	Bluebird Buses	J702KCU	Busways
J105WSC	Ribble	J231JJR	Transit	J502GCD	Stagecoach South	J702YRM	Stagecoach South
J106WSC	Ribble	J231XKY	East London	J503FPS	Bluebird Buses	J703YRM	Stagecoach South
J107WSC	Ribble	J263KRN	Ribble	J503GCD	Stagecoach South	J711CYG	East London
J108WSC	Ribble	J264KRN	Ribble	J504FPS	Bluebird Buses	J712CYG	East London
J109WSC	Ribble	J277OSJ	Western	J504GCD	Stagecoach South	J714CYG	East London
J110WSC	Ribble	J301BRM	Western	J505FPS	Bluebird Buses	J716CYG	East London
J112WSC	Ribble	J302BRM	Western	J505GCD	Stagecoach South	J717CYG	East London
J113WSC	Ribble	J302TUH	Red & White	J506FPS	Bluebird Buses	J718CYG	East London
J114WSC	Ribble	J303BRM	Western	J506GCD	Stagecoach South	J719CYG	East London
J115WSC	Ribble	J303TUH	Red & White	J507FPS	Bluebird Buses	J720CYG	East London
J116WSC	Ribble	J304BRM	Western	J507GCD	Stagecoach South	J720GAP	Stagecoach South
J120AAO	Cumberland	J304THP	Midland Red	J508FPS	Bluebird Buses	J721CYG	East London
J120AHH	Cumberland	J304UKG	Red & White	J508GCD	Stagecoach South	J721GAP	Stagecoach South
J120XHH	Bluebird Buses	J305BRM	Western	J509FPS	Bluebird Buses	J722CYG	East London
J121AAO	Cumberland	J305THP	Midland Red	J509GCD	Stagecoach South	J722GAP	Stagecoach South
J121AHH	Cumberland	J305UKG	Red & White	J510FPS	Bluebird Buses	J723CYG	East London
J121XHH	Bluebird Buses	J306BRM	Western	J510GCD	Stagecoach South	J724CYG	East London
J122AAO	Cumberland	J306UKG	Red & White	J511FPS	Bluebird Buses	J725CYG	East London
J122AHH	Ribble	J307BRM	Western	J511GCD	Stagecoach South	J726CYG	East London
J122XHH	Bluebird Buses	J307UKG	Red & White	J512FPS	Bluebird Buses	J727CYG	East London
J123AHH	Ribble	J308BRM	Western	J512GCD	Stagecoach South	J728CYG	East London
J123XHH	Cumberland	J309BRM	Western	J513GCD	Stagecoach South	J729CYG	East London
J124AHH	Ribble	J310BRM	Western	J514GCD	Stagecoach South	J739CWT	Cambus
J124XHH	Cumberland	J349XET	East Midland	J515GCD	Stagecoach South	J740CWT	Cambus
J125XHH	Cumberland	J350XET	East Midland	J516GCD	Stagecoach South	J741CWT	Cambus
J126XHH	Cumberland	J351XET	East Midland	J517GCD	Stagecoach South	J742CWT	Cambus
J127XHH	Cumberland	J352XET	East Midland	J518GCD	Stagecoach South	J743CWT	Cambus
J132HMT	East London	J353XET	East Midland	J519GCD	Stagecoach South	J744CWT	Cambus
J133HMT	East London	J371BNW	Busways	J520GCD	Stagecoach South	J752CWT	United Counties
J134HMT	East London	J372BNW	Busways	J521GCD	Stagecoach South	J753CWT	United Counties
J135HMT	East London	J373BNW	Busways	J522GCD	Stagecoach South	J797MHF	Red & White
J136HMT	East London	J374BNW	Busways	J523GCD	Stagecoach South	J801WFS	Fife Scottish
J137HMT	East London	J375BNW	Busways	J524GCD	Stagecoach South	J802WFS	Fife Scottish
J138HMT	East London	J376BNW	Busways	J525GCD	Stagecoach South	J803WFS	Fife Scottish
J139HMT	East London	J377BNW	Busways	J526GCD	Stagecoach South	J804WFS	Fife Scottish
J140HMT	East London	J378BNW	Busways	J527GCD	Stagecoach South	J805DWW	Cambus
J141HMT	East London	J379BNW	Busways	J528GCD	Stagecoach South	J805WFS	Fife Scottish
J142HMT	East London	J380BNW	Busways	J529GCD	Stagecoach South	J806DWW	Cambus
J143HMT	East London	J401LKO	Stagecoach South	J530GCD	Stagecoach South	J806WFS	Fife Scottish
J144HMT	East London	J402LKO	Stagecoach South	J531GCD	Stagecoach South	J807DWW	Cambus
J145HMT	East London	J403LKO	Stagecoach South	J532GCD	Stagecoach South	J807WFS	Fife Scottish
J176MCW	Ribble	J407PRW	Midland Red	J533GCD	Stagecoach South	J808WFS	United Counties
J177MCW	Ribble	J408PRW	Midland Red	J534GCD	Stagecoach South	J811NKK	Stagecoach South
J196YSS	Bluebird Buses	J408TEW	Cambus	J535GCD	Stagecoach South	J812NKK	Stagecoach South
J197YSS	Bluebird Buses	J409PRW	Midland Red	J536GCD	Stagecoach South	J813NKK	Stagecoach South
J198HFR	Ribble	J409TEW	Cambus	J537GCD	Stagecoach South	J814NKK	Stagecoach South
J198YSS	Bluebird Buses	J410PRW	Midland Red	J538GCD	Stagecoach South	J822HMC	East London
J199HFR	Cumberland	J411PRW	Midland Red	J539GCD	Stagecoach South	J823HMC	East London
J199YSS	Bluebird Buses	J411WSC	Ribble	J540GCD	Stagecoach South	J824HMC	East London
J201HFR	Cumberland	J412PRW	Midland Red	J541GCD	Stagecoach South	J825HMC	East London
J202HFR	Cumberland	J413PRW	Cheltenham & Glos	J542GCD	Stagecoach South	J826HMC	East London
J203HFR	Cumberland	J413PRW	Midland Red	J543GCD	Stagecoach South	J827HMC	East London
J204HFR	Cumberland	J414PRW	Midland Red	J544GCD	Stagecoach South	J828HMC	East London
J205HFR	Cumberland	J415PRW	Midland Red	J545GCD	Stagecoach South	J829HMC	East London
J206HFR	Cumberland	J416PRW	Midland Red	J546GCD	Stagecoach South	J856NKK	Stagecoach South
J207HFR	Cumberland	J417PRW	Midland Red	J547GCD	Stagecoach South	J901UKV	Transit
J208HFR	Cumberland	J418PRW	Midland Red	J548GCD	Stagecoach South	J909NKP	Stagecoach South
J209HFR	Cumberland	J420HDS	Oxford	J549GCD	Stagecoach South	J917LEM	Western
J210HFR	Cumberland	J424HDS	Oxford	J550GCD	Stagecoach South	J919LEM	Western
J213AET	East Midland	J430HDS	United Counties	J551GCD	Stagecoach South	J960DWX	Cambus
J214AET	East Midland	J439HDS	United Counties	J552GCD	Stagecoach South	J961DWX	Cambus
J215AET	East Midland	J445HDS	United Counties	J620GCR	United Counties	J962DWX	Cambus
J216AET	East Midland	J446HDS	United Counties	J621GCR	United Counties	JAH552D	Cambus
J216XKY	Western	J450HDS	United Counties	J622GCR	United Counties	JAJ137W	Transit
J217AET	East Midland	J454JRH	Red & White	J623GCR	Stagecoach South	JAJ138W	Transit
J217XKY	Western	J456FSR	Oxford	J624GCR	Stagecoach South	JAJ139W	Transit
J218AET	East Midland	J460YDT	Western	J701KCU	Busways	JAJ140W	Transit
J219AET	East Midland	J501FPS	Bluebird Buses	J701YRM	Stagecoach South	JAJ141W	Transit

260

Reg	Operator	Reg	Operator	Reg	Operator	Reg	Operator
JAJ142W	Transit	JOX504P	Midland Red	K128DAO	Cumberland	K354ANV	United Counties
JAJ143W	Transit	JPU817	Cumberland	K128SRH	East London	K354DWJ	East Midland
JAJ144W	Transit	JSA101V	Bluebird Buses	K129DAO	Cumberland	K355ANV	United Counties
JAJ145W	Transit	JSA102V	Bluebird Buses	K129SRH	East London	K355DWJ	East Midland
JAJ146W	Transit	JSA103V	Bluebird Buses	K130DAO	Cumberland	K356ANV	United Counties
JAK209W	Bluebird Buses	JSA104V	Bluebird Buses	K130SRH	East London	K356DWJ	East Midland
JAK210W	Bluebird Buses	JSD595W	Western	K131DAO	Cumberland	K357ANV	United Counties
JAK211W	East Midland	JTF971W	Western	K131SRH	East London	K357DWJ	East Midland
JAK212W	Bluebird Buses	JUB650V	Devon	K132DAO	Cumberland	K358ANV	United Counties
JCK848W	Ribble	JWV253W	Stagecoach South	K132SRH	East London	K358DWJ	East Midland
JCK849W	Stagecoach South	JWV255W	Stagecoach South	K133DAO	Cumberland	K359ANV	United Counties
JDZ2359	Selkent	JWV268W	Stagecoach South	K133SRH	East London	K359DWJ	East Midland
JDZ2360	Selkent	JWV269W	Stagecoach South	K134DAO	Cumberland	K360DWJ	East Midland
JDZ2361	Selkent	JWV274W	Stagecoach South	K134SRH	East London	K361DWJ	East Midland
JDZ2362	Selkent	JWV976W	Stagecoach South	K135DAO	Cumberland	K362DWJ	East Midland
JDZ2363	Selkent	K26WBV	Ribble	K135SRH	East London	K363DWJ	East Midland
JDZ2364	Selkent	K27WBV	Ribble	K150DNV	United Counties	K390KUA	Cambus
JDZ2365	Selkent	K75XCW	Ribble	K151DNV	United Counties	K391KUA	Cambus
JDZ2371	Selkent	K91BNY	Red & White	K152DNV	United Counties	K392KUA	Cambus
JFR2W	Cumberland	K92BNY	Red & White	K153DNV	United Counties	K393KUA	Cambus
JFR3W	Ribble	K93BNY	Red & White	K154DNV	United Counties	K402EDT	Red & White
JFR4W	Ribble	K94AAX	Red & White	K162FYG	Busways	K420ARW	Midland Red
JFR5W	Ribble	K95AAX	Red & White	K163FYG	Busways	K421ARW	Midland Red
JFR6W	Ribble	K96AAX	Red & White	K164FYG	Busways	K422ARW	Midland Red
JFR7W	Ribble	K97XNY	Red & White	K165FYG	Busways	K423ARW	Midland Red
JFR8W	Ribble	K98XNY	Red & White	K166FYG	Busways	K424ARW	Midland Red
JFR9W	Ribble	K101JWJ	East Midland	K171CAV	Cambus	K425ARW	Midland Red
JFR10W	Ribble	K101XHG	Bluebird Buses	K172CAV	Cambus	K449YCW	Cumberland
JFR11W	Ribble	K102JWJ	East Midland	K173CAV	Cambus	K450YCW	Cumberland
JFR12W	Ribble	K102XHG	Bluebird Buses	K174CAV	Cambus	K485FFS	Fife Scottish
JFR13W	Ribble	K103JWJ	East Midland	K175CAV	Cambus	K486FFS	Fife Scottish
JHU899X	Cheltenham & Glos	K103XHG	Bluebird Buses	K176CAV	Cambus	K487FFS	Fife Scottish
JHU912X	Cheltenham & Glos	K104JWJ	East Midland	K177CAV	Cambus	K488FFS	Fife Scottish
JIL5279	Manchester	K104XHG	Bluebird Buses	K208OHS	Western	K489FFS	Fife Scottish
JIL7606	Manchester	K105JWJ	East Midland	K209OHS	Western	K490FFS	Fife Scottish
JIL7607	Manchester	K105XHG	Bluebird Buses	K211SRH	East London	K491FFS	Fife Scottish
JIL7608	Manchester	K106JWJ	East Midland	K235NHC	Stagecoach South	K492FFS	Fife Scottish
JIL7609	Manchester	K106XHG	Bluebird Buses	K236NHC	Stagecoach South	K493FFS	Fife Scottish
JIL7610	Manchester	K107JWJ	East Midland	K237NHC	Stagecoach South	K494FFS	Fife Scottish
JIL8374	Manchester	K107XHG	Bluebird Buses	K238NHC	Stagecoach South	K508ESS	Bluebird Buses
JJD392D	East London	K108XHG	Bluebird Buses	K239NHC	Stagecoach South	K509ESS	Bluebird Buses
JJD399D	East London	K109SRH	East London	K240NHC	Stagecoach South	K510ESS	Bluebird Buses
JJD402D	East London	K109XHG	Bluebird Buses	K306ARW	Midland Red	K511ESS	Bluebird Buses
JJD415D	East London	K110SRH	Selkent	K308YKG	Cheltenham & Glos	K515ESS	Bluebird Buses
JJD429D	East London	K110XHG	Bluebird Buses	K309YKG	Red & White	K518ESS	Bluebird Buses
JJD435D	East London	K112SRH	Selkent	K310YKG	Red & White	K521EFL	Midland Red
JJD437D	East London	K112XHG	Ribble	K311YKG	Red & White	K522EFL	Midland Red
JJD444D	East London	K113SRH	East London	K312YKG	Red & White	K523EFL	Midland Red
JJD445D	East London	K113XHG	Cumberland	K313YKG	Red & White	K524EFL	Midland Red
JJD450D	East London	K114SRH	East London	K314YKG	Red & White	K525EFL	Midland Red
JJD451D	East London	K114XHG	Cumberland	K315YKG	Red & White	K526EFL	Midland Red
JJD456D	East London	K115SRH	East London	K316YKG	Red & White	K527EFL	Midland Red
JJD462D	East London	K115XHG	Ribble	K317YKG	Red & White	K528EFL	Midland Red
JJD470D	East London	K116SRH	East London	K318YKG	Red & White	K529EFL	Midland Red
JJD481D	East London	K116XHG	Ribble	K319YKG	Red & White	K530EFL	Midland Red
JJD488D	East London	K117SRH	Selkent	K320FYG	Red & White	K553NHC	Stagecoach South
JJD493D	East London	K117XHG	Cumberland	K320YKG	Red & White	K554NHC	Stagecoach South
JJD495D	East London	K118SRH	Selkent	K321YKG	Red & White	K556NHC	Stagecoach South
JJD496D	East London	K118XHG	Ribble	K322YKG	Red & White	K557NHC	Stagecoach South
JJD497D	East London	K119SRH	East London	K323YKG	Red & White	K558NHC	Stagecoach South
JJD541D	East London	K120SRH	Selkent	K324YKG	Red & White	K559NHC	Stagecoach South
JJD550D	East London	K120XHG	Ribble	K325YKG	Red & White	K561GSA	Bluebird Buses
JJD565D	East London	K121SRH	East London	K342PJR	Transit	K561NHC	Stagecoach South
JJD581D	East London	K121XHG	Cumberland	K343PJR	Transit	K562GSA	Bluebird Buses
JJD592D	East London	K122SRH	East London	K344PJR	Transit	K562NHC	Stagecoach South
JJG898P	Stagecoach South	K123SRH	Selkent	K345PJR	Transit	K563GSA	Bluebird Buses
JND260V	Bluebird Buses	K124SRH	East London	K350ANV	United Counties	K563NHC	Stagecoach South
JNJ194V	Stagecoach South	K125SRH	East London	K351ANV	United Counties	K564GSA	Bluebird Buses
JOU160P	Cheltenham & Glos	K126SRH	East London	K352ANV	United Counties	K564NHC	Stagecoach South
JOX503P	Midland Red	K127SRH	Selkent	K353ANV	United Counties	K565GSA	Bluebird Buses

K565NHC	Stagecoach South	K627YVN	Transit	K715PCN	Busways	K752DAO	Cumberland
K566GSA	Bluebird Buses	K628UFR	Ribble	K716ASC	Stagecoach South	K753DAO	Cumberland
K566NHC	Stagecoach South	K628YVN	Transit	K716DAO	Cumberland	K754DAO	Cumberland
K567GSA	Bluebird Buses	K629YVN	Transit	K717ASC	Stagecoach South	K755DAO	Cumberland
K567NHC	Stagecoach South	K630HWX	East London	K717DAO	Cumberland	K756DAO	Cumberland
K568GSA	Bluebird Buses	K630YVN	Transit	K717PCN	Busways	K757DAO	Cumberland
K568NHC	Stagecoach South	K631HWX	East London	K717UTT	Devon	K758DAO	Cumberland
K569GSA	Bluebird Buses	K632HWX	East London	K718ASC	Fife Scottish	K758FYG	United Counties
K569NHC	Stagecoach South	K633HWX	East London	K718DAO	Cumberland	K759DAO	Cumberland
K570GSA	Bluebird Buses	K634HWX	East London	K718PCN	Busways	K759FYG	United Counties
K570NHC	Stagecoach South	K635HWX	East London	K718UTT	Devon	K760DAO	Cumberland
K571DFS	Transit	K655NHC	Stagecoach South	K719ASC	Fife Scottish	K760FYG	United Counties
K571LTS	Bluebird Buses	K655UNH	United Counties	K719DAO	Cumberland	K761DAO	Cumberland
K571NHC	Stagecoach South	K656UNH	United Counties	K719UTT	Devon	K761FYG	United Counties
K572DFS	Transit	K657UNH	United Counties	K720ASC	Fife Scottish	K762DAO	Cumberland
K572LTS	Bluebird Buses	K658UNH	United Counties	K720DAO	Cumberland	K763DAO	Cumberland
K572NHC	Stagecoach South	K659UNH	United Counties	K720PCN	Busways	K764DAO	Cumberland
K573DFS	Transit	K660NHC	Stagecoach South	K720UTT	Devon	K765DAO	Cumberland
K573LTS	Bluebird Buses	K660UNH	United Counties	K721ASC	Fife Scottish	K766DAO	Cumberland
K573NHC	Stagecoach South	K661UNH	United Counties	K721DAO	Cumberland	K767DAO	Cumberland
K574DFS	Western	K662UNH	United Counties	K721PCN	Busways	K768DAO	Cumberland
K574LTS	Bluebird Buses	K663UNH	United Counties	K721UTT	Devon	K769DAO	Cumberland
K574NHC	Stagecoach South	K664UNH	United Counties	K722ASC	Fife Scottish	K770DAO	Cumberland
K575DFS	East Midland	K665UNH	United Counties	K722DAO	Cumberland	K771DAO	Cumberland
K575LTS	Bluebird Buses	K667UNH	United Counties	K722PCN	Busways	K772DAO	Cumberland
K575NHC	Stagecoach South	K668UNH	United Counties	K722UTT	Devon	K773DAO	Cumberland
K576DFS	Transit	K669UNH	United Counties	K723ASC	Fife Scottish	K774DAO	Cumberland
K576LTS	Bluebird Buses	K670UNH	United Counties	K723DAO	Cumberland	K775DAO	Cumberland
K576NHC	Stagecoach South	K699ERM	Cumberland	K723PNL	Busways	K776DAO	Cumberland
K577DFS	Transit	K700DAO	Cumberland	K724ASC	Fife Scottish	K777DAO	Cumberland
K577LTS	Bluebird Buses	K701DAO	Cumberland	K724DAO	Cumberland	K778DAO	Cumberland
K577NHC	Stagecoach South	K701NDO	East Midland	K724PNL	Busways	K779DAO	Cumberland
K578LTS	Bluebird Buses	K702DAO	Cumberland	K724UTT	Devon	K780DAO	Cumberland
K578NHC	Stagecoach South	K702NDO	East Midland	K725ASC	Fife Scottish	K781DAO	Cumberland
K579NHC	Stagecoach South	K702UTT	Devon	K725DAO	Cumberland	K783DAO	Cumberland
K580NHC	Stagecoach South	K703DAO	Cumberland	K725PNL	Busways	K784DAO	Cumberland
K584ODY	Stagecoach South	K703NDO	East Midland	K725UTT	Devon	K785DAO	Cumberland
K585ODY	Stagecoach South	K703PCN	Busways	K726DAO	Cumberland	K786DAO	Cumberland
K586ODY	Stagecoach South	K704ERM	Cumberland	K726PNL	Busways	K787DAO	Cumberland
K587ODY	Stagecoach South	K704NDO	East Midland	K726UTT	Devon	K788DAO	Cumberland
K588ODY	Stagecoach South	K704PCN	Busways	K727DAO	Cumberland	K789DAO	Stagecoach South
K601ESH	Fife Scottish	K705DAO	Cumberland	K727PNL	Busways	K790DAO	Stagecoach South
K602ESH	Fife Scottish	K705PCN	Busways	K727UTT	Devon	K791DAO	Stagecoach South
K603ESH	Fife Scottish	K706DAO	Cumberland	K728DAO	Cumberland	K801OMW	Circle Line
K604ESH	Fife Scottish	K706PCN	Busways	K728PNL	Busways	K802OMW	Circle Line
K605ESH	Fife Scottish	K707DAO	Cumberland	K729DAO	Cumberland	K803WFJ	Devon
K610UFR	Ribble	K707PCN	Busways	K730DAO	Cumberland	K804WFJ	Devon
K611UFR	Ribble	K708DAO	Cumberland	K730UTT	Devon	K805WFJ	Devon
K612UFR	Ribble	K708PCN	Busways	K731DAO	Cumberland	K806WFJ	Devon
K613UFR	Ribble	K709ASC	United Counties	K731UTT	Devon	K816WFJ	Devon
K614UFR	Ribble	K709DAO	Cumberland	K732DAO	Cumberland	K821TKP	Stagecoach South
K615UFR	Cumberland	K709PCN	Busways	K732UTT	Devon	K821WFJ	Devon
K616UFR	Ribble	K710ASC	United Counties	K733DAO	Cumberland	K822TKP	Stagecoach South
K617UFR	Ribble	K710DAO	Cumberland	K734DAO	Cumberland	K822WFJ	Devon
K618UFR	Ribble	K710PCN	Busways	K735DAO	Cumberland	K823TKP	Stagecoach South
K619UFR	Ribble	K711DAO	Cumberland	K736DAO	Cumberland	K823WFJ	Devon
K620UFR	Ribble	K711PCN	Busways	K737DAO	Cumberland	K824TKP	Stagecoach South
K620XOD	Devon	K711UTT	Devon	K738DAO	Cumberland	K824WFJ	Devon
K621UFR	Ribble	K712DAO	Cumberland	K739DAO	Cumberland	K825TKP	Stagecoach South
K622UFR	Cumberland	K712PCN	Busways	K740DAO	Ribble	K846LMK	East London
K622YVN	Transit	K713ASC	United Counties	K741DAO	Cumberland	K847LMK	East London
K623UFR	Cumberland	K713DAO	Cumberland	K742DAO	Cumberland	K848LMK	East London
K623YVN	Transit	K713PCN	Busways	K743DAO	Cumberland	K849LMK	East London
K624UFR	Ribble	K713UTT	Devon	K744DAO	Cumberland	K850LMK	East London
K624YVN	Transit	K714ASC	Stagecoach South	K745DAO	Cumberland	K851LMK	East London
K625UFR	Cumberland	K714DAO	Cumberland	K746DAO	Cumberland	K852LMK	East London
K625YVN	Transit	K714PCN	Busways	K748DAO	Cumberland	K853LMK	East London
K626UFR	Cumberland	K714UTT	Devon	K749DAO	Cumberland	K853ODY	Stagecoach South
K626YVN	Transit	K715ASC	Stagecoach South	K750DAO	Cumberland	K854LMK	East London
K627UFR	Ribble	K715DAO	Cumberland	K751DAO	Cumberland	K854ODY	Stagecoach South

Reg	Operator	Reg	Operator	Reg	Operator	Reg	Operator
K855LMK	East London	K974HUB	Cambus	KYV311X	East London	KYV511X	Stagecoach South
K855ODY	Stagecoach South	K975KUB	Cambus	KYV318X	East London	KYV512X	East London
K856LMK	East London	KAJ214W	Transit	KYV320X	East London	KYV513X	East London
K856ODY	Stagecoach South	KAJ215W	Transit	KYV326X	East London	KYV514X	East London
K857LMK	East London	KAJ216W	Transit	KYV331X	East London	KYV515X	East London
K857ODY	Stagecoach South	KAJ217W	Transit	KYV334X	East London	KYV517X	East London
K858LMK	East London	KAJ218W	Transit	KYV340X	East London	KYV521X	East London
K858ODY	Stagecoach South	KAJ219W	Transit	KYV345X	Stagecoach South	KYV522X	East London
K859LMK	East London	KBB118D	Busways	KYV348X	Stagecoach South	KYV523X	Stagecoach South
K859ODY	Stagecoach South	KDW342P	Manchester	KYV360X	East London	KYV525X	East London
K860LMK	East London	KHH376W	Cheltenham & Glos	KYV361X	Stagecoach South	KYV526X	East London
K860ODY	Stagecoach South	KHH377W	Ribble	KYV366X	East London	KYV527X	East London
K861LMK	East London	KHH378W	Western	KYV368X	Selkent	KYV529X	East London
K861ODY	Stagecoach South	KHT122P	Circle Line	KYV378X	East London	KYV531X	East London
K862LMK	East London	KHT124P	Midland Red	KYV379X	East London	KYV532X	East London
K862ODY	Stagecoach South	KKY222W	Bluebird Buses	KYV380X	East London	KYV533X	East London
K863LMK	East London	KMA399T	Western	KYV386X	East London	KYV535X	East London
K863ODY	Stagecoach South	KPA366P	Stagecoach South	KYV387X	East London	KYV536X	East London
K864LMK	East London	KPA369P	Stagecoach South	KYV394X	East London	KYV537X	East London
K864ODY	Stagecoach South	KPA374P	Stagecoach South	KYV395X	East London	KYV539X	East London
K865LMK	East London	KPA379P	Stagecoach South	KYV397X	Stagecoach South	KYV540X	East London
K865ODY	Stagecoach South	KPA388P	Stagecoach South	KYV406X	East London	KYV541X	East London
K866LMK	East London	KPA389P	Stagecoach South	KYV410X	Western	KYV542X	Red & White
K866ODY	Stagecoach South	KRM430W	Bluebird Buses	KYV420X	Stagecoach South	KYV543X	East London
K867LMK	East London	KRM431W	Cumberland	KYV428X	East London	KYV544X	East London
K867ODY	Stagecoach South	KRM432W	Cumberland	KYV434X	East London	KYV545X	East London
K868LMK	East London	KRM433W	Cumberland	KYV437X	East London	KYV546X	East London
K868ODY	Stagecoach South	KRM434W	Cumberland	KYV439X	Selkent	KYV548X	East London
K869LMK	East London	KRM435W	Cumberland	KYV441X	East London	KYV549X	East London
K869ODY	Stagecoach South	KRM436W	Cumberland	KYV442X	Stagecoach South	L26JSA	Bluebird Buses
K870LMK	East London	KRM437W	Cumberland	KYV444X	East London	L27JSA	Bluebird Buses
K870ODY	Stagecoach South	KRN103T	Cumberland	KYV445X	East London	L28JSA	Bluebird Buses
K871GHH	Cumberland	KRN105T	Cumberland	KYV446X	East London	L31HHN	Transit
K871LMK	East London	KRN113T	Cumberland	KYV447X	Selkent	L32HHN	Transit
K871ODY	Stagecoach South	KRN119T	Cumberland	KYV448X	East London	L33HHN	Transit
K872GHH	Cumberland	KRS531V	Bluebird Buses	KYV451X	Stagecoach South	L34HHN	Transit
K872ODY	Stagecoach South	KRS532V	Bluebird Buses	KYV453X	East London	L35HHN	Transit
K873GHH	Cumberland	KRS540V	Western	KYV454X	East London	L36HHN	Transit
K873ODY	Stagecoach South	KRS542V	Western	KYV455X	Fife Scottish	L37HHN	Transit
K874GHH	Cumberland	KRS682V	Bluebird Buses	KYV456X	East London	L79CWO	Red & White
K874ODY	Stagecoach South	KRU838W	Stagecoach South	KYV458X	East London	L81CWO	Red & White
K875GHH	Cumberland	KRU843W	United Counties	KYV460X	East London	L81YBB	Busways
K875ODY	Stagecoach South	KRU845W	United Counties	KYV461X	East London	L82CWO	Red & White
K876GHH	Cumberland	KRU847W	United Counties	KYV462X	East London	L82YBB	Busways
K876ODY	Stagecoach South	KRU852W	United Counties	KYV465X	East London	L83CWO	Red & White
K877GHH	Cumberland	KSD62W	Western	KYV466X	East London	L83YBB	Busways
K877ODY	Stagecoach South	KSU463	East Midland	KYV467X	East London	L84CWO	Red & White
K878GHH	Cumberland	KVF245V	Cambus	KYV469X	East London	L84YBB	Busways
K878ODY	Stagecoach South	KVF246V	Cambus	KYV470X	East London	L85CWO	Red & White
K879ODY	Stagecoach South	KVF247V	Red & White	KYV471X	East London	L86CWO	Red & White
K880ODY	Stagecoach South	KVF248V	Red & White	KYV472X	Selkent	L87CWO	Red & White
K910TKP	Stagecoach South	KVF249V	Circle Line	KYV473X	East London	L89CWO	Red & White
K911RGE	Cambus	KVF250V	Cambus	KYV474X	Stagecoach South	L100JLB	Bluebird Buses
K912RGE	Cambus	KWA213W	Bluebird Buses	KYV476X	East London	L101GHN	Transit
K913VDV	Devon	KWA214W	East Midland	KYV480X	East London	L101JSA	Bluebird Buses
K924VDV	Devon	KWA215W	New Zealand	KYV486X	East London	L101SDY	Ribble
K925VDV	Devon	KWA216W	New Zealand	KYV488X	East London	L102GHN	Transit
K926VDV	Devon	KWA218W	East Midland	KYV490X	East London	L102JSA	Bluebird Buses
K927VDV	Devon	KWA219W	Bluebird Buses	KYV492X	East London	L102SDY	Ribble
K963HUB	Cambus	KWA221W	East Midland	KYV495X	East London	L103GHN	Transit
K964HUB	Cambus	KWA223W	East Midland	KYV497X	East London	L103SDY	Ribble
K965HUB	Cambus	KWA224W	East Midland	KYV498X	Selkent	L104SDY	Ribble
K966HUB	Cambus	KYN282X	Devon	KYV500X	East London	L105SDY	Ribble
K967HUB	Cambus	KYN285X	East London	KYV501X	East London	L106SDY	Ribble
K968HUB	Cambus	KYN286X	East London	KYV502X	East London	L107SDY	Ribble
K969HUB	Cambus	KYN288X	Stagecoach South	KYV503X	East London	L108LHL	East Midland
K970HUB	Cambus	KYN298X	East London	KYV504X	East London	L109LHL	East Midland
K971HUB	Cambus	KYN305X	Stagecoach South	KYV505X	East London	L119DRN	Ribble
K972HUB	Cambus	KYN306X	East London	KYV506X	East London	L122DRN	Cumberland
K973HUB	Cambus	KYN487X	Stagecoach South	KYV508X	East London	L123DRN	Cumberland

Reg	Operator	Reg	Operator	Reg	Operator	Reg	Operator
L124XHG	Cumberland	L206YAG	Selkent	L304PSC	Fife Scottish	L374JBD	United Counties
L125DRN	Ribble	L207YAG	Selkent	L305PSC	Fife Scottish	L375JBD	United Counties
L125NAO	Cumberland	L208FDV	Devon	L306PSC	Fife Scottish	L376JBD	United Counties
L126DRN	Cumberland	L208PSB	Western	L307PSC	Fife Scottish	L377JBD	United Counties
L126NAO	Cumberland	L208YAG	Selkent	L307SKV	Midland Red	L378JBD	United Counties
L127DRN	Cumberland	L209FDV	Devon	L308PSC	Fife Scottish	L379JBD	United Counties
L127NAO	Cumberland	L209YAG	Selkent	L308YDU	Midland Red	L380JBD	United Counties
L128DRN	Ribble	L210FDV	Devon	L309PSC	Fife Scottish	L381NBD	United Counties
L136VRH	East London	L210YAG	Selkent	L309YDU	Midland Red	L382NBD	United Counties
L137VRH	East London	L211FDV	Devon	L310PSC	Fife Scottish	L383NBD	United Counties
L138BFV	Ribble	L211YAG	Selkent	L310YDU	Midland Red	L401JBD	United Counties
L138VRH	East London	L212FDV	Devon	L311YDU	Midland Red	L402JBD	United Counties
L139BFV	Ribble	L212GJO	Oxford	L312YDU	Midland Red	L403JBD	United Counties
L139VRH	East London	L214FDV	Devon	L313YDU	Midland Red	L404JBD	United Counties
L140BFV	Ribble	L237CCW	Ribble	L314YDU	Midland Red	L405JBD	United Counties
L140VRH	East London	L238CCW	Transit	L315JSA	Bluebird Buses	L406JBD	United Counties
L141BFV	Ribble	L239CCW	Ribble	L315YDU	Midland Red	L407JBD	United Counties
L141VRH	East London	L240CCW	Ribble	L316JSA	Bluebird Buses	L408JBD	United Counties
L142BFV	Ribble	L241CCK	Ribble	L316YDU	Midland Red	L409JBD	United Counties
L142VRH	East London	L241SDY	Stagecoach South	L317YDU	Midland Red	L410JBD	United Counties
L143BFV	Ribble	L242CCK	Transit	L318BOD	Devon	L411JBD	United Counties
L143VRH	East London	L242SDY	Stagecoach South	L318YDU	Midland Red	L412JBD	United Counties
L144BFV	Ribble	L243CCK	Transit	L319YDU	Midland Red	L413JBD	United Counties
L144VRH	East London	L243SDY	Stagecoach South	L320YDU	Midland Red	L414JBD	United Counties
L145BFV	Ribble	L244CCK	Transit	L321YDU	Midland Red	L414SFL	Red & White
L145VRH	East London	L244SDY	Stagecoach South	L322YDU	Midland Red	L415JBD	United Counties
L146BFV	Ribble	L245CCK	Transit	L323YDU	Midland Red	L416JBD	United Counties
L146VRH	East London	L245SDY	Stagecoach South	L324YDU	Midland Red	L417JBD	United Counties
L148BFV	Ribble	L246CCK	Transit	L325YDU	Midland Red	L418JBD	United Counties
L149BFV	Ribble	L246SDY	Stagecoach South	L326CHB	Red & White	L419JBD	United Counties
L150BFV	Ribble	L247CCK	Transit	L326YKV	Midland Red	L420JBD	United Counties
L151BFV	Ribble	L247FDV	Oxford	L327CHB	Red & White	L421JBD	United Counties
L152BFV	Cumberland	L247SDY	Stagecoach South	L327YKV	Midland Red	L422MVV	United Counties
L153BFV	Ribble	L248CCK	Cheltenham & Glos	L328CHB	Red & White	L423MVV	Fife Scottish
L154BFV	Cumberland	L248FDV	Oxford	L328YKV	Midland Red	L423XVV	United Counties
L155BFV	Ribble	L248SDY	Stagecoach South	L329CHB	Red & White	L424MVV	Fife Scottish
L155JNH	United Counties	L249CCK	Transit	L329YKV	Midland Red	L424XVV	United Counties
L155LBW	Oxford	L249SDY	Stagecoach South	L330CHB	Cheltenham & Glos	L425MVV	Fife Scottish
L156BFV	Ribble	L250CCK	Transit	L330YKV	Midland Red	L425XVV	United Counties
L156JNH	United Counties	L250SDY	Stagecoach South	L331CHB	Red & White	L426MVV	Fife Scottish
L156LBW	Oxford	L251CCK	Ribble	L334FWO	Red & White	L427MVV	Fife Scottish
L157BFV	Ribble	L252CCK	Ribble	L335FWO	Red & White	L428MVV	Fife Scottish
L157JNH	United Counties	L253CCK	Ribble	L336FWO	Red & White	L435LWA	East Midland
L157LBW	Oxford	L254CCK	Transit	L337FWO	Red & White	L436LWA	East Midland
L158BFV	Ribble	L255CCK	Ribble	L338FWO	Red & White	L437LWA	East Midland
L158JNH	United Counties	L256CCK	Ribble	L339FWO	Red & White	L438LWA	East Midland
L158LBW	Oxford	L262VSU	Western	L339KCK	East Midland	L439LWA	East Midland
L159CCW	Ribble	L267CCK	Fife Scottish	L340FWO	Red & White	L440LWA	East Midland
L159JNH	United Counties	L268CCK	Fife Scottish	L340KCK	East Midland	L441LWA	East Midland
L159LBW	Oxford	L269CCK	Fife Scottish	L341FWO	Red & White	L442LWA	East Midland
L160BFV	Cumberland	L270EHB	Red & White	L341KCK	East Midland	L443LWA	East Midland
L160JNH	United Counties	L270LHH	Cumberland	L342FWO	Red & White	L445FFR	Ribble
L161CCW	Ribble	L271LHH	Ribble	L342KCK	East Midland	L445LWA	East Midland
L161JNH	United Counties	L272LHH	Ribble	L343JBD	United Counties	L446FFR	Ribble
L162JNH	United Counties	L273LHH	Ribble	L343KCK	East Midland	L446LWA	East Midland
L178KHG	Ribble	L274LHH	Ribble	L344KCK	East Midland	L447FFR	Ribble
L179KHG	Ribble	L275JAO	Cumberland	L360JBD	United Counties	L447LWA	East Midland
L188SDY	Stagecoach South	L276JAO	Cumberland	L361JBD	United Counties	L448FFR	Ribble
L193FDV	Devon	L277JAO	Ribble	L362JBD	United Counties	L448LWA	East Midland
L194FDV	Devon	L278JAO	Ribble	L363JBD	United Counties	L449LWA	East Midland
L195FDV	Devon	L279JAO	Ribble	L364JBD	United Counties	L450LWA	East Midland
L197FDV	Devon	L281JAO	Ribble	L365JBD	United Counties	L451LWA	East Midland
L201FDV	Devon	L282JAO	Cumberland	L366JBD	United Counties	L451YAC	Midland Red
L201YAG	Selkent	L283JAO	Ribble	L367JBD	United Counties	L452LWA	East Midland
L202YAG	Selkent	L301JSA	Bluebird Buses	L368JBD	United Counties	L452YAC	Midland Red
L203FDV	Devon	L301PSC	Fife Scottish	L369JBD	United Counties	L453LHL	East Midland
L203YAG	Selkent	L302JSA	Bluebird Buses	L370JBD	United Counties	L453YAC	Midland Red
L204FDV	Devon	L302PSC	Fife Scottish	L371JBD	United Counties	L454YAC	Midland Red
L204YAG	Selkent	L303JSA	Bluebird Buses	L372JBD	United Counties	L455YAC	Midland Red
L205YAG	Selkent	L303PSC	Fife Scottish	L373JBD	United Counties	L456YAC	Midland Red

Reg	Operator	Reg	Operator	Reg	Operator	Reg	Operator
L547CDV	Devon	L657MFL	Cambus	L712JUD	Oxford	L802HJO	Oxford
L550JFS	Bluebird Buses	L658HKS	Fife Scottish	L713JUD	Oxford	L803HJO	Oxford
L577NSB	Western	L658MFL	Cambus	L714JUD	Oxford	L803XDG	Cheltenham & Glos
L578HSG	Fife Scottish	L659HKS	Fife Scottish	L715JUD	East London	L804HJO	Oxford
L578NSB	Western	L659MFL	Cambus	L716JUD	East London	L804XDG	Cheltenham & Glos
L579HSG	Fife Scottish	L660HKS	Ribble	L717JUD	East London	L805XDG	Cheltenham & Glos
L579JSA	Bluebird Buses	L660MFL	Cambus	L718JUD	East London	L806XDG	Cheltenham & Glos
L580HSG	Fife Scottish	L661MFL	Cambus	L719JUD	East London	L826BKK	Stagecoach South
L580JSA	Bluebird Buses	L661MSF	Ribble	L720JUD	East London	L827BKK	Stagecoach South
L581HSG	Fife Scottish	L662MFL	Cambus	L721JUD	East London	L828BKK	Stagecoach South
L581JSA	Bluebird Buses	L662MSF	Ribble	L722JUD	East London	L829BKK	Stagecoach South
L582HSG	Fife Scottish	L663MFL	Cambus	L723JUD	Oxford	L830BKK	Stagecoach South
L582JSA	Western	L663MSF	Ribble	L724JUD	Oxford	L831CDG	Cheltenham & Glos
L583HSG	Fife Scottish	L664MFL	Cambus	L729VNL	Busways	L832CDG	Cheltenham & Glos
L583JSA	Western	L664MSF	Ribble	L730VNL	Busways	L833CDG	Cheltenham & Glos
L584HSG	Fife Scottish	L665MFL	Cambus	L731LWA	East Midland	L834CDG	Cheltenham & Glos
L584JSA	Western	L665MSF	Ribble	L731VNL	Busways	L835CDG	Cheltenham & Glos
L585HSG	Fife Scottish	L667MFL	Cambus	L732LWA	East Midland	L836CDG	Cheltenham & Glos
L585JSA	Bluebird Buses	L667MSF	Ribble	L732VNL	Busways	L837CDG	Cheltenham & Glos
L586HSG	Fife Scottish	L668MFL	Cambus	L733LWA	East Midland	L838CDG	Cheltenham & Glos
L586JSA	Bluebird Buses	L668MSF	Ribble	L733VNL	Busways	L839CDG	Cheltenham & Glos
L587HSG	Fife Scottish	L669MFL	Cambus	L734LWA	East Midland	L839MWT	Red & White
L587JSA	Bluebird Buses	L669MSF	Ribble	L734VNL	Busways	L840CDG	Cheltenham & Glos
L588HSG	Fife Scottish	L671HNV	United Counties	L735LWA	East Midland	L840MWT	Red & White
L588JSA	Bluebird Buses	L672HNV	United Counties	L735VNL	Busways	L841CDG	Cheltenham & Glos
L589HSG	Fife Scottish	L673HNV	United Counties	L736LWA	East Midland	L842CDG	Cheltenham & Glos
L590HSG	Fife Scottish	L674HNV	United Counties	L736VNL	Busways	L881SDY	Stagecoach South
L601VCD	Stagecoach South	L675HNV	United Counties	L737LWA	East Midland	L882LFS	Western
L602VCD	Stagecoach South	L676HNV	United Counties	L737VNL	Busways	L882SDY	Stagecoach South
L603VCD	Stagecoach South	L677HNV	United Counties	L738LWA	East Midland	L883LFS	Western
L609TDY	Stagecoach South	L678HNV	United Counties	L738VNL	Busways	L883SDY	Stagecoach South
L616TDY	Stagecoach South	L679HNV	United Counties	L739LWA	East Midland	L884SDY	Stagecoach South
L617TDY	Stagecoach South	L680HNV	United Counties	L739VNL	Busways	L885SDY	Stagecoach South
L618TDY	Stagecoach South	L681HNV	United Counties	L740LWA	East Midland	L886SDY	Stagecoach South
L624TDY	Stagecoach South	L682HNV	United Counties	L740VNL	Busways	L887SDY	Stagecoach South
L625TDY	Stagecoach South	L683HNV	United Counties	L741LWA	East Midland	L916UGA	Western
L626TDY	Stagecoach South	L684HNV	United Counties	L741VNL	Busways	L929CTT	Devon
L627TDY	Stagecoach South	L685CDD	Red & White	L742LWA	East Midland	L930CTT	Devon
L628TDY	Stagecoach South	L685JBD	United Counties	L742VNL	Busways	L931CTT	Devon
L629BFV	Ribble	L686CDD	Cheltenham & Glos	L743LWA	East Midland	L932CTT	Devon
L629TDY	Stagecoach South	L687CDD	Cheltenham & Glos	L743VNL	Busways	L933CTT	Devon
L630BFV	Ribble	L688CDD	Cheltenham & Glos	L744LWA	East Midland	L934CTT	Devon
L630TDY	Stagecoach South	L689CDD	Cheltenham & Glos	L744VNL	Busways	L935CTT	Devon
L631BFV	Ribble	L690CDD	Cheltenham & Glos	L745LWA	East Midland	L936CTT	Devon
L631TDY	Stagecoach South	L691CDD	Cheltenham & Glos	L745VNL	Busways	L937CTT	Devon
L632BFV	Ribble	L692CDD	Cheltenham & Glos	L746LWA	East Midland	L938CTT	Devon
L632TDY	Stagecoach South	L693CDD	Cheltenham & Glos	L746VNL	Busways	L939CTT	Devon
L633BFV	Ribble	L694CDD	Cheltenham & Glos	L748LWA	East Midland	L940CTT	Devon
L633TDY	Stagecoach South	L695CDD	Cheltenham & Glos	L748VNL	Busways	L941CTT	Devon
L634BFV	Ribble	L696CDD	Cheltenham & Glos	L749LWA	East Midland	L942CTT	Devon
L634TDY	Stagecoach South	L701FWO	Red & White	L749VNL	Busways	L943CTT	Devon
L635BFV	Ribble	L702FWO	Red & White	L750LWA	East Midland	L945EOD	Devon
L635TDY	Stagecoach South	L703FWO	Red & White	L750VNL	Busways	L946EOD	Devon
L636BFV	Ribble	L704FWO	Red & White	L751LHL	East Midland	L947EOD	Devon
L637LDT	East Midland	L705FWO	Red & White	L751VNL	Busways	L948EOD	Devon
L638LDT	East Midland	L705HFU	East Midland	L752VNL	Busways	L949EOD	Devon
L639LDT	East Midland	L706FWO	Red & White	L753VNL	Busways	L950EOD	Devon
L640LDT	East Midland	L706HFU	East Midland	L754VNL	Busways	LAG188V	East Midland
L641LDT	East Midland	L707FWO	Red & White	L755VNL	Busways	LAG189V	East Midland
L642LDT	East Midland	L707HFU	East Midland	L756VNL	Busways	LAT505V	Transit
L643LDT	East Midland	L708FWO	Red & White	L757VNL	Busways	LAT506V	Transit
L651HKS	Fife Scottish	L708HFU	East Midland	L758VNL	Busways	LAT514V	Transit
L652HKS	Fife Scottish	L709FWO	Cheltenham & Glos	L759VNL	Busways	LBD920V	United Counties
L653HKS	Fife Scottish	L709HFU	East Midland	L760ARG	Busways	LBD921V	United Counties
L654HKS	Fife Scottish	L709JUD	Oxford	L761ARG	Busways	LBD923V	United Counties
L655HKS	Fife Scottish	L710FWO	Cheltenham & Glos	L762ARG	Busways	LBN201P	Busways
L655MFL	Cambus	L710JUD	Oxford	L763ARG	Busways	LBN202P	Busways
L656HKS	Fife Scottish	L711FWO	Cheltenham & Glos	L764ARG	Busways	LCU112	Busways
L656MFL	Cambus	L711JUD	Oxford	L765ARG	Busways	LDS201A	Bluebird Buses
L657HKS	Fife Scottish	L712FWO	Cheltenham & Glos	L801HJO	Oxford	LDS210A	Bluebird Buses

LEO736Y	Fife Scottish	M64HHB	Red & White	M191HTT	Devon	M314PKS	Fife Scottish
LFF875	East London	M64VJO	Oxford	M192HTT	Devon	M315DGP	Selkent
LFJ852W	United Counties	M65HHB	Red & White	M193HTT	Devon	M315PKS	Fife Scottish
LFJ855W	United Counties	M65VJO	Oxford	M194HTT	Devon	M316DGP	Selkent
LFJ858W	Ribble	M67HHB	Red & White	M201DRG	Busways	M317DGP	Selkent
LFJ859W	Ribble	M67VJO	Oxford	M201LHP	Midland Red	M317RSO	Bluebird Buses
LFJ861W	Ribble	M68HHB	Red & White	M202DRG	Busways	M318DGP	Selkent
LFJ862W	United Counties	M68VJO	Oxford	M202LHP	Midland Red	M318RSO	Bluebird Buses
LFJ863W	United Counties	M69HHB	Red & White	M203DRG	Busways	M319DGP	Selkent
LFJ864W	United Counties	M69VJO	Oxford	M203LHP	Midland Red	M319RSO	Bluebird Buses
LFJ865W	United Counties	M71HHB	Red & White	M204DRG	Busways	M320DGP	Selkent
LFJ866W	Ribble	M71VJO	Oxford	M204LHP	Midland Red	M320RSO	Bluebird Buses
LFJ869W	United Counties	M73HHB	Red & White	M205LHP	Midland Red	M321RSO	Bluebird Buses
LFJ870W	Stagecoach South	M73VJO	Oxford	M209LHP	Midland Red	M331LHP	Midland Red
LFJ874W	Stagecoach South	M74HHB	Red & White	M210LHP	Midland Red	M332DRP	United Counties
LFJ875W	Stagecoach South	M74VJO	Oxford	M220DWV	Stagecoach South	M332LHP	Midland Red
LFJ878W	United Counties	M75VJO	Oxford	M223SVN	Transit	M334DRP	United Counties
LFJ879W	United Counties	M76HHB	Red & White	M224SVN	Transit	M334LHP	Midland Red
LFJ880W	Stagecoach South	M76VJO	Oxford	M225SVN	Transit	M335DRP	United Counties
LFJ881W	Stagecoach South	M78HHB	Red & White	M226SVN	Transit	M335LHP	Midland Red
LFJ882W	Ribble	M78VJO	Oxford	M226UTM	Devon	M336DRP	United Counties
LFJ883W	Ribble	M79VJO	Oxford	M227SVN	Transit	M336LHP	Midland Red
LFJ884W	Ribble	M81WBW	Oxford	M227UTM	Devon	M337DRP	United Counties
LFJ885W	Ribble	M82WBW	Oxford	M228UTM	Devon	M337LHP	Midland Red
LFR860X	Cheltenham & Glos	M83WBW	Oxford	M229UTM	Devon	M338DRP	United Counties
LFR861X	Cheltenham & Glos	M84WBW	Oxford	M230TBV	Ribble	M338LHP	Midland Red
LFR862X	United Counties	M85WBW	Oxford	M230UTM	Devon	M339DRP	United Counties
LFR864X	United Counties	M86WBW	Oxford	M231TBV	Ribble	M339LHP	Midland Red
LFR866X	Ribble	M87WBW	Oxford	M231UTM	Devon	M340DRP	United Counties
LFR871X	Ribble	M89WBW	Oxford	M232TBV	Ribble	M340LHP	Midland Red
LFR873X	Cheltenham & Glos	M91WBW	Oxford	M232UTM	Devon	M341DRP	United Counties
LFR877X	Ribble	M92WBW	Oxford	M233TBV	Ribble	M341LHP	Midland Red
LFV205X	Ribble	M93WBW	Oxford	M233UTM	Devon	M342DRP	United Counties
LHT725P	Midland Red	M94WBW	Oxford	M234TBV	Ribble	M342LHP	Midland Red
LIB1182	Manchester	M95WBW	Oxford	M234UTM	Devon	M343DRP	United Counties
LIL3317	Manchester	M96WBW	Oxford	M235TBV	Ribble	M343LHP	Midland Red
LIL4612	Manchester	M97WBW	Oxford	M235UTM	Devon	M344DRP	United Counties
LJC800	Cumberland	M98WBW	Oxford	M236TBV	Ribble	M344JBO	Red & White
LJY145	Cumberland	M100AAB	Western	M236UTM	Devon	M344LHP	Midland Red
LPF605P	Stagecoach South	M101CCD	Red & White	M237UTM	Devon	M345DRP	United Counties
LSD732W	Western	M101WBW	Oxford	M238UTM	Devon	M345JBO	Red & White
LSJ871W	Western	M102CCD	Fife Scottish	M239UTM	Devon	M345LHP	Midland Red
LSJ872W	Western	M102WBW	Oxford	M240UTM	Devon	M346DRP	United Counties
LSV670	Oxford	M103CCD	Fife Scottish	M241UTM	Devon	M346JBO	Red & White
LSX16P	Fife Scottish	M103WBW	Oxford	M242UTM	Devon	M346KWK	Midland Red
LSX17P	Fife Scottish	M103XBW	Oxford	M243UTM	Devon	M347DRP	United Counties
LSX32P	Fife Scottish	M104CCD	Fife Scottish	M244UTM	Devon	M347JBO	Red & White
LUA273V	Cumberland	M104PVN	Transit	M245UTM	Devon	M348DRP	United Counties
LUA275V	Cumberland	M104XBW	Oxford	M246UTM	Devon	M348JBO	Red & White
LWS33Y	Cheltenham & Glos	M105CCD	Stagecoach South	M247UTM	Devon	M349DRP	United Counties
LWS34Y	Cheltenham & Glos	M105PVN	Transit	M248UTM	Devon	M349JBO	Red & White
LWS35Y	Cheltenham & Glos	M105XBW	Oxford	M249UTM	Devon	M350JBO	Red & White
LWS36Y	Cheltenham & Glos	M106CCD	Stagecoach South	M250UTM	Devon	M351JBO	Red & White
LWS37Y	Cheltenham & Glos	M106PVN	Transit	M301DGP	Selkent	M352JBO	Red & White
LWS38Y	Cheltenham & Glos	M106XBW	Oxford	M302DGP	Selkent	M353JBO	Red & White
LWS39Y	Cheltenham & Glos	M107CCD	Red & White	M303DGP	Selkent	M354JBO	Red & White
LWS40Y	Cheltenham & Glos	M107PVN	Transit	M304DGP	Selkent	M355JBO	Red & White
LWS41Y	Cheltenham & Glos	M107XBW	Oxford	M305DGP	Selkent	M356JBO	Red & White
LWU466V	Red & White	M108CCD	Stagecoach South	M306DGP	Selkent	M357JBO	Red & White
LWU468V	Devon	M108PVN	Transit	M307DGP	Selkent	M358JBO	Red & White
LWU470V	Devon	M151FGB	Western	M308DGP	Selkent	M359JBO	Red & White
M38PVN	Transit	M160CCD	Western	M309DGP	Selkent	M360JBO	Red & White
M39PVN	Transit	M161CCD	Western	M310DGP	Selkent	M361LAX	Red & White
M40PVN	Transit	M162CCD	Western	M311DGP	Selkent	M362LAX	Red & White
M41PVN	Transit	M163CCD	Western	M311YSC	Stagecoach South	M363LAX	Red & White
M42PVN	Transit	M164CCD	Western	M312DGP	Selkent	M364LAX	Red & White
M59VJO	Oxford	M164SCK	Ribble	M312YSC	Stagecoach South	M365LAX	Red & White
M61VJO	Oxford	M165CCD	Western	M313DGP	Selkent	M366LAX	Red & White
M62VJO	Oxford	M165SCK	Ribble	M313YSC	Stagecoach South	M367LAX	Red & White
M63VJO	Oxford	M166CCD	Western	M314DGP	Selkent	M368LAX	Red & White

M369LAX	Red & White	M482ASW	Western	M636BCD	Stagecoach South	M711FMR	Cheltenham & Glos
M370LAX	Red & White	M483ASW	Western	M636HDV	Devon	M711KRH	Transit
M371LAX	Red & White	M484ASW	Western	M637BCD	Stagecoach South	M712FMR	Cheltenham & Glos
M395KVR	Western	M485ASW	Western	M637HDV	Devon	M712KRH	Transit
M396KVR	Western	M486ASW	Western	M638BCD	Stagecoach South	M713FMR	Cheltenham & Glos
M397KVR	Western	M487ASW	Western	M638HDV	Devon	M713KRH	Transit
M401SPY	Transit	M488ASW	Western	M639BCD	Stagecoach South	M714FMR	Cheltenham & Glos
M402SPY	Transit	M489ASW	Western	M639HDV	Devon	M714KRH	Transit
M403SPY	Transit	M490ASW	Western	M640HDV	Devon	M715FMR	Cheltenham & Glos
M404BFG	Stagecoach South	M491ASW	Western	M641HDV	Devon	M715KRH	Transit
M404OKM	Stagecoach South	M492ASW	Western	M648FYS	Western	M716KRH	Transit
M404SPY	Transit	M527RSO	Bluebird Buses	M649FYS	Western	M717KRH	Transit
M405BFG	Stagecoach South	M528RSO	Bluebird Buses	M650BCD	Stagecoach South	M718BCS	Western
M405OKM	Stagecoach South	M529RSO	Bluebird Buses	M650FYS	Western	M718KRH	Transit
M405SPY	Transit	M530RSO	Bluebird Buses	M651BCD	Stagecoach South	M719BCS	Western
M406BFG	Stagecoach South	M531RSO	Bluebird Buses	M651FYS	Western	M720BCS	Western
M406OKM	Stagecoach South	M532RSO	Bluebird Buses	M652BCD	Stagecoach South	M721BCS	Western
M406SPY	Transit	M533RSO	Bluebird Buses	M652FYS	Western	M722BCS	Western
M407BFG	Stagecoach South	M534RSO	Bluebird Buses	M653FYS	Western	M723BCS	Western
M407OKM	Stagecoach South	M535RSO	Bluebird Buses	M654FYS	Western	M724BCS	Western
M407SPY	Transit	M536RSO	Bluebird Buses	M655FYS	Western	M725BCS	Western
M408BFG	Stagecoach South	M537RSO	Bluebird Buses	M656FYS	Western	M726BCS	Western
M408OKM	Stagecoach South	M538RSO	Bluebird Buses	M657FYS	Western	M727BCS	Western
M408SPY	Transit	M539RSO	Bluebird Buses	M658FYS	Western	M732BSJ	Western
M409BFG	Stagecoach South	M540RSO	Bluebird Buses	M659FYS	Western	M733BSJ	Western
M409SPY	Transit	M541RSO	Bluebird Buses	M660FYS	Western	M734BSJ	Western
M410BFG	Stagecoach South	M542RSO	Bluebird Buses	M661FYS	Western	M735BSJ	Western
M410SPY	Transit	M543RSO	Bluebird Buses	M662ECD	Stagecoach South	M736BSJ	Western
M411RRN	East Midland	M543SPY	Transit	M662FYS	Western	M737BSJ	Western
M412RRN	East Midland	M544RSO	Bluebird Buses	M663ECD	Stagecoach South	M738BSJ	Western
M413RRN	East Midland	M544SPY	Transit	M663FYS	Western	M739BSJ	Western
M414RRN	East Midland	M545SPY	Transit	M664ECD	Stagecoach South	M740BSJ	Western
M451VCW	Ribble	M546SPY	Transit	M664FYS	Western	M741BSJ	Western
M452VCW	Ribble	M547SPY	Transit	M665ECD	Stagecoach South	M741PRS	Manchester
M453VCW	Ribble	M548SPY	Transit	M665FYS	Western	M742PRS	Manchester
M454VCW	Ribble	M549SPY	Transit	M667ECD	Stagecoach South	M743PRS	Manchester
M454VHE	Manchester	M550SPY	Transit	M667FYS	Western	M744PRS	Manchester
M455VCW	Cumberland	M551SPY	Transit	M668ECD	Stagecoach South	M745PRS	Manchester
M455VHE	Manchester	M552SPY	Transit	M668FYS	Western	M746PRS	Manchester
M456VCW	Cumberland	M562JTG	Red & White	M669ECD	Stagecoach South	M748PRS	Manchester
M456VHE	Manchester	M589OSO	Bluebird Buses	M670ECD	Stagecoach South	M749PRS	Manchester
M457VCW	Cumberland	M590OSO	Bluebird Buses	M670SSX	Fife Scottish	M750LAX	Red & White
M457VHE	Manchester	M591OSO	Bluebird Buses	M671SSX	Fife Scottish	M750PRS	Manchester
M458VCW	Cumberland	M592OSO	Bluebird Buses	M672SSX	Fife Scottish	M751LAX	Red & White
M458VHE	Manchester	M593OSO	Bluebird Buses	M673SSX	Fife Scottish	M752LAX	Red & White
M459VCW	Cumberland	M594OSO	Bluebird Buses	M674SSX	Western	M753LAX	Red & White
M459VHE	Manchester	M595OSO	Bluebird Buses	M675SSX	Western	M754LAX	Red & White
M460VCW	Cumberland	M596OSO	Bluebird Buses	M676SSX	Western	M755LAX	Red & White
M460VHE	Manchester	M597OSO	Bluebird Buses	M677SSX	Western	M756LAX	Red & White
M461VCW	Cumberland	M598OSO	Bluebird Buses	M678SSX	Western	M757LAX	Red & White
M461VHE	Manchester	M601VHE	East Midland	M679SSX	Western	M758LAX	Red & White
M462VCW	Cumberland	M602VHE	East Midland	M680SSX	Western	M759LAX	Red & White
M462VHE	Manchester	M603VHE	East Midland	M681SSX	Western	M75HHB	Red & White
M463VCW	Cumberland	M604VHE	East Midland	M697EDD	Cheltenham & Glos	M760LAX	Red & White
M466ASW	Western	M605VHE	East Midland	M698EDD	Cheltenham & Glos	M761LAX	Red & White
M467ASW	Western	M606VHE	East Midland	M699EDD	Cheltenham & Glos	M762LAX	Red & White
M468ASW	Western	M607VHE	East Midland	M701EDD	Cheltenham & Glos	M763LAX	Red & White
M469ASW	Western	M608WET	East Midland	M702EDD	Cheltenham & Glos	M764LAX	Red & White
M470ASW	Western	M609WET	East Midland	M703EDD	Cheltenham & Glos	M765RAX	Red & White
M471ASW	Western	M615APN	Stagecoach South	M704JDG	Cheltenham & Glos	M766DRG	Busways
M472ASW	Western	M622HDV	Devon	M705JDG	Cheltenham & Glos	M766RAX	Red & White
M473ASW	Western	M623HDV	Devon	M706JDG	Cheltenham & Glos	M767DRG	Busways
M474ASW	Western	M624HDV	Devon	M707JDG	Cheltenham & Glos	M767RAX	Red & White
M475ASW	Western	M625HDV	Devon	M707KRH	Transit	M768DRG	Busways
M476ASW	Western	M625KKG	Red & White	M708JDG	Cheltenham & Glos	M768RAX	Red & White
M477ASW	Western	M626HDV	Devon	M708KRH	Transit	M769DRG	Busways
M478ASW	Western	M627HDV	Devon	M709JDG	Cheltenham & Glos	M769RAX	Red & White
M479ASW	Western	M628HDV	Devon	M709KRH	Transit	M770DRG	Busways
M480ASW	Western	M629HDV	Devon	M710JDG	Cheltenham & Glos	M770RAX	Red & White
M481ASW	Western	M630HDV	Devon	M710KRH	Transit	M770TFS	Fife Scottish

In addition to the Alexander PS model, Stagecoach operate seventy three Northern Counties Palatine buses, seventy on Volvo B10M chassis (Manchester 25, Stagecoach South 13 and Transit 32); two on Scania (at Busways) and one on a Dennis Dart (at Red & White). Pictured in Hull is Transit 716, M716KRH. *B Ridgeway.*

M771DRG	Busways	M817KRH	Transit	M945JBO	Red & White	MDS866V	Ribble
M771TFS	Fife Scottish	M818KRH	Transit	M945TSX	Fife Scottish	MFN115R	Stagecoach South
M772BCS	Western	M819KRH	Transit	M946JBO	Red & White	MFN946F	Stagecoach South
M772TFS	Fife Scottish	M843EMW	Cheltenham & Glos	M946TSX	Fife Scottish	MFV30T	Ribble
M773BCS	Western	M844EMW	Cheltenham & Glos	M947JBO	Red & White	MFV35T	Ribble
M773TFS	Fife Scottish	M845EMW	Cheltenham & Glos	M947TSX	Fife Scottish	MFV36T	Ribble
M774TFS	Fife Scottish	M846HDF	Manchester	M948JBO	Red & White	MHS4P	Bluebird Buses
M775TFS	Fife Scottish	M847HDF	Cheltenham & Glos	M948TSX	Fife Scottish	MHS5P	Bluebird Buses
M776TFS	Fife Scottish	M847PRS	Manchester	M949EGE	Western	MIB7416	Bluebird Buses
M778TFS	Fife Scottish	M866LNY	Red & White	M949JBO	Red & White	MIL4693	Western
M779TFS	Fife Scottish	M869ASW	Western	M949TSX	Fife Scottish	MNC495W	Manchester
M780TFS	Fife Scottish	M870ASW	Western	M950EGE	Western	MNC498W	Manchester
M782PRS	Ribble	M871ASW	Western	M950JBO	Red & White	MNS6Y	Fife Scottish
M783PRS	Ribble	M872ASW	Western	M950TSX	Fife Scottish	MNS7Y	Fife Scottish
M784PRS	Western	M889ECD	Stagecoach South	M951DRG	Busways	MNS8Y	Fife Scottish
M785PRS	Western	M890ECD	Stagecoach South	M951JBO	Red & White	MNS9Y	Fife Scottish
M786PRS	Western	M901DRG	Busways	M951TSX	Fife Scottish	MNS10Y	Fife Scottish
M787PRS	Western	M902DRG	Busways	M952DRG	Busways	MOU739R	Cheltenham & Glos
M788PRS	Western	M911WJK	Stagecoach South	M952TSX	Fife Scottish	MRJ37W	Manchester
M789PRS	Western	M912WJK	Stagecoach South	M953DRG	Busways	MRJ38W	Manchester
M790PRS	Western	M913WJK	Stagecoach South	M953TSX	Fife Scottish	MRJ40W	Manchester
M791PRS	Western	M914WJK	Stagecoach South	M954DRG	Busways	MRJ41W	Manchester
M792PRS	Western	M915WJK	Stagecoach South	M954TSX	Fife Scottish	MRJ42W	Manchester
M793PRS	Western	M916WJK	Stagecoach South	M955TSX	Fife Scottish	MRJ43W	Manchester
M794PRS	Ribble	M917WJK	Stagecoach South	M956TSX	Fife Scottish	MRJ44W	Manchester
M795PRS	Ribble	M918WJK	Stagecoach South	M975WWR	Cambus	MRJ45W	Manchester
M796PRS	Ribble	M940JBO	Red & White	M976WWR	Cambus	MRJ47W	Manchester
M797PRS	Ribble	M941JBO	Red & White	M977WWR	Cambus	MRJ48W	Manchester
M798PRS	Ribble	M942JBO	Red & White	M978WWR	Cambus	MRJ51W	Manchester
M799PRS	Ribble	M942TSX	East Midland	M979VWY	Cambus	MRJ52W	Manchester
M808JTY	East Midland	M943JBO	Red & White	MBE613R	East Midland	MRJ53W	Manchester
M808WWR	Cambus	M943TSX	East Midland	MDS858V	Ribble	MRJ54W	Manchester
M809WWR	Cambus	M944JBO	Red & White	MDS859V	Ribble	MRJ66W	Manchester
M810WWR	Cambus	M944TSX	Fife Scottish	MDS865V	Western	MRJ67W	Manchester

Reg	Operator	Reg	Operator	Reg	Operator	Reg	Operator
MRJ71W	Manchester	N132AET	East Midland	N202LFV	Ribble	N312AMC	East London
MRJ270W	East Midland	N132VAO	Cumberland	N202LPN	Stagecoach South	N312XRP	United Counties
MRJ275W	Cumberland	N132YRM	Cumberland	N202LTN	Busways	N313AMC	East London
MSO10W	Western	N133AET	East Midland	N202UHH	Cumberland	N313XRP	United Counties
MSO13W	Red & White	N133YRM	Cumberland	N203CUD	Oxford	N314AMC	East London
MSO14W	Red & White	N134AET	East Midland	N203LPN	Stagecoach South	N314XRP	United Counties
MSO17W	Ribble	N135AET	East Midland	N203LTN	Busways	N315AMC	East London
MSO18W	Western	N136AET	East Midland	N203UHH	Cumberland	N315XRP	United Counties
MSU345	Fife Scottish	N136MPN	Stagecoach South	N204CUD	Oxford	N316AMC	East London
MSU466	Western	N137AET	East Midland	N204LPN	Stagecoach South	N316VMS	Fife Scottish
MUA872P	Cheltenham & Glos	N138AET	East Midland	N204LTN	Busways	N316XRP	United Counties
MUR214L	Red & White	N139AET	East Midland	N204UHH	Cumberland	N317AMC	East London
MVK500R	Busways	N140AET	East Midland	N205CUD	Oxford	N317VMS	Fife Scottish
MVK521R	Midland Red	N141AET	East Midland	N205LTN	Busways	N317XRP	United Counties
MVK532R	Busways	N142AET	East Midland	N205UHH	Cumberland	N318AMC	East London
MVK544R	Busways	N142XSA	Western	N206CUD	Oxford	N318VMS	Fife Scottish
MVK551R	Busways	N143AET	East Midland	N206LTN	Busways	N318XRP	United Counties
MVK558R	Midland Red	N143XSA	Western	N206TDU	Midland Red	N319AMC	East London
MWG622X	East Midland	N144AET	East Midland	N206UHH	Cumberland	N319VMS	Fife Scottish
MWG623X	East Midland	N144XSA	Western	N207LTN	Busways	N319XRP	United Counties
MWG624X	East Midland	N145XSA	Western	N207TDU	Midland Red	N320AMC	East London
N41MJO	Oxford	N146XSA	Western	N207UHH	Cumberland	N320VMS	Fife Scottish
N42MJO	Oxford	N148XSA	Bluebird Buses	N208LTN	Busways	N320XRP	United Counties
N43MJO	Oxford	N149XSA	Bluebird Buses	N208TDU	Midland Red	N321AMC	East London
N45MJO	Oxford	N150XSA	Bluebird Buses	N208UHH	Cumberland	N321HGK	Selkent
N46MJO	Oxford	N151MTG	Red & White	N209LTN	Busways	N321VMS	Fife Scottish
N47EJO	Oxford	N151XSA	Bluebird Buses	N209UHH	Cumberland	N321XRP	United Counties
N47MJO	Oxford	N152MTG	Red & White	N210LTN	Busways	N322AMC	East London
N48EJO	Oxford	N152XSA	Bluebird Buses	N210UHH	Cumberland	N322HGK	Selkent
N48MJO	Oxford	N153MTG	Red & White	N211LTN	Busways	N322VMS	Fife Scottish
N51KBW	Oxford	N153XSA	Bluebird Buses	N211TDU	Midland Red	N322XRP	United Counties
N52KBW	Oxford	N154MTG	Red & White	N211UHH	Cumberland	N323AMC	East London
N53KBW	Oxford	N154XSA	Bluebird Buses	N212LTN	Busways	N323HGK	Selkent
N54KBW	Oxford	N155MTG	Red & White	N212TDU	Midland Red	N323VMS	Fife Scottish
N56KBW	Oxford	N156MTG	Red & White	N212UHH	Cumberland	N323XRP	United Counties
N57KBW	Oxford	N157MTG	Red & White	N213LTN	Busways	N324AMC	East London
N58KBW	Oxford	N158MTG	Red & White	N213TDU	Midland Red	N324HGK	Selkent
N59KBW	Oxford	N159MTG	Red & White	N213UHH	Cumberland	N324VMS	Fife Scottish
N61KBW	Oxford	N160MTG	Red & White	N214LTN	Busways	N324XRP	United Counties
N62KBW	Oxford	N176LCK	Ribble	N214TDU	Midland Red	N325AMC	East London
N62MTG	Red & White	N177LCK	Ribble	N214UHH	Cumberland	N325HGK	Selkent
N63KBW	Oxford	N178LCK	Ribble	N215LTN	Busways	N325NPN	Manchester
N63MTG	Red & White	N179LCK	Ribble	N215TDU	Midland Red	N325VMS	Fife Scottish
N64KBW	Oxford	N180LCK	Ribble	N215UHH	Cumberland	N325XRP	United Counties
N91RVK	Busways	N182CMJ	Devon	N216LTN	Busways	N326AMC	East London
N95ALS	Fife Scottish	N183CMJ	Midland Red	N216TDU	Midland Red	N326HGK	Selkent
N96ALS	Fife Scottish	N188GFR	Ribble	N217LTN	Busways	N326NPN	Manchester
N97ALS	Fife Scottish	N189GFR	Ribble	N247XSA	Western	N326VMS	Fife Scottish
N116YHH	Cumberland	N190GFR	Ribble	N301AMC	East London	N326XRP	United Counties
N117YHH	Cumberland	N191LPN	Stagecoach South	N301XRP	United Counties	N327AMC	East London
N118YHH	Cumberland	N192LPN	Stagecoach South	N302AMC	East London	N327HGK	Selkent
N119YHH	Cumberland	N193LPN	Stagecoach South	N302XRP	United Counties	N327NPN	Manchester
N120YHH	Cumberland	N194LFV	Ribble	N303AMC	East London	N327VMS	Fife Scottish
N121YHH	Cumberland	N194LPN	Stagecoach South	N303XRP	United Counties	N327XRP	Cumberland
N122YHH	Cumberland	N195LFV	Ribble	N304AMC	East London	N328HGK	Selkent
N123YHH	Cumberland	N195LPN	Stagecoach South	N304XRP	United Counties	N328NPN	Manchester
N124YHH	Cumberland	N196LFV	Ribble	N305AMC	East London	N328VMS	Fife Scottish
N125YHH	Cumberland	N196LPN	Stagecoach South	N305XRP	United Counties	N328XRP	Cumberland
N126YRM	Cumberland	N197LFV	Ribble	N306AMC	East London	N329HGK	Selkent
N127YRM	Cumberland	N197LPN	Stagecoach South	N306XRP	United Counties	N329NPN	Manchester
N128VAO	Cumberland	N198LFV	Ribble	N307AMC	East London	N329VMS	Fife Scottish
N128YRM	Cumberland	N198LPN	Stagecoach South	N307XRP	United Counties	N329XRP	Cumberland
N129VAO	Cumberland	N199LFV	Ribble	N308AMC	East London	N330HGK	Selkent
N129YRM	Cumberland	N199LPN	Stagecoach South	N308XRP	United Counties	N330NPN	Manchester
N130AET	East Midland	N201CUD	Oxford	N309AMC	East London	N331HGK	Selkent
N130VAO	Cumberland	N201LFV	Ribble	N309XRP	United Counties	N331NPN	Manchester
N130YRM	Cumberland	N201LPN	Stagecoach South	N310AMC	East London	N332HGK	Selkent
N131AET	East Midland	N201LTN	Busways	N310XRP	United Counties	N332NPN	Manchester
N131VAO	Cumberland	N201UHH	Cumberland	N311AMC	East London	N333NPN	Manchester
N131YRM	Cumberland	N202CUD	Oxford	N311XRP	United Counties	N334HGK	Selkent

Reg	Operator	Reg	Operator	Reg	Operator	Reg	Operator
N334NPN	Manchester	N361AVV	Midland Red	N404LDF	Cheltenham & Glos	N456PAP	Stagecoach South
N335HGK	Selkent	N361LPN	Stagecoach South	N404WVR	Manchester	N456VOD	Ribble
N335NPN	Manchester	N362AVV	Midland Red	N405LDF	Cheltenham & Glos	N457PAP	Stagecoach South
N336HGK	Selkent	N362LPN	Stagecoach South	N405WVR	Manchester	N457VOD	Ribble
N336NPN	Manchester	N363AVV	Midland Red	N406LDF	Cheltenham & Glos	N458PAP	Stagecoach South
N337HGK	Selkent	N363LPN	Stagecoach South	N406WVR	Manchester	N458VOD	Ribble
N337NPN	Manchester	N364AVV	Midland Red	N407LDF	Cheltenham & Glos	N459PAP	Stagecoach South
N338HGK	Selkent	N364LPN	Stagecoach South	N407WVR	Manchester	N459VOD	Ribble
N338NPN	Manchester	N365AVV	Midland Red	N408LDF	Cheltenham & Glos	N460PAP	Stagecoach South
N339HGK	Selkent	N365LPN	Stagecoach South	N408WVR	Manchester	N460VOD	Ribble
N339NPN	Manchester	N366AVV	Midland Red	N409LDF	Cheltenham & Glos	N461PAP	Stagecoach South
N340HGK	Selkent	N366LPN	Stagecoach South	N409WVR	Manchester	N461RVK	Busways
N341HGK	Selkent	N367AVV	Midland Red	N410MBW	East London	N461VOD	Ribble
N341KKH	Transit	N367LPN	Stagecoach South	N410WVR	Manchester	N462PAP	Stagecoach South
N341MPN	Stagecoach South	N368AVV	Midland Red	N411MBW	East London	N462RVK	Busways
N342HGK	Selkent	N368LPN	Stagecoach South	N411WVR	Manchester	N462VOD	Ribble
N342KKH	Transit	N369AVV	Midland Red	N412MBW	East London	N463HRN	Ribble
N342MPN	Stagecoach South	N369LPN	Stagecoach South	N412WVR	Manchester	N463PAP	Stagecoach South
N343HGK	Selkent	N370AVV	Midland Red	N413MBW	East London	N463RVK	Busways
N343KKH	Transit	N370LPN	Stagecoach South	N413WVR	Manchester	N463VOD	Ribble
N343MPN	Stagecoach South	N371AVV	Midland Red	N414MBW	East London	N464HRN	Ribble
N344HGK	Selkent	N371LPN	Stagecoach South	N414WVR	Manchester	N464PAP	Stagecoach South
N344KKH	Transit	N372AVV	Midland Red	N415MBW	East London	N464RVK	Busways
N344MPN	Stagecoach South	N372LPN	Stagecoach South	N415WVR	Manchester	N464VOD	Ribble
N345HGK	Selkent	N372PNY	Red & White	N416MBW	East London	N465PAP	Stagecoach South
N345KKH	Transit	N373LPN	Stagecoach South	N416WVR	Manchester	N465RVK	Busways
N345MPN	Stagecoach South	N373PNY	Red & White	N417MBW	East London	N465VOD	Ribble
N346HGK	Selkent	N374LPN	Stagecoach South	N417WVR	Manchester	N466PAP	Stagecoach South
N346KKH	Transit	N374PNY	Red & White	N418MBW	East London	N466RVK	Busways
N346MPN	Stagecoach South	N375LPN	Stagecoach South	N418WVR	Manchester	N466VOD	Ribble
N347AVV	Midland Red	N375PNY	Red & White	N419MBW	East London	N467PAP	Stagecoach South
N347HGK	Selkent	N376LPN	Stagecoach South	N419WVR	Manchester	N467RVK	Busways
N347KKH	Transit	N376PNY	Red & White	N420MBW	East London	N467VOD	Ribble
N347MPN	Stagecoach South	N377LPN	Stagecoach South	N420WVR	Manchester	N468RVK	Busways
N348AVV	Midland Red	N377PNY	Red & White	N421MBW	East London	N468VOD	Ribble
N348HGK	Selkent	N378LPN	Stagecoach South	N421WVR	Manchester	N469RVK	Busways
N348KKH	Transit	N378PNY	Red & White	N422MBW	East London	N470RVK	Busways
N348MPN	Stagecoach South	N379LPN	Stagecoach South	N422WVR	Manchester	N471RVK	Busways
N349AVV	Midland Red	N379PNY	Red & White	N423MBW	East London	N472RVK	Busways
N349HGK	Selkent	N380LPN	Stagecoach South	N423WVR	Manchester	N473RVK	Busways
N349MPN	Stagecoach South	N380PNY	Red & White	N424MBW	East London	N474RVK	Busways
N350AVV	Midland Red	N381LPN	Stagecoach South	N424WVR	Manchester	N475RVK	Busways
N350HGK	Selkent	N381PNY	Red & White	N425MBW	East London	N476RVK	Busways
N350MPN	Stagecoach South	N382LPN	Stagecoach South	N425WVR	Manchester	N477RVK	Busways
N350YFL	Cambus	N382PNY	Red & White	N426MBW	East London	N478RVK	Busways
N351AVV	Midland Red	N383LPN	Stagecoach South	N426WVR	Manchester	N479RVK	Busways
N351HGK	Selkent	N383PNY	Red & White	N427MBW	East London	N480RVK	Busways
N351MPN	Stagecoach South	N384LPN	Stagecoach South	N427WVR	Manchester	N481RVK	Busways
N351YFL	Cambus	N384PNY	Red & White	N428WVR	Manchester	N482RVK	Busways
N352AVV	Midland Red	N385LPN	Stagecoach South	N429WVR	Manchester	N483RVK	Busways
N352HGK	Selkent	N386LPN	Stagecoach South	N430WVR	Manchester	N484RVK	Busways
N352MPN	Stagecoach South	N387LPN	Stagecoach South	N445XVA	Cambus	N485RVK	Busways
N352YFL	Cambus	N388LPN	Stagecoach South	N446TOS	Western	N486RVK	Busways
N353AVV	Midland Red	N389LPN	Stagecoach South	N446XVA	Cambus	N487RVK	Busways
N353HGK	Selkent	N390LPN	Stagecoach South	N447XVA	Cambus	N488RVK	Busways
N353MPN	Stagecoach South	N391LPN	Stagecoach South	N448XVA	Cambus	N489RVK	Busways
N354AVV	Midland Red	N392LPN	Stagecoach South	N449XVA	Cambus	N490RVK	Busways
N354MPN	Stagecoach South	N393LPN	Stagecoach South	N450XVA	Cambus	N491RVK	Busways
N355AVV	Midland Red	N394LPN	Stagecoach South	N451PAP	Stagecoach South	N492RVK	Busways
N355MPN	Stagecoach South	N395LPN	Stagecoach South	N451VOD	Ribble	N493RVK	Busways
N356AVV	Midland Red	N396LPN	Stagecoach South	N451XVA	Cambus	N494RVK	Busways
N356MPN	Stagecoach South	N397LPN	Stagecoach South	N452PAP	Stagecoach South	N495RVK	Busways
N357AVV	Midland Red	N398LPN	Stagecoach South	N452VOD	Ribble	N496RVK	Busways
N357MPN	Stagecoach South	N399LPN	Stagecoach South	N452XVA	Cambus	N497RVK	Busways
N358AVV	Midland Red	N401LDF	Cheltenham & Glos	N453PAP	Stagecoach South	N498RVK	Busways
N358MPN	Stagecoach South	N401WVR	Manchester	N453VOD	Ribble	N499RVK	Busways
N359AVV	Midland Red	N402LDF	Cheltenham & Glos	N454PAP	Stagecoach South	N501RVK	Busways
N359MPN	Stagecoach South	N402WVR	Manchester	N454VOD	Ribble	N506BJA	Devon
N360AVV	Midland Red	N403LDF	Cheltenham & Glos	N455PAP	Stagecoach South	N507BJA	Devon
N360LPN	Stagecoach South	N403WVR	Manchester	N455VOD	Ribble	N508BJA	Devon

N509BJA	Devon	N626VSS	Western	N720RDD	Cheltenham & Glos	N790VRM	Cumberland
N510BJA	Devon	N627VSS	Western	N721LTN	Busways	N801DNE	Manchester
N511BJA	Devon	N628VSS	Western	N721RDD	Cheltenham & Glos	N802DNE	Manchester
N512BJA	Devon	N629VSS	Western	N722LTN	Busways	N803DNE	Manchester
N513BJA	Devon	N630VSS	Western	N722RDD	Cheltenham & Glos	N804DNE	Manchester
N514BJA	Devon	N631VSS	Western	N723LTN	Busways	N805DNE	Manchester
N515BJA	Devon	N632VSS	Western	N723RDD	Cheltenham & Glos	N806DNE	Manchester
N516BJA	Devon	N633VSS	Western	N724LTN	Busways	N807DNE	Manchester
N517BJA	Devon	N634VSS	Western	N724RDD	Cheltenham & Glos	N808DNE	Manchester
N518BJA	Devon	N635VSS	Western	N725LTN	Busways	N809DNE	Manchester
N518XER	Cambus	N636VSS	Bluebird Buses	N725RDD	Cheltenham & Glos	N810DNE	Manchester
N519BJA	Ribble	N637VSS	Bluebird Buses	N726LTN	Busways	N811DNE	Manchester
N519XER	Cambus	N638VSS	Bluebird Buses	N726RDD	Cheltenham & Glos	N812DNE	Manchester
N520BJA	Ribble	N639VSS	Bluebird Buses	N727LTN	Busways	N813DNE	Manchester
N520XER	Cambus	N640LPN	Stagecoach South	N727RDD	Cheltenham & Glos	N814DNE	Manchester
N550MTG	Red & White	N640VSS	Bluebird Buses	N728LTN	Busways	N815DNE	Manchester
N551MTG	Red & White	N641LPN	Stagecoach South	N728RDD	Cheltenham & Glos	N816DNE	Manchester
N551VDC	Transit	N641VSS	Cambus	N729LTN	Busways	N817DNE	Manchester
N552VDC	Transit	N642LPN	Stagecoach South	N729RDD	Cheltenham & Glos	N818DNE	Manchester
N553VDC	Transit	N642VSS	Cambus	N730LTN	Busways	N849VHH	Western
N561SJF	Fife Scottish	N643LPN	Stagecoach South	N730RDD	Cheltenham & Glos	N850VHH	Western
N562SJF	Fife Scottish	N643VSS	Cambus	N731LTN	Busways	N851VHH	Western
N582XSA	Bluebird Buses	N644LPN	Stagecoach South	N731RDD	Cheltenham & Glos	N852VHH	Western
N583XSA	Bluebird Buses	N644VSS	Cambus	N732LTN	Busways	N853VHH	Western
N584XSA	Bluebird Buses	N645LPN	Stagecoach South	N732RDD	Cheltenham & Glos	N854VHH	Western
N599DWY	Devon	N645VSS	Manchester	N733LTN	Busways	N855VHH	Western
N601KGF	Selkent	N646VSS	Manchester	N733RDD	Cheltenham & Glos	N856VHH	Western
N601VSS	Western	N647VSS	Manchester	N734LTN	Busways	N857VHH	Western
N602KGF	Selkent	N648VSS	Manchester	N734RDD	Cheltenham & Glos	N858VHH	Western
N602VSS	Western	N649VSS	Manchester	N735LTN	Busways	N859VHH	Western
N603KGF	Selkent	N650VSS	Manchester	N735RDD	Cheltenham & Glos	N860VHH	Western
N603VSS	Western	N651VSS	Manchester	N736LTN	Busways	N861VHH	Western
N604KGF	Selkent	N652VSS	Manchester	N737LTN	Busways	N862VHH	Western
N604VSS	Western	N653VSS	Manchester	N738LTN	Busways	N863VHH	Western
N605KGF	Selkent	N654VSS	Manchester	N739LTN	Busways	N864VHH	Western
N605VSS	Western	N655VSS	Manchester	N740LTN	Busways	N865VHH	Western
N606KGF	Selkent	N656VSS	Manchester	N752CKU	East Midland	N866VHH	Western
N606VSS	Western	N657VSS	Manchester	N753CKU	East Midland	N879AVV	Manchester
N607KGF	Selkent	N658VSS	Manchester	N754CKU	East Midland	N880AVV	Manchester
N607VSS	Western	N659VSS	Manchester	N755CKU	East Midland	N881AVV	Manchester
N608KGF	Selkent	N660VSS	Manchester	N756CKU	East Midland	N882AVV	Manchester
N608VSS	Western	N661VSS	Manchester	N757CKU	East Midland	N883AVV	Manchester
N609KGF	Selkent	N662VSS	Manchester	N758CKU	East Midland	N884AVV	Manchester
N609VSS	Western	N663VSS	Manchester	N759CKU	East Midland	N885AVV	Manchester
N610KGF	Selkent	N664VSS	Manchester	N760CKU	East Midland	N901PFC	Oxford
N610VSS	Western	N665VSS	Manchester	N761CKU	East Midland	N902PFC	Oxford
N611LGC	Selkent	N701LTN	Busways	N762EWG	East Midland	N903PFC	Oxford
N611VSS	Western	N702LTN	Busways	N763EWG	East Midland	N905NAP	Stagecoach South
N612LGC	Selkent	N703LTN	Busways	N764EWG	East Midland	N906NAP	Stagecoach South
N612VSS	Western	N704LTN	Busways	N765EWG	East Midland	N907NAP	Stagecoach South
N613LGC	Selkent	N705LTN	Busways	N766EWG	East Midland	N908NAP	Stagecoach South
N613VSS	Cambus	N706LTN	Busways	N767EWG	East Midland	N909NAP	Stagecoach South
N614LGC	Selkent	N707LTN	Busways	N768EWG	East Midland	N910NAP	Stagecoach South
N614VSS	Cambus	N708LTN	Busways	N769EWG	East Midland	N911NAP	Stagecoach South
N615VSS	Cambus	N709LTN	Busways	N770EWG	East Midland	N912NAP	Stagecoach South
N616USS	Western	N710LTN	Busways	N771EWG	East Midland	N913NAP	Stagecoach South
N616VSS	Cambus	N711LTN	Busways	N772EWG	East Midland	N914NAP	Stagecoach South
N617USS	Western	N712LTN	Busways	N772RVK	Busways	N915NAP	Stagecoach South
N617VSS	Cambus	N713LTN	Busways	N773EWG	East Midland	N916NAP	Stagecoach South
N618USS	Bluebird Buses	N714LTN	Busways	N773RVK	Busways	N917NAP	Stagecoach South
N618VSS	Cambus	N715LTN	Busways	N774RVK	Busways	N918NAP	Stagecoach South
N619USS	Bluebird Buses	N716KAM	Cheltenham & Glos	N774EWG	East Midland	N919NAP	Stagecoach South
N619VSS	Cambus	N716LTN	Busways	N775EWG	East Midland	N920NAP	Stagecoach South
N620USS	Bluebird Buses	N717KAM	Cheltenham & Glos	N775RVK	Busways	N921NAP	Stagecoach South
N620VSS	Cambus	N717LTN	Busways	N776EWG	East Midland	N922NAP	Stagecoach South
N621VSS	Western	N718LTN	Busways	N776RVK	Busways	N923NAP	Stagecoach South
N622VSS	Western	N718RDD	Cheltenham & Glos	N778RVK	Busways	N924NAP	Stagecoach South
N623VSS	Western	N719LTN	Busways	N779RVK	Busways	N925NAP	Stagecoach South
N624VSS	Western	N719RDD	Cheltenham & Glos	N780RVK	Busways	N926NAP	Stagecoach South
N625VSS	Western	N720LTN	Busways	N789VRM	Cumberland	N927NAP	Stagecoach South

Reg	Operator	Reg	Operator	Reg	Operator	Reg	Operator
N928NAP	Stagecoach South	NDZ3135	East London	NOE573R	Red & White	NUW604Y	Transit
N929NAP	Stagecoach South	NDZ3136	East London	NOE576R	Red & White	NUW605Y	United Counties
N930NAP	Stagecoach South	NDZ3137	East London	NOE578R	Midland Red	NUW606Y	Transit
N931NAP	Stagecoach South	NDZ3138	East London	NOE582R	Midland Red	NUW608Y	United Counties
N932NAP	Stagecoach South	NDZ3139	East London	NOE586R	Midland Red	NUW609Y	East London
N933NAP	Stagecoach South	NDZ3140	East London	NOE587R	Midland Red	NUW610Y	United Counties
N934NAP	Stagecoach South	NDZ3141	East London	NOE590R	Midland Red	NUW611Y	Stagecoach South
N935NAP	Stagecoach South	NDZ3142	East London	NOE595R	Ribble	NUW613Y	East London
N936NAP	Stagecoach South	NDZ3143	East London	NOE602R	Midland Red	NUW614Y	East London
N937NAP	Stagecoach South	NDZ3144	East London	NOE603R	Midland Red	NUW616Y	Selkent
N938NAP	Stagecoach South	NDZ3145	East London	NOE604R	Midland Red	NUW617Y	East London
N939NAP	Stagecoach South	NDZ3146	East London	NOE605R	Midland Red	NUW618Y	Western
N940NAP	Stagecoach South	NDZ3147	East London	NOE606R	Midland Red	NUW619Y	Red & White
N941NAP	Stagecoach South	NDZ3148	East London	NPA229W	Western	NUW621Y	East London
N942NAP	Stagecoach South	NDZ3149	East London	NPJ476R	Stagecoach South	NUW622Y	Fife Scottish
N943NAP	Stagecoach South	NDZ3150	East London	NPJ477R	Stagecoach South	NUW623Y	Fife Scottish
N944NAP	Stagecoach South	NDZ3151	East London	NPJ480R	Stagecoach South	NUW625Y	East London
N945NAP	Stagecoach South	NDZ3152	East London	NRP580V	East Midland	NUW626Y	Fife Scottish
N946NAP	Stagecoach South	NDZ3153	East London	NSG636A	Bluebird Buses	NUW627Y	East London
N947NAP	Stagecoach South	NDZ3154	East London	NSJ550X	Western	NUW629Y	East London
N948NAP	Stagecoach South	NDZ3155	East London	NSP334R	Fife Scottish	NUW630Y	East London
N949NAP	Stagecoach South	NDZ3156	East London	NSP336R	Fife Scottish	NUW631Y	East London
N950NAP	Stagecoach South	NDZ3157	East London	NTC132Y	Cheltenham & Glos	NUW632Y	East London
N951NAP	Stagecoach South	NDZ3158	East London	NUF276	Bluebird Buses	NUW633Y	East London
N952NAP	Stagecoach South	NDZ3159	East London	NUM341V	Devon	NUW634Y	Transit
N953NAP	Stagecoach South	NFB603R	Circle Line	NUW550Y	East London	NUW636Y	East London
N954NAP	Stagecoach South	NFN81R	Stagecoach South	NUW551Y	East London	NUW637Y	East London
N955NAP	Stagecoach South	NFN88R	Stagecoach South	NUW552Y	East London	NUW639Y	East London
N956NAP	Stagecoach South	NFS170Y	Fife Scottish	NUW553Y	East London	NUW640Y	East London
N957NAP	Stagecoach South	NFS171Y	Fife Scottish	NUW554Y	Fife Scottish	NUW641Y	East London
N958NAP	Stagecoach South	NFS172Y	Fife Scottish	NUW556Y	East London	NUW642Y	Transit
N959NAP	Stagecoach South	NFS173Y	Fife Scottish	NUW557Y	United Counties	NUW643Y	Transit
N960NAP	Stagecoach South	NFS174Y	Fife Scottish	NUW558Y	Fife Scottish	NUW644Y	East London
N961NAP	Stagecoach South	NFS175Y	Fife Scottish	NUW559Y	East London	NUW645Y	Stagecoach South
N962NAP	Stagecoach South	NFS176Y	Fife Scottish	NUW560Y	Fife Scottish	NUW646Y	Red & White
N963NAP	Stagecoach South	NFS177Y	Fife Scottish	NUW562Y	Fife Scottish	NUW647Y	Stagecoach South
N964NAP	Stagecoach South	NFS178Y	Fife Scottish	NUW563Y	East London	NUW648Y	Transit
N965NAP	Stagecoach South	NFS179Y	Fife Scottish	NUW564Y	East London	NUW649Y	Transit
N966NAP	Stagecoach South	NFX667	Stagecoach South	NUW565Y	United Counties	NUW650Y	East London
N967NAP	Stagecoach South	NHH378W	Cumberland	NUW566Y	Fife Scottish	NUW651Y	Red & White
N968NAP	Stagecoach South	NHH382W	Cheltenham & Glos	NUW568Y	United Counties	NUW652Y	East London
N969NAP	Stagecoach South	NHL301X	East Midland	NUW569Y	East London	NUW653Y	East London
N970NAP	Stagecoach South	NHL302X	East Midland	NUW571Y	Fife Scottish	NUW657Y	East London
N971NAP	Stagecoach South	NHL303X	East Midland	NUW572Y	Fife Scottish	NUW658Y	East London
N972NAP	Stagecoach South	NHL304X	East Midland	NUW573Y	East London	NUW659Y	Transit
N973NAP	Stagecoach South	NHL305X	East Midland	NUW575Y	Fife Scottish	NUW660Y	East London
N974NAP	Stagecoach South	NHU670R	Cheltenham & Glos	NUW576Y	United Counties	NUW662Y	East London
N975NAP	Stagecoach South	NHU671R	Midland Red	NUW577Y	Fife Scottish	NUW663Y	Stagecoach South
N976NAP	Stagecoach South	NHU672R	Midland Red	NUW578Y	East London	NUW664Y	Transit
N977NAP	Stagecoach South	NIB4138	Bluebird Buses	NUW579Y	United Counties	NUW665Y	East London
N978NAP	Devon	NIB5232	Bluebird Buses	NUW580Y	East London	NUW666Y	Transit
N979NAP	Devon	NIB5233	Bluebird Buses	NUW581Y	East London	NUW668Y	Transit
N980NAP	Devon	NIB5455	Bluebird Buses	NUW582Y	Fife Scottish	NUW669Y	East London
N981NAP	Devon	NLP388V	Western	NUW584Y	United Counties	NUW670Y	Stagecoach South
N982NAP	Devon	NLS983W	Western	NUW585Y	East London	NUW671Y	Stagecoach South
NAK29X	Midland Red	NLS985W	Western	NUW586Y	Fife Scottish	NUW672Y	Stagecoach South
NDZ3015	East London	NLS987W	Red & White	NUW587Y	Fife Scottish	NUW673Y	Transit
NDZ3016	East London	NLS989W	Western	NUW588Y	United Counties	NUW674Y	Western
NDZ3017	East London	NML607E	East London	NUW589Y	East London	NUW675Y	Transit
NDZ3018	East London	NML610E	East London	NUW590Y	United Counties	NWO457R	Red & White
NDZ3019	East London	NML616E	East London	NUW592Y	East London	NWO461R	Red & White
NDZ3020	East London	NML624E	East London	NUW594Y	Stagecoach South	NWO468R	Red & White
NDZ3021	East London	NML639E	East London	NUW595Y	United Counties	NWS288R	Cheltenham & Glos
NDZ3022	East London	NML641E	East London	NUW596Y	Stagecoach South	NWS289R	Cheltenham & Glos
NDZ3023	East London	NML642E	East London	NUW597Y	East London	OCU815R	Busways
NDZ3024	East London	NML657E	East London	NUW598Y	East London	OCU816R	Busways
NDZ3025	East London	NMY643E	Bluebird Buses	NUW600Y	East London	OCU818R	Busways
NDZ3026	East London	NOE553R	Midland Red	NUW601Y	Fife Scottish	OCU819R	Busways
NDZ3133	East London	NOE571R	Midland Red	NUW602Y	United Counties	OCU820R	Busways
NDZ3134	East London	NOE572R	Red & White	NUW603Y	East London	OCU821R	Busways

OCU822R	Busways	ORJ77W	Manchester	P118XCN	Busways	P220HBD	Midland Red
OFB965R	Cambus	ORJ78W	Manchester	P119XCN	Busways	P224VCK	Ribble
OFV14X	Ribble	ORJ79W	Manchester	P120XCN	Busways	P225VCK	Ribble
OFV15X	Ribble	ORJ80W	Manchester	P121XCN	Busways	P226VCK	Ribble
OFV16X	Cumberland	ORJ81W	Manchester	P122XCN	Busways	P227VCK	Ribble
OFV17X	Cumberland	ORJ91W	Manchester	P123XCN	Busways	P228VCK	Ribble
OFV18X	Ribble	ORJ92W	Manchester	P124XCN	Busways	P229VCK	Ribble
OFV19X	Ribble	ORJ93W	Manchester	P125XCN	Busways	P230VCK	Ribble
OFV20X	Ribble	ORJ94W	Manchester	P126XCN	Busways	P231VCK	Ribble
OFV21X	Ribble	ORJ95W	Manchester	P127XCN	Ribble	P232VCK	Ribble
OFV22X	Ribble	ORJ98W	Manchester	P128XCN	Ribble	P233VCK	Ribble
OFV23X	Ribble	ORJ100W	Manchester	P129XCN	Ribble	P234VCK	Ribble
OHV680Y	Selkent	OSC49V	Fife Scottish	P130XCN	Ribble	P235VCK	Ribble
OHV684Y	Western	OSC50V	Fife Scottish	P131XCN	Ribble	P255ASA	Western
OHV686Y	East London	OSC51V	Fife Scottish	P132XCN	Ribble	P260VPN	Ribble
OHV688Y	Stagecoach South	OSC53V	Fife Scottish	P133XCN	Ribble	P260WPN	Stagecoach South
OHV691Y	East London	OSC54V	Fife Scottish	P134XCN	Ribble	P261VPN	Ribble
OHV697Y	Stagecoach South	OSC56V	Fife Scottish	P135XCN	Busways	P261WPN	Stagecoach South
OHV699Y	East London	OSC57V	Fife Scottish	P145KWJ	East Midland	P262VPN	Ribble
OHV700Y	Western	OSC60V	Fife Scottish	P146KWJ	East Midland	P262WPN	Stagecoach South
OHV710Y	Western	OSC61V	Fife Scottish	P148ASA	Western	P263VPN	Ribble
OHV714Y	Western	OSC62V	Fife Scottish	P148KWJ	East Midland	P263WPN	Stagecoach South
OHV719Y	Red & White	OSC63V	Fife Scottish	P149ASA	Western	P264VPN	Stagecoach South
OHV721Y	Selkent	OSC64V	Fife Scottish	P149KWJ	East Midland	P265VPN	Stagecoach South
OHV724Y	Stagecoach South	OSC66V	Fife Scottish	P150ASA	Western	P266VPN	Stagecoach South
OHV728Y	Western	OSJ634R	Bluebird Buses	P150KWJ	East Midland	P267VPN	Stagecoach South
OHV729Y	Devon	OSJ635R	Bluebird Buses	P151ASA	Western	P268VPN	Stagecoach South
OHV731Y	Stagecoach South	OSJ636R	Western	P151KWJ	East Midland	P269VPN	Stagecoach South
OHV738Y	Devon	OSJ643R	Bluebird Buses	P152ASA	Western	P270VPN	Ribble
OHV740Y	Selkent	OSJ644R	Bluebird Buses	P152KWJ	East Midland	P271VPN	Ribble
OHV743Y	Stagecoach South	OSK784	Bluebird Buses	P153ASA	Western	P272VPN	Ribble
OHV744Y	Stagecoach South	OSR195R	Ribble	P153KWJ	East Midland	P273VPN	Ribble
OHV748Y	Selkent	OSR197R	Ribble	P154ASA	Western	P274VPN	Ribble
OHV749Y	Fife Scottish	OUF262W	Stagecoach South	P154KWJ	East Midland	P275VPN	Ribble
OHV751Y	Fife Scottish	OWB30X	East Midland	P156ASA	Western	P276VPN	Stagecoach South
OHV759Y	Stagecoach South	OWB31X	East Midland	P156KWJ	East Midland	P277VPN	Stagecoach South
OHV761Y	Stagecoach South	OWB32X	East Midland	P157ASA	Western	P278VPN	Stagecoach South
OHV762Y	Glasgow	OWB33X	East Midland	P157KWJ	East Midland	P279VPN	Stagecoach South
OHV769Y	Stagecoach South	OWB34X	East Midland	P158ASA	Western	P281VPN	Stagecoach South
OHV770Y	Selkent	P21HMF	East London	P158KWJ	East Midland	P282VPN	Stagecoach South
OHV771Y	Selkent	P23HMF	East London	P159ASA	Western	P283VPN	Stagecoach South
OHV772Y	Selkent	P24HMF	East London	P159KAK	East Midland	P284VPN	Stagecoach South
OHV780Y	Western	P25HMF	East London	P160ASA	Western	P285VPN	Stagecoach South
OHV784Y	Stagecoach South	P26HMF	East London	P160KAK	East Midland	P286VPN	Stagecoach South
OHV785Y	Selkent	P27HMF	East London	P161TDW	Red & White	P287VPN	Stagecoach South
OHV789Y	Fife Scottish	P28HMF	East London	P162TDW	Red & White	P288VPN	Stagecoach South
OHV791Y	Fife Scottish	P29HMF	East London	P163TNY	Red & White	P289VPN	Stagecoach South
OHV797Y	Selkent	P31HMF	East London	P164TNY	Red & White	P290VPN	Stagecoach South
OHV800Y	Western	P54XBO	Red & White	P165TNY	Red & White	P315EFL	Cambus
OHV801Y	Fife Scottish	P56XBO	Red & White	P166TNY	Red & White	P316EFL	Cambus
OHV802Y	East London	P57XBO	Red & White	P167TNY	Red & White	P317EFL	Cambus
OHV802Y	Fife Scottish	P58XBO	Red & White	P168KBD	United Counties	P318EFL	Cambus
OHV804Y	Selkent	P59VTG	Red & White	P168TNY	Red & White	P319EFL	Cambus
OHV805Y	Selkent	P61VTG	Red & White	P169KBD	United Counties	P320EFL	Cambus
OHV809Y	Western	P92URG	Busways	P169TNY	Red & White	P321EFL	Cambus
OHV810Y	Selkent	P101HNH	Midland Red	P170KBD	United Counties	P321JND	Manchester
OHV812Y	Selkent	P102HNH	Midland Red	P170TNY	Red & White	P322EFL	Cambus
OHV813Y	Selkent	P103HNH	Midland Red	P171KBD	United Counties	P322JND	Manchester
OHV814Y	Selkent	P104HNH	Midland Red	P171TNY	Red & White	P323EFL	Cambus
OIW7024	Western	P105HNH	Midland Red	P172KBD	United Counties	P323JND	Manchester
OIW7025	Western	P107FRS	Glasgow	P173KBD	United Counties	P324EFL	Cambus
OJL822Y	East Midland	P108DCW	Ribble	P178PRH	Transit	P324JND	Manchester
OJL823Y	East Midland	P108FRS	Glasgow	P179PRH	Transit	P325JND	Manchester
OMS910W	Bluebird Buses	P109DCW	Ribble	P180PRH	Transit	P326JND	Manchester
ONH846P	Midland Red	P109FRS	Glasgow	P181PRH	Transit	P327JND	Manchester
ONH927V	Circle Line	P110DCW	Ribble	P198OSE	Western	P328JND	Manchester
ORJ72W	Manchester	P110FRS	Glasgow	P199OSE	Western	P329JND	Manchester
ORJ74W	Manchester	P112DCW	Ribble	P217HBD	Midland Red	P330JND	Manchester
ORJ75W	Manchester	P113DCW	Ribble	P218HBD	Midland Red	P331JND	Manchester
ORJ76W	Manchester	P114DCW	Ribble	P219HBD	Midland Red	P332JND	Manchester

Reg	Operator	Reg	Operator	Reg	Operator	Reg	Operator
P334JND	Manchester	P391LPS	Western	P538ESA	Glasgow	P561PNE	Manchester
P335JND	Manchester	P392LPS	Western	P538HMP	East London	P562EFL	Cambus
P336JND	Manchester	P393LPS	Western	P538PNE	Manchester	P562PNE	Manchester
P337JND	Manchester	P394LPS	Western	P539EFL	Cambus	P563EFL	Cambus
P338JND	Manchester	P395BRS	Western	P539ESA	Glasgow	P563MSX	Fife Scottish
P339JND	Manchester	P396BRS	Western	P539HMP	East London	P563PNE	Manchester
P340JND	Manchester	P397BRS	Western	P539PNE	Manchester	P564EFL	Cambus
P341ASO	Bluebird Buses	P398BRS	Western	P540EFL	Cambus	P564MSX	Fife Scottish
P341JND	Manchester	P418KWF	East Midland	P540ESA	Glasgow	P564PNE	Manchester
P342ASO	Bluebird Buses	P419KWF	East Midland	P540HMP	East London	P565EFL	Cambus
P342JND	Manchester	P420KWF	East Midland	P540PNE	Manchester	P565MSX	Fife Scottish
P343ASO	Bluebird Buses	P450KRP	United Counties	P541EFL	Cambus	P565PNE	Manchester
P343JND	Manchester	P451KRP	United Counties	P541ESA	Glasgow	P566EFL	Cambus
P344ASO	Bluebird Buses	P452KRP	United Counties	P541HMP	East London	P566MSX	Fife Scottish
P344JND	Manchester	P455EEF	Transit	P541PNE	Manchester	P566PNE	Manchester
P345ASO	Bluebird Buses	P456EEF	Transit	P542EFL	Cambus	P567EFL	Cambus
P345JND	Manchester	P457EEF	Transit	P542ESA	Glasgow	P567MSX	Fife Scottish
P346ASO	Bluebird Buses	P458EEF	Transit	P542HMP	East London	P568EFL	Cambus
P346JND	Manchester	P459EEF	Transit	P542PNE	Manchester	P568MSX	Fife Scottish
P347ASO	Bluebird Buses	P460EEF	Transit	P543EFL	Cambus	P569EFL	Cambus
P347JND	Manchester	P461EEF	Transit	P543ESA	Glasgow	P569MSX	Fife Scottish
P348ASO	Bluebird Buses	P491BRS	Bluebird Buses	P543HMP	East London	P570EFL	Cambus
P348JND	Manchester	P492BRS	Bluebird Buses	P543PNE	Manchester	P571EFL	Cambus
P349ASO	Bluebird Buses	P493BRS	Bluebird Buses	P544EFL	Cambus	P572EFL	Cambus
P349JND	Manchester	P494BRS	Bluebird Buses	P544ESA	Glasgow	P573EFL	Cambus
P349NKH	Transit	P495BRS	Bluebird Buses	P544PNE	Manchester	P574EFL	Cambus
P350ASO	Bluebird Buses	P496BRS	Bluebird Buses	P545EFL	Cambus	P575EFL	Cambus
P350JND	Manchester	P497BRS	Bluebird Buses	P545ESA	Glasgow	P576EFL	Cambus
P350NKH	Transit	P498BRS	Bluebird Buses	P545PNE	Manchester	P577EFL	Cambus
P351ASO	Bluebird Buses	P499BRS	Bluebird Buses	P546EFL	Cambus	P578EFL	Cambus
P351JND	Manchester	P526EFL	Cambus	P546ESA	Glasgow	P579EFL	Cambus
P351NKH	Transit	P527EFL	Cambus	P546PNE	Manchester	P601JBU	Manchester
P352ASO	Bluebird Buses	P527HMP	East London	P547EFL	Cambus	P602JBU	Manchester
P352JND	Manchester	P528EFL	Cambus	P547ESA	Glasgow	P603JBU	Manchester
P352NKH	Transit	P528HMP	East London	P547PNE	Manchester	P604JBU	Manchester
P353JND	Manchester	P529EFL	Cambus	P548EFL	Cambus	P605JBU	Manchester
P353NKH	Transit	P529HMP	East London	P548ESA	Glasgow	P606CMS	Fife Scottish
P354JND	Manchester	P530EFL	Cambus	P548PNE	Manchester	P607CMS	Fife Scottish
P354NKH	Transit	P530ESA	Glasgow	P549EFL	Cambus	P608CMS	Fife Scottish
P355JND	Manchester	P530HMP	East London	P549ESA	Glasgow	P609CMS	Fife Scottish
P356JND	Manchester	P530PNE	Manchester	P549PNE	Manchester	P610CMS	Fife Scottish
P357JND	Manchester	P531EFL	Cambus	P550EFL	Cambus	P610SEV	East London
P361DSA	Glasgow	P531ESA	Glasgow	P550ESA	Glasgow	P611CMS	Fife Scottish
P362DSA	Glasgow	P531HMP	East London	P550PNE	Manchester	P611SEV	East London
P363DSA	Glasgow	P531PNE	Manchester	P551EFL	Cambus	P612CMS	Fife Scottish
P364APM	Cambus	P532EFL	Cambus	P551ESA	Glasgow	P613CMS	Fife Scottish
P364DSA	Glasgow	P532ESA	Glasgow	P551PNE	Manchester	P613SEV	East London
P365DSA	Glasgow	P532HMP	East London	P552EFL	Cambus	P615PGP	Selkent
P366DSA	Glasgow	P532PNE	Manchester	P552ESA	Glasgow	P616PGP	Selkent
P367DSA	Glasgow	P5332NE	Manchester	P552PNE	Manchester	P617PGP	Selkent
P368DSA	Glasgow	P533EFL	Cambus	P5534FL	Cambus	P618PGP	Selkent
P369DSA	Glasgow	P533ESA	Glasgow	P553ESA	Glasgow	P619PGP	Selkent
P370DSA	Glasgow	P533HMP	East London	P553PNE	Manchester	P620PGP	Selkent
P371DSA	Glasgow	P534EFL	Cambus	P554EFL	Cambus	P621PGP	Selkent
P372DSA	Glasgow	P534ESA	Glasgow	P554ESA	Glasgow	P622ESO	Bluebird Buses
P373DSA	Glasgow	P534HMP	East London	P554PNE	Manchester	P622PGP	Selkent
P374DSA	Glasgow	P534PNE	Manchester	P556EFL	Cambus	P623PGP	Selkent
P375DSA	Glasgow	P535EFL	Cambus	P556ESA	Glasgow	P624PGP	Selkent
P376DSA	Glasgow	P535ESA	Glasgow	P556PNE	Manchester	P625NSE	Bluebird Buses
P377DSA	Glasgow	P535HMP	East London	P557EFL	Cambus	P625PGP	Selkent
P378DSA	Glasgow	P535PNE	Manchester	P557ESA	Glasgow	P626NSE	Bluebird Buses
P379DSA	Glasgow	P536EFL	Cambus	P557PNE	Manchester	P626PGP	Selkent
P380DSA	Glasgow	P536ESA	Glasgow	P558EFL	Cambus	P627ESO	Bluebird Buses
P381DSA	Glasgow	P536HMP	East London	P558ESA	Glasgow	P627PGP	Selkent
P382DSA	Glasgow	P536PNE	Manchester	P558PNE	Manchester	P628PGP	Selkent
P383DSA	Glasgow	P537EFL	Cambus	P559EFL	Cambus	P629PGP	Selkent
P384DSA	Glasgow	P537ESA	Glasgow	P559ESA	Glasgow	P630PGP	Selkent
P385DSA	Glasgow	P537HMP	East London	P559PNE	Manchester	P631PGP	Selkent
P386DSA	Glasgow	P537PNE	Manchester	P560ESA	Glasgow	P632PGP	Selkent
P390LPS	Western	P538EFL	Cambus	P561EFL	Cambus	P633PGP	Selkent

Reg	Operator	Reg	Operator	Reg	Operator	Reg	Operator
P634PGP	Selkent	P802XTA	Devon	P852GND	Manchester	PEF148X	Transit
P636PGP	Selkent	P803GMU	East London	P852SMR	Cheltenham & Glos	PEF149X	Transit
P637PGP	Selkent	P803NJN	East London	P853GND	Manchester	PES190Y	Bluebird Buses
P638PGP	Selkent	P803XTA	Devon	P853SMR	Cheltenham & Glos	PEU511R	Midland Red
P639PGP	Selkent	P804GMU	East London	P854GND	Manchester	PEU515R	Circle Line
P640PGP	Selkent	P804NJN	East London	P854SMR	Cheltenham & Glos	PEX620W	Stagecoach South
P644SEV	East London	P804XTA	Devon	P855GND	Manchester	PEX621W	Stagecoach South
P645SEV	East London	P805GMU	East London	P856GND	Manchester	PFN873	Stagecoach South
P646SEV	East London	P805NJN	East London	P857GND	Manchester	PHW985S	Red & White
P670EWB	Fife Scottish	P805XTA	Devon	P858GND	Manchester	PHW988S	Cheltenham & Glos
P671EWB	Fife Scottish	P806GMU	East London	P859GND	Manchester	PHW989S	Cheltenham & Glos
P686JBD	United Counties	P806NJN	East London	P860GND	Manchester	PIB8109	Midland Red
P687JBD	United Counties	P806XTA	Devon	P861GND	Manchester	PJI4314	East Midland
P688JBD	United Counties	P807GMU	East London	P862GND	Manchester	PJI4316	East Midland
P689JBD	United Counties	P807NJN	East London	P863GND	Manchester	PJI4983	Western
P690JBD	United Counties	P808GMU	East London	P864GND	Manchester	PJJ344S	Stagecoach South
P691JBD	United Counties	P809GMU	East London	P865GND	Manchester	PKG741R	Red & White
P692JBD	United Counties	P810GMU	East London	P866GND	Manchester	PMT199X	Stagecoach South
P701BTA	Devon	P811GMU	East London	P867GND	Manchester	PRA109R	Bluebird Buses
P702BTA	Devon	P812GMU	East London	P868GND	Manchester	PRA110R	Bluebird Buses
P703BTA	Devon	P813GMU	East London	P869MNE	Manchester	PRA112R	Bluebird Buses
P704BTA	Devon	P814GMU	East London	P870MNE	Manchester	PRX189B	Transit
P705BTA	Devon	P815GMU	East London	P871MNE	Manchester	PS2743	East Midland
P706BTA	Devon	P816GMU	East London	P872MNE	Manchester	PSU443	East Midland
P707BTA	Devon	P817GMU	East London	P873MNE	Manchester	PSU764	East Midland
P708BTA	Devon	P818GMU	East London	P874MNE	Manchester	PSU787	Cumberland
P709BTA	Devon	P819GMU	East London	P875MNE	Manchester	PSU788	Cumberland
P710BTA	Devon	P819GNC	Manchester	P876MNE	Manchester	PSX180Y	Fife Scottish
P711BTA	Devon	P820GMU	East London	P877MNE	Manchester	PSX181Y	Fife Scottish
P712BTA	Devon	P820GNC	Manchester	P878MNE	Manchester	PSX182Y	Fife Scottish
P713BTA	Devon	P821FVU	Manchester	P879MNE	Manchester	PSX183Y	Fife Scottish
P714BTA	Devon	P821GMU	East London	P880MNE	Manchester	PSX185Y	Fife Scottish
P716GND	Manchester	P822FVU	Manchester	P881MNE	Manchester	PSX186Y	Fife Scottish
P717GND	Manchester	P822GMU	East London	P882MNE	Manchester	PSX187Y	Fife Scottish
P718GND	Manchester	P823FVU	Manchester	P883MNE	Manchester	PSX188Y	Fife Scottish
P719GND	Manchester	P823GMU	East London	P884MNE	Manchester	PSX189Y	Fife Scottish
P720GND	Manchester	P824FVU	Manchester	P885MNE	Manchester	PUK621R	Midland Red
P721GND	Manchester	P824GMU	East London	P886MNE	Manchester	PUK622R	Midland Red
P722GND	Manchester	P825FVU	Manchester	P887MNE	Manchester	PUK623R	Midland Red
P723GND	Manchester	P825GMU	East London	P889MNE	Manchester	PUK624R	Midland Red
P724GND	Manchester	P826FVU	Manchester	P890MNE	Manchester	PUK625R	Midland Red
P725GND	Manchester	P826GMU	East London	P891MNE	Manchester	PUK626R	Midland Red
P726GND	Manchester	P827FVU	Manchester	P892MNE	Manchester	PUK627R	Midland Red
P727GND	Manchester	P828FEF	Transit	P893MNE	Manchester	PUK628R	Midland Red
P728GND	Manchester	P828FVU	Manchester	P894MNE	Manchester	PUK629R	Midland Red
P729GND	Manchester	P829FEF	Transit	P901SMR	Cheltenham & Glos	PWY37W	Cambus
P730GND	Manchester	P829FVU	Manchester	P902SMR	Cheltenham & Glos	PWY40W	Devon
P771TTG	Red & White	P830FEF	Transit	P903SMR	Cheltenham & Glos	PWY45W	Cambus
P772TTG	Red & White	P830FVU	Manchester	P904SMR	Cheltenham & Glos	PWY47W	Cambus
P773TTG	Red & White	P831FVU	Manchester	P905SMR	Cheltenham & Glos	PWY48W	Devon
P774TTG	Red & White	P832FVU	Manchester	P906SMR	Cheltenham & Glos	PWY49W	Cambus
P780WCN	Busways	P833FVU	Manchester	P907SMR	Cheltenham & Glos	PWY50W	Cambus
P781WCN	Busways	P834FVU	Manchester	P908SMR	Cheltenham & Glos	PYE841Y	East Midland
P782WCN	Busways	P835FVU	Manchester	P909SMR	Cheltenham & Glos	PYE842Y	East Midland
P783WCN	Busways	P836GND	Manchester	P910SMR	Cheltenham & Glos	R34AKV	Midland Red
P784WCN	Busways	P837GND	Manchester	P911SMR	Cheltenham & Glos	R35AKV	Midland Red
P785WCN	Busways	P838GND	Manchester	P912SMR	Cheltenham & Glos	R36AKV	Midland Red
P786WVK	Busways	P839GND	Manchester	P913SMR	Cheltenham & Glos	R36LSO	Glasgow
P787WVK	Busways	P840GND	Manchester	P914SMR	Cheltenham & Glos	R37AKV	Midland Red
P788WVK	Busways	P841GND	Manchester	P973UBV	Fife Scottish	R38AKV	Midland Red
P789WVK	Busways	P842GND	Manchester	P974UBV	Fife Scottish	R39AKV	Midland Red
P790WVK	Busways	P843GND	Manchester	P975UBV	Fife Scottish	R63UFC	Oxford
P791WVK	Busways	P844GND	Manchester	P976UBV	Fife Scottish	R64UFC	Oxford
P792WVK	Busways	P845GND	Manchester	P977UBV	Ribble	R65UFC	Oxford
P793WVK	Busways	P846GND	Manchester	P978UBV	Ribble	R82SEF	Transit
P801GMU	East London	P847GND	Manchester	P979UBV	Ribble	R82XNO	Selkent
P801NJN	East London	P848GND	Manchester	PCD73R	Stagecoach South	R83SEF	Transit
P801XTA	Devon	P849GND	Manchester	PCD79R	Stagecoach South	R83XNO	Selkent
P802GMU	East London	P850GND	Manchester	PCD80R	Stagecoach South	R84SEF	Transit
P802NJN	East London	P851GND	Manchester	PEF147X	Transit	R84XNO	Selkent

Reg	Operator	Reg	Operator	Reg	Operator	Reg	Operator
R85SEF	Transit	R150VPU	East London	R242KRG	Busways	R453RCE	Cambus
R85XNO	Selkent	R151VPU	East London	R243KRG	Busways	R454RCE	Cambus
R86XNO	Selkent	R152VPU	East London	R244KRG	Busways	R455RCE	Cambus
R87XNO	Selkent	R153VPU	East London	R245KRG	Busways	R456RCE	Cambus
R89XNO	Selkent	R154VPU	East London	R246KRG	Busways	R462LSO	Western
R91XNO	Selkent	R155VPU	East London	R246NBV	Ribble	R462SEF	Transit
R92XNO	Selkent	R156VPU	East London	R247KRG	Busways	R463LSO	Western
R93XNO	Selkent	R157VPU	East London	R247NBV	Ribble	R463SEF	Transit
R94XNO	Selkent	R158VPU	East London	R248KRG	Busways	R464LSO	Western
R95XNO	Selkent	R159VPU	East London	R248NBV	Ribble	R464SEF	Transit
R96XNO	Selkent	R160VPU	East London	R249KRG	Busways	R465LSO	Western
R97XNO	Selkent	R161VPU	East London	R249NBV	Ribble	R465SEF	Transit
R99XNO	Selkent	R162VPU	East London	R250KRG	Busways	R466LSO	Western
R101KRG	Busways	R163VPU	East London	R250NBV	Ribble	R466SEF	Transit
R102KRG	Busways	R164VPU	East London	R251KRG	Busways	R467LSO	Western
R103KRG	Busways	R165VPU	East London	R251NBV	Ribble	R467SEF	Transit
R103LSO	Western	R166VPU	East London	R252KRG	Busways	R468LSO	Western
R104KRG	Busways	R167VPU	East London	R252NBV	Ribble	R468SEF	Transit
R104LSO	Western	R168VPU	East London	R253KRG	Busways	R469LSO	Western
R105KRG	Busways	R169VPU	East London	R253NBV	Ribble	R469MVN	Transit
R105LSO	Western	R170VPU	East London	R254KRG	Busways	R470LSO	Western
R107KRG	Busways	R171VPU	East London	R254NBV	Ribble	R470MVN	Transit
R108KRG	Busways	R172VPU	East London	R255KRG	Busways	R471LSO	Western
R109KRG	Busways	R173VPU	East London	R255NBV	Ribble	R471MVN	Transit
R110KRG	Busways	R174DNH	United Counties	R256KRG	Busways	R472MVN	Transit
R112KRG	Busways	R174VPU	East London	R256NBV	Ribble	R473MCW	Ribble
R112OPS	Glasgow	R175DNH	United Counties	R257KRG	Busways	R474MCW	Ribble
R113KRG	Busways	R175VPU	East London	R257NBV	Ribble	R475MCW	Ribble
R113OPS	Glasgow	R176DNH	United Counties	R258NBV	Ribble	R476MCW	Ribble
R114KRG	Busways	R176VPU	East London	R259NBV	Ribble	R477MCW	Ribble
R114OPS	Glasgow	R177DNH	United Counties	R260NBV	Ribble	R478MCW	Ribble
R114VPU	East London	R177VPU	East London	R261NBV	Ribble	R479MCW	Ribble
R115KRG	Busways	R178DNH	United Counties	R262NBV	Ribble	R480MCW	Ribble
R115OPS	Glasgow	R178VPU	East London	R263NBV	Ribble	R481MCW	Ribble
R115VPU	East London	R179DNH	United Counties	R264NBV	Ribble	R482MCW	Ribble
R116KRG	Busways	R179VPU	East London	R265NBV	Ribble	R501UWL	Oxford
R116OPS	Glasgow	R180DNH	United Counties	R266NBV	Ribble	R501YWC	Selkent
R116VPU	East London	R180VPU	East London	R267NBV	Ribble	R502KSA	Glasgow
R117KRG	Busways	R181DNH	United Counties	R268NBV	Ribble	R502UWL	Oxford
R117OPS	Glasgow	R181VPU	East London	R330HFS	Fife Scottish	R502YWC	Selkent
R117VPU	East London	R182DNH	United Counties	R331HFS	Fife Scottish	R503KSA	Western
R118KRG	Busways	R183DNH	United Counties	R332HFS	Fife Scottish	R503UWL	Oxford
R118OPS	Glasgow	R184DNH	United Counties	R334HFS	Fife Scottish	R503YWC	Selkent
R118VPU	East London	R185DNH	United Counties	R335HFS	Fife Scottish	R504KSA	Glasgow
R119KRG	Busways	R186DNH	United Counties	R336HFS	Fife Scottish	R504UWL	Oxford
R119OPS	Western	R188XNO	Selkent	R337HFS	Fife Scottish	R504YWC	Selkent
R119VPU	East London	R190XNO	Selkent	R338HFS	Fife Scottish	R505UWL	Oxford
R120KRG	Busways	R203DHB	Red & White	R339HFS	Fife Scottish	R505YWC	Selkent
R120OPS	Glasgow	R204DHB	Red & White	R340HFS	Fife Scottish	R506UWL	Oxford
R120VPU	Selkent	R205DHB	Red & White	R341HFS	Fife Scottish	R506YWC	Selkent
R121KRG	Busways	R206DHB	Red & White	R342HFS	Fife Scottish	R507UWL	Oxford
R121OPS	Western	R207DHB	Red & White	R353LER	Cambus	R507YWC	Selkent
R121VPU	Selkent	R207XNO	Selkent	R354LER	Cambus	R508UWL	Oxford
R122KRG	Busways	R208DHB	Red & White	R355LER	Cambus	R508YWC	Selkent
R122VPU	Selkent	R208XNO	East London	R356LER	Cambus	R509UWL	Oxford
R123KRG	Busways	R209XNO	East London	R365JVA	Cambus	R509YWC	Selkent
R123VPU	Selkent	R210XNO	Selkent	R366JVA	Cambus	R510UWL	Oxford
R124KRG	Busways	R221CRW	Midland Red	R414XFC	Oxford	R510YWC	Selkent
R124VPU	Selkent	R223CRW	Midland Red	R415XFC	Oxford	R511UWL	Oxford
R125KRG	Busways	R224CRW	Midland Red	R416XFC	Oxford	R511YWC	Selkent
R125VPU	Selkent	R225CRW	Midland Red	R417XFC	Oxford	R512UWL	Oxford
R126KRG	Busways	R226CRW	Midland Red	R418XFC	Oxford	R512YWC	Selkent
R126VPU	Selkent	R227CRW	Midland Red	R419XFC	Oxford	R513KSA	Glasgow
R127KRG	Busways	R228CRW	Midland Red	R420XFC	Oxford	R513UWL	Oxford
R127VPU	Selkent	R236KRG	Busways	R421XFC	Oxford	R513YWC	Selkent
R128KRG	Busways	R237KRG	Busways	R422XFC	Oxford	R514KSA	Glasgow
R128VPU	Selkent	R238KRG	Busways	R423XFC	Oxford	R514YWC	Selkent
R129VPU	Selkent	R239KRG	Busways	R424XFC	Oxford	R515KSA	Glasgow
R148VPU	East London	R240KRG	Busways	R425XFC	Oxford	R515YWC	Selkent
R149VPU	East London	R241KRG	Busways	R426XFC	Oxford	R516YWC	Selkent

Reg	Operator	Reg	Operator	Reg	Operator	Reg	Operator
R517YWC	Selkent	R693DNH	United Counties	R807YUD	Oxford	R921XVM	Manchester
R518YWC	Selkent	R694DNH	United Counties	R808YUD	Oxford	R922XVM	Manchester
R539GSF	Fife Scottish	R695DNH	United Counties	R809YUD	Oxford	R923XVM	Manchester
R541GSF	Fife Scottish	R696DNH	United Counties	R810YUD	Oxford	R924XVM	Manchester
R542GSF	Fife Scottish	R697DNH	United Counties	R811YUD	Oxford	R925XVM	Manchester
R543GSF	Fife Scottish	R698DNH	United Counties	R812YUD	Oxford	R926XVM	Manchester
R550JDF	Cheltenham & Glos	R699DNH	United Counties	R813YUD	Oxford	R927XVM	Manchester
R551JDF	Cheltenham & Glos	R701DNH	United Counties	R814YUD	Oxford	R928XVM	Manchester
R552JDF	Cheltenham & Glos	R701DNJ	Stagecoach South	R815YUD	Oxford	R929XVM	Manchester
R553JDF	Cheltenham & Glos	R701YWC	East London	R816YUD	Oxford	R930XVM	Manchester
R554JDF	Cheltenham & Glos	R702DNH	United Counties	R817YUD	Oxford	R931XVM	Manchester
R560DRP	United Counties	R702DNJ	Stagecoach South	R818YUD	Oxford	R932XVM	Manchester
R561DRP	United Counties	R702YWC	East London	R819YUD	Oxford	R933XVM	Manchester
R562DRP	United Counties	R703DNH	United Counties	R821YUD	Oxford	R934XVM	Manchester
R563DRP	United Counties	R703DNJ	Stagecoach South	R822YUD	Oxford	R935XVM	Manchester
R564DRP	United Counties	R703YWC	East London	R823YUD	Oxford	R936XVM	Manchester
R565DRP	United Counties	R704DNJ	Stagecoach South	R824YUD	Oxford	R937XVM	Manchester
R566DRP	United Counties	R704YWC	East London	R825YUD	Oxford	R938XVM	Manchester
R567DRP	United Counties	R705DNJ	Stagecoach South	R826YUD	Oxford	R939XVM	Manchester
R568DRP	United Counties	R705YWC	East London	R827YUD	Oxford	R940XVM	Manchester
R580JVA	Cambus	R706DNJ	Stagecoach South	R828YUD	Oxford	R941XVM	Manchester
R581JVA	Cambus	R706YUD	Oxford	R829YUD	Oxford	R942XVM	Manchester
R582JVA	Cambus	R706YWC	East London	R831OVN	Transit	R943XVM	Manchester
R583JVA	Cambus	R707DNJ	Stagecoach South	R832OVN	Transit	R944XVM	Manchester
R584JVA	Cambus	R707YWC	East London	R833OVN	Transit	R945XVM	Manchester
R585JVA	Cambus	R708DNJ	Stagecoach South	R834OVN	Transit	R946XVM	Manchester
R586JVA	Cambus	R708YWC	East London	R835OVN	Transit	R947XVM	Manchester
R595LSO	Western	R709DNJ	Stagecoach South	R836OVN	Transit	R948XVM	Manchester
R596LSO	Western	R709YWC	East London	R837OVN	Transit	R949XVM	Manchester
R601KDD	Cheltenham & Glos	R710DNJ	Stagecoach South	R838OVN	Transit	R950XVM	Manchester
R602KDD	Cheltenham & Glos	R710YWC	East London	R839OVN	Transit	R951XVM	Manchester
R603KDD	Cheltenham & Glos	R711DNJ	Stagecoach South	R840OVN	Transit	R952XVM	Manchester
R604KDD	Cheltenham & Glos	R711YWC	East London	R895XVM	Manchester	R953XVM	Manchester
R606KDD	Cheltenham & Glos	R712XAR	East London	R896XVM	Manchester	R954XVM	Manchester
R607KDD	Cheltenham & Glos	R712YWC	East London	R897XVM	Manchester	R955XVM	Manchester
R608KDD	Cheltenham & Glos	R713YWC	East London	R898XVM	Manchester	R956XVM	Manchester
R609KDD	Cheltenham & Glos	R714YWC	East London	R899XVM	Manchester	R957XVM	Manchester
R610KDD	Cheltenham & Glos	R715YWC	East London	R901FDV	Devon	R958XVM	Manchester
R611KDD	Cheltenham & Glos	R716YWC	East London	R901XVM	Manchester	R959XVM	Manchester
R612KDD	Cheltenham & Glos	R717YWC	East London	R902XVM	Manchester	R960XVM	Manchester
R613KDD	Cheltenham & Glos	R718YWC	East London	R903XVM	Manchester	R961XVM	Manchester
R614KDD	Cheltenham & Glos	R720YUD	Oxford	R904XFC	Oxford	R962XVM	Manchester
R615KDD	Cheltenham & Glos	R747XAR	East London	R904XVM	Manchester	R963XVM	Manchester
R616KDD	Cheltenham & Glos	R751BDV	Devon	R905XFC	Oxford	R964XVM	Manchester
R636RSE	Bluebird Buses	R775CDW	Red & White	R905XVM	Manchester	R965XVM	Manchester
R637RSE	Bluebird Buses	R776CDW	Red & White	R906XFC	Oxford	R966XVM	Manchester
R638RSE	Bluebird Buses	R778CDW	Red & White	R906XVM	Manchester	R967XVM	Manchester
R639RSE	Bluebird Buses	R779CDW	Red & White	R907XFC	Oxford	R968XVM	Manchester
R640RSE	Bluebird Buses	R780CDW	Red & White	R907XVM	Manchester	R969XVM	Manchester
R641LSO	Bluebird Buses	R781CDW	Red & White	R908XFC	Oxford	R970XVM	Manchester
R642LSO	Bluebird Buses	R782CDW	Red & White	R908XVM	Manchester	R971XVM	Manchester
R643LSO	Bluebird Buses	R783CDW	Red & White	R909XFC	Oxford	R972XVM	Manchester
R644LSO	Bluebird Buses	R784CDW	Red & White	R909XVM	Manchester	R973XVM	Manchester
R645LSO	Bluebird Buses	R785DHB	Red & White	R910XFC	Oxford	R974XVM	Manchester
R646LSO	Bluebird Buses	R787DHB	Red & White	R910XVM	Manchester	R975XVM	Manchester
R647LSO	Bluebird Buses	R788DHB	Red & White	R911XFC	Oxford	R976XVM	Manchester
R648LSO	Bluebird Buses	R789DHB	Red & White	R912XFC	Oxford	R977XVM	Manchester
R649LSO	Bluebird Buses	R790DHB	Red & White	R912XVM	Manchester	R978XVM	Manchester
R650LSO	Bluebird Buses	R791DHB	Red & White	R913XVM	Manchester	R979XVM	Manchester
R651VSE	Bluebird Buses	R791PAO	Cumberland	R914XVM	Manchester	R980XVM	Manchester
R652VSE	Bluebird Buses	R792DHB	Red & White	R915GMW	Cheltenham & Glos	R981XVM	Manchester
R653VSE	Bluebird Buses	R792PAO	Cumberland	R915XVM	Manchester	R982XVM	Manchester
R654VSE	Bluebird Buses	R793URM	Cumberland	R916GMW	Cheltenham & Glos	R983XVM	Manchester
R663TKU	East Midland	R794URM	Cumberland	R916XVM	Manchester	R984XVM	Manchester
R664TKU	East Midland	R795URM	Cumberland	R917GMW	Cheltenham & Glos	R985XVM	Manchester
R668LFV	Ribble	R801YUD	Oxford	R917XVM	Manchester	R986XVM	Manchester
R669LFV	Ribble	R802YUD	Oxford	R918GMW	Cheltenham & Glos	R987XVM	Manchester
R670LFV	Ribble	R803YUD	Oxford	R918XVM	Manchester	R988XVM	Manchester
R671LFV	Ribble	R804YUD	Oxford	R919XVM	Manchester	R989XVM	Manchester
R672LFV	Ribble	R805YUD	Oxford	R920XVM	Manchester	R990XVM	Manchester

Reg	Operator	Reg	Operator	Reg	Operator
R991XVM	Manchester	RJT155R	Bluebird Buses	SHE306Y	East Midland	SNV936W	United Counties
R992XVM	Manchester	RNV413V	Midland Red	SHE307Y	East Midland	SNV937W	United Counties
R993XVM	Manchester	RRM383X	Western	SHE308Y	East Midland	SSA2X	Bluebird Buses
R994XVM	Manchester	RRM384X	Ribble	SHE309Y	East Midland	SSA3X	Bluebird Buses
R995XVM	Manchester	RRM385X	Cheltenham & Glos	SHE310Y	East Midland	SSA4X	Bluebird Buses
R996XVM	Manchester	RRM386X	Ribble	SHE311Y	East Midland	SSA5X	Bluebird Buses
R997DBA	Manchester	RRP858R	Ribble	SHH387X	Ribble	SSA6X	Bluebird Buses
RAH264W	Cambus	RRP862R	United Counties	SHH388X	Ribble	SSA7X	Bluebird Buses
RAH265W	Devon	RRP863R	United Counties	SHH389X	Cheltenham & Glos	STW24W	Cambus
RAH268W	Devon	RRS46R	Bluebird Buses	SHH390X	Ribble	SUB790W	Cambus
RBJ36W	Ribble	RRS47R	Bluebird Buses	SHH392X	Midland Red	SUB792W	Cambus
RBZ2621	Glasgow	RRS50R	Bluebird Buses	SHH393X	Western	SUB793W	Cambus
RBZ3427	Western	RRS53R	Bluebird Buses	SHN401R	Transit	SUB795W	Cambus
RBZ3428	Western	RSC190Y	Fife Scottish	SHN407R	Transit	SVK627G	Busways
RBZ3429	Western	RSC191Y	Fife Scottish	SIB8243	Stagecoach South	SVV586W	East Midland
RBZ4209	Western	RSC192Y	Fife Scottish	SJI2054	Manchester	SVV589W	Midland Red
RBZ4241	Western	RSC194Y	Fife Scottish	SJI4558	Manchester	SYC852	Stagecoach South
RBZ4243	Glasgow	RSG814V	Red & White	SJI4559	Manchester	TAE639S	Midland Red
RBZ4245	Western	RSG815V	Red & White	SJI4560	Manchester	TAE641S	Cheltenham & Glos
RBZ4281	Western	RSG823V	Red & White	SJW515	Bluebird Buses	TAE642S	Cheltenham & Glos
RBZ4359	Western	RSG824V	Red & White	SKG908S	Red & White	TAE644S	Cheltenham & Glos
RBZ5459	Western	RSG825V	Red & White	SKG923S	Red & White	TBC1X	Western
RBZ5491	Western	RUF40R	Transit	SKL680X	Stagecoach South	TBC2X	Busways
RBZ5492	Western	RUF41R	Manchester	SKL681X	Stagecoach South	TCK841	Cumberland
RBZ5493	Western	RVB978S	Fife Scottish	SKL682X	Stagecoach South	TEL490R	Stagecoach South
RBZ5494	Western	RYK815Y	Selkent	SKL683X	Stagecoach South	THX401S	East London
RBZ5495	Western	RYK816Y	Selkent	SKL685X	Stagecoach South	THX402S	East London
RBZ5496	Western	RYK818Y	Selkent	SKY31Y	East Midland	TJI2488	Manchester
RBZ5497	Glasgow	RYK819Y	Fife Scottish	SKY32Y	East Midland	TKG518J	Red & White
RBZ5497	Western	RYK820Y	Fife Scottish	SMK661F	East London	TMS404X	Western
RBZ5498	Western	RYK821Y	Selkent	SMK665F	East London	TMS405X	Western
RBZ5503	Western	RYK822Y	Selkent	SMK670F	East London	TMS406X	Western
RCS382	Western	SAE752S	Cheltenham & Glos	SMK671F	East London	TMS407X	Western
RCU833S	Busways	SAE753S	Midland Red	SMK666F	East London	TOF707S	Midland Red
RCU834S	Busways	SAE754S	Circle Line	SMK705F	East London	TOF708S	Midland Red
RCU837S	Busways	SAE756S	Cheltenham & Glos	SMK709F	East London	TOF709S	Midland Red
RCU838S	Busways	SAG518W	Transit	SMK723F	East London	TOF710S	Midland Red
RDZ6115	East London	SAG522W	Transit	SMK738F	East London	TRN481V	Ribble
RDZ6116	East London	SAG524W	Transit	SMK743F	East London	TRN482V	Circle Line
RDZ6117	East London	SAG525W	Transit	SMK748F	East London	TRN810V	Cumberland
RDZ6118	East London	SAG526W	Transit	SMK749F	East London	TSJ31S	Western
RDZ6119	East London	SAG527W	Transit	SMK760F	East London	TSJ32S	Western
RDZ6120	East London	SAG528W	Transit	SND106X	Manchester	TSJ33S	Western
RDZ6121	East London	SAO410R	Bluebird Buses	SND107X	Manchester	TSJ67S	Western
RDZ6122	East London	SAO412R	Bluebird Buses	SND108X	Manchester	TSJ70S	Western
RDZ6123	East London	SCK224X	Ribble	SND109X	Manchester	TSJ71S	Western
RDZ6124	East London	SCK225X	Ribble	SND110X	Manchester	TSJ76S	Western
RDZ6125	East London	SCK226X	Ribble	SND111X	Manchester	TSJ78S	Western
RDZ6126	East London	SCN248S	Busways	SND116X	Manchester	TSJ79S	Western
RDZ6127	East London	SCN249S	Transit	SND118X	Manchester	TSJ80S	Western
RDZ6128	East London	SCN250S	Circle Line	SND119X	Manchester	TSJ85S	Western
RDZ6129	East London	SCN251S	Busways	SND120X	Manchester	TSO12X	Bluebird Buses
RDZ6130	East London	SCN252S	Midland Red	SND121X	Manchester	TSO13X	Bluebird Buses
REU311S	Cheltenham & Glos	SCN253S	Midland Red	SND124X	Manchester	TSO14X	Bluebird Buses
REU316S	Manchester	SCN254S	Busways	SND125X	Manchester	TSO15X	Bluebird Buses
RFS579V	Western	SCN255S	Circle Line	SND141X	Manchester	TSO17X	Bluebird Buses
RFS582V	Ribble	SCN256S	Circle Line	SND143X	Manchester	TSO20X	Bluebird Buses
RFS583V	Western	SCN259S	Busways	SND144X	Manchester	TSO21X	Bluebird Buses
RFS584V	Ribble	SCN264S	Circle Line	SND145X	Manchester	TSO23X	Bluebird Buses
RGV37W	Ribble	SCN265S	Midland Red	SND432X	Ribble	TSO24X	Bluebird Buses
RGV38W	Ribble	SCN267S	Busways	SND451X	Manchester	TSO29X	Bluebird Buses
RGV39W	Ribble	SCN268S	Busways	SND452X	Manchester	TSO30X	Bluebird Buses
RGV40W	Ribble	SCN270S	Busways	SND455X	Manchester	TSO31X	Bluebird Buses
RHG880X	Cheltenham & Glos	SCN276S	Midland Red	SND472X	Manchester	TSO32X	Bluebird Buses
RHG884X	Cumberland	SCN277S	Busways	SNS825W	Cheltenham & Glos	TSU638	Bluebird Buses
RIB4309	Bluebird Buses	SCN279S	Busways	SNS826W	Western	TSV718	Bluebird Buses
RIW3364	Circle Line	SCN281S	Midland Red	SNS831W	Ribble	TSV719	Bluebird Buses
RJA702R	Western	SCN282S	Busways	SNV930W	United Counties	TSV720	Bluebird Buses
RJA729R	Manchester	SCN283S	Busways	SNV931W	United Counties	TSV721	Bluebird Buses
RJT146R	Stagecoach South	SFL373R	Cambus	SNV935W	United Counties	TSV722	Bluebird Buses

278

Reg	Operator	Reg	Operator	Reg	Operator	Reg	Operator
TSV778	Bluebird Buses	UWV623S	Stagecoach South	VVV965W	United Counties	WLT978	Western
TSV779	Bluebird Buses	UWW3X	Cambus	VVV966W	United Counties	WPC316X	Ribble
TSV780	Bluebird Buses	UWW4X	Cambus	VVV967W	United Counties	WSK219	Ribble
TSV781	Bluebird Buses	UWW7X	Cheltenham & Glos	VWA34Y	East Midland	WUH166T	Devon
TWF201Y	East Midland	UWW8X	Cambus	VWA35Y	East Midland	WVM884S	Western
TWF202Y	East Midland	VAE499T	Cheltenham & Glos	VWA36Y	East Midland	WVM888S	Western
TWS906T	Cheltenham & Glos	VAE501T	Cheltenham & Glos	WAO396Y	Ribble	WVT618	Stagecoach South
TWS909T	Red & White	VAE502T	Circle Line	WAO397Y	Circle Line	WYJ169S	Stagecoach South
TWS913T	Cheltenham & Glos	VAH278X	Cambus	WAO398Y	Cumberland	WYV3T	East London
TWS914T	Cheltenham & Glos	VAH279X	Cambus	WAO643Y	Bluebird Buses	WYV4T	East London
UCS659	Western	VAH280X	Cambus	WAO645Y	Cumberland	WYV5T	Western
UDT312Y	East Midland	VBA161S	Western	WAS765V	Red & White	WYV6T	East London
UDT313Y	East Midland	VBA166S	Red & White	WAS767V	Red & White	WYV7T	East London
UF4813	Stagecoach South	VBA178S	Red & White	WAS768V	Western	WYV8T	East London
UFG48S	Stagecoach South	VBA188S	Red & White	WAS771V	Western	WYV9T	Selkent
UFG49S	Transit	VBA190S	Red & White	WAX194S	Red & White	WYV10T	Selkent
UFG52S	Transit	VCS376	Western	WBN474T	Manchester	WYV11T	East London
UFS875R	Fife Scottish	VCS391	Western	WBR248	Busways	WYV12T	East London
UFS876R	Fife Scottish	VCU302T	Busways	WDA1T	Red & White	WYV13T	East London
UFS877R	Fife Scottish	VCU303T	Busways	WDA2T	Red & White	WYV14T	East London
UFS878R	Fife Scottish	VCU304T	Midland Red	WDA5T	Red & White	WYV15T	East London
UHG757R	Stagecoach South	VCU310T	Midland Red	WDZ2104	Western	WYV16T	East London
UIB3076	Western	VCW196V	Ribble	WDZ4138	Western	WYV17T	Selkent
UIB3541	Western	VDV150S	Manchester	WDZ6951	Western	WYV18T	East London
UIB3542	Western	VDV135S	Devon	WDZ6962	Western	WYV19T	Selkent
UIB3543	Western	VEF150Y	Transit	WDZ6974	Western	WYV20T	Selkent
ULS660T	Western	VEF151Y	Transit	WDZ6975	Western	WYV21T	East London
UM7681	Western	VEF152Y	Transit	WFM801K	Manchester	WYV22T	East London
UMO180N	Stagecoach South	VEF153Y	Transit	WFS135W	Bluebird Buses	WYV23T	East London
UNA772S	Western	VEU231T	Cheltenham & Glos	WFS136W	Western	WYV24T	East London
UNA824S	Western	VEX289X	Cambus	WFS137W	Bluebird Buses	WYV25T	East London
UNA840S	Midland Red	VEX291X	Cambus	WFS138W	Western	WYV26T	Selkent
UNA863S	Western	VEX293X	Cambus	WFS141W	Fife Scottish	WYV27T	Western
UOT648	Bluebird Buses	VEX295X	Cambus	WFS142W	Western	WYV28T	East London
URM801Y	Cumberland	VEX296X	Cambus	WFS147W	Western	WYV29T	Western
URM802Y	Cumberland	VEX298X	Cambus	WJM825T	Stagecoach South	WYV30T	East London
URP939W	United Counties	VEX299X	Cambus	WJM826T	Stagecoach South	WYV31T	East London
URP940W	United Counties	VEX300X	Cambus	WJM828T	Stagecoach South	WYV32T	East London
URP941W	United Counties	VEX301X	Cambus	WJM829T	Stagecoach South	WYV33T	East London
URP943W	Cambus	VEX303X	Cambus	WJM832T	Stagecoach South	WYV34T	East London
URP944W	United Counties	VEX304X	Cambus	WLT380	Cumberland	WYV35T	East London
URP945W	United Counties	VFV7V	Ribble	WLT415	Western	WYV36T	East London
USJ491Y	Western	VFX984S	Stagecoach South	WLT416	Western	WYV37T	Selkent
USK625	East London	VLT104	Western	WLT439	Western	WYV38T	Selkent
UTX726S	Red & White	VLT14	Selkent	WLT447	Western	WYV39T	East London
UVF623X	Circle Line	VLT154	Western	WLT461	Selkent	WYV40T	Selkent
UVK287T	Busways	VLT20	Selkent	WLT465	Western	WYV49T	Western
UVK289T	Busways	VLT255	United Counties	WLT491	Selkent	WYV56T	Western
UVK290T	Busways	VLT272	Bluebird Buses	WLT501	Western	WYV63T	East London
UVK295T	Busways	VLT37	Western	WLT512	United Counties	WYV66T	Selkent
UVK299T	Busways	VLT77	Fife Scottish	WLT526	Western	XDU599	Western
UVK300T	Busways	VNB132L	Manchester	WLT528	United Counties	XDV602S	Cheltenham & Glos
UWA150S	East Midland	VOD593S	Cheltenham & Glos	WLT538	Western	XDV606S	Cheltenham & Glos
UWA151S	East Midland	VOD596S	Cheltenham & Glos	WLT546	Western	XFF813	East London
UWP105	Glasgow	VOD597S	Cheltenham & Glos	WLT575	Selkent	XFF814	East London
UWV604S	Devon	VOD604S	Stagecoach South	WLT613	East London	XGR728R	Midland Red
UWV605S	Bluebird Buses	VOD605S	Stagecoach South	WLT682	United Counties	XGS736S	East Midland
UWV607S	Western	VRN827Y	Ribble	WLT697	Western	XIA586	Stagecoach South
UWV608S	Bluebird Buses	VRN828Y	Ribble	WLT706	Cumberland	XIA857	Stagecoach South
UWV609S	Bluebird Buses	VRN829Y	Cumberland	WLT713	Circle Line	XJJ650V	Stagecoach South
UWV610S	Cumberland	VRN830Y	Ribble	WLT720	Western	XJJ651V	Stagecoach South
UWV611S	Bluebird Buses	VRR447	Cumberland	WLT727	Western	XJJ652V	Stagecoach South
UWV612S	Cumberland	VTV170S	Midland Red	WLT774	Western	XJJ653V	Stagecoach South
UWV613S	Bluebird Buses	VTV171S	Bluebird Buses	WLT794	Western	XJJ654V	Stagecoach South
UWV614S	Devon	VVV949W	United Counties	WLT809	Western	XJJ655V	Stagecoach South
UWV617S	Fife Scottish	VVV950W	United Counties	WLT824	Cumberland	XJJ657V	Stagecoach South
UWV618S	Cumberland	VVV952W	United Counties	WLT830	Western	XJJ658V	Stagecoach South
UWV620S	Cumberland	VVV961W	United Counties	WLT874	Western	XJJ659V	Stagecoach South
UWV621S	Stagecoach South	VVV962W	United Counties	WLT886	East London	XJJ660V	Stagecoach South
UWV622S	Cumberland	VVV963W	United Counties	WLT908	United Counties	XJJ661V	Stagecoach South

The first example of Alexander's ALX300 model made its appearance at the 1997 Bus and Coach show, but was not available for photography before the book went to press. The vehicle carries the new Stagecoach *Lo-Liner* name which is to be used throughout the fleet. However, the name was applied to Busway's newly delivered 1101, R101KRG and is seen here on an ALX200 shortly after delivery. During 1998 the Alexander ALX300 will be delivered on a batch of Volvo B10Bs for Busways and 150 MAN 18.220 chassis, the first of which are due in Spring. *Stagecoach Busways*

XJJ662V	Stagecoach South	XSJ653T	Western	YBO16T	Midland Red	YRN820V	Ribble
XJJ663V	Stagecoach South	XSJ654T	Western	YBO18T	Midland Red	YRN821V	Stagecoach South
XJJ664V	Stagecoach South	XSJ655T	Western	YBO150T	Red & White	YSD350L	Western
XJJ665V	Stagecoach South	XSJ656T	Western	YCD73T	Stagecoach South	YSF98S	Western
XJJ667V	Stagecoach South	XSJ657T	Western	YCD74T	Stagecoach South	YSF100S	Western
XJJ668V	Stagecoach South	XSJ658T	Circle Line	YCD76T	Stagecoach South	YSJ14T	Western
XJJ669V	Stagecoach South	XSJ659T	Western	YCD77T	Stagecoach South	YSO33Y	Bluebird Buses
XJJ670V	Stagecoach South	XSJ660T	Western	YCD82T	Stagecoach South	YSO34Y	Bluebird Buses
XMS253R	Transit	XSJ661T	Circle Line	YDC21Y	Transit	YSO35Y	Bluebird Buses
XMS422Y	Western	XSJ662T	Western	YDC23Y	Transit	YSO36Y	Bluebird Buses
XMS423Y	Western	XSJ666T	Western	YDC25Y	Transit	YSO37Y	Bluebird Buses
XOV753T	Midland Red	XSJ667T	Western	YDG616	Cumberland	YSO38Y	Bluebird Buses
XOV754T	Midland Red	XSJ668T	Western	YEL2T	Cheltenham & Glos	YSO39Y	Bluebird Buses
XOV755T	Midland Red	XSJ669T	Western	YEU446V	Midland Red	YSO40Y	Bluebird Buses
XOV756T	Midland Red	XSL596A	East London	YFB972V	Cheltenham & Glos	YSO41Y	Bluebird Buses
XOV760T	Midland Red	XSU612	Stagecoach South	YFB973V	Cheltenham & Glos	YSO42Y	Bluebird Buses
XRC487	Bluebird Buses	XSU682	Stagecoach South	YFS304W	Western	YSO43Y	Bluebird Buses
XRM772Y	Bluebird Buses	XSU906	Ribble	YFS308W	Western	YSV730	Western
XRN44V	Ribble	XYK976	East London	YFS309W	Western	YSV735	Western
XRN45V	Ribble	XYK976	Stagecoach South	YFS310W	Western	YSX932W	Red & White
XRN46V	Ribble	YAE516V	Manchester	YJV806	Cheltenham & Glos	YSX933W	Red & White
XRN47V	Ribble	YAJ154Y	Transit	YLJ332	Stagecoach South	YSX934W	Red & White
XRN48V	Ribble	YAJ155Y	Transit	YLP528	Red & White	YSX935W	Red & White
XRN49V	Ribble	YAJ156Y	Transit	YRN815V	Ribble	YTS820A	East London
XRR175S	Cumberland	YAJ157Y	Transit	YRN816V	Stagecoach South	YVN521T	Transit
XSJ651T	Western	YAY21Y	Transit	YRN817V	Ribble	YYS174	Western

ISBN 1 897990 25 1

Published by *British Bus Publishing Ltd*
The Vyne, 16 St Margaret's Drive, Wellington,Telford, England, TF1 3PH
Fax/Answerphone (+44) (0) 1952 255669